The Best of the World's Classics

VOL. VII

CONTINENTAL EUROPE—I

RABELAIS

VOLTAIRE

HUGO

MONTAIGNE

THE BEST
OF THE
WORLD'S
CLASSICS

RESTRICTED
TO PROSE

HENRY CABOT LODGE
EDITOR-IN-CHIEF

FRANCIS W. HALSEY
ASSOCIATE EDITOR

With an Introduction, Biographical and Explanatory
Notes, etc.

IN TEN VOLUMES

Vol. VII
CONTINENTAL EUROPE—I

FUNK & WAGNALLS COMPANY
NEW YORK AND LONDON

CONTENTS

CONTENTS

CONTENTS

CONTENTS

viii

CONTENTS

CONTENTS

CONTENTS

ST. AURELIUS AUGUSTINE

Born in Numidia, Africa, in 354 A.D., died in 430; educated at Carthage; taught rhetoric at Carthage; removed to Rome in 383; going thence to Milan in 384, where he became a friend of St. Ambrose; converted from Manicheanism to Christianity by his mother Monica, and baptized by St. Ambrose in 387; made Bishop of Hippo in North Africa in 395; became a champion of orthodoxy and the most celebrated of the fathers of the Latin branch of the Church; his "Confessions" published in 397.

IMPERIAL POWER FOR GOOD AND BAD MEN[1]

LET us examine the nature of the spaciousness and continuance of empire, for which men give their gods such great thanks; to whom also they exhibited plays (that were so filthy both in actors and the action) without any offense of honesty. But, first, I would make a little inquiry, seeing you can not show such estates to be anyway happy, as are in continual wars, being still in terror, trouble, and guilt of shedding human blood, tho it be their foes; what reason then or what wisdom shall any man show in glorying in the largeness of empire, all their joy being but as a glass, bright and brittle, and evermore in fear and danger of breaking? To dive the deeper into this matter, let us not give the sails of our souls to every air of human breath, nor suffer our understanding's

[1] From "De Civitate Dei," Book IV, Chapter III, published in 426. This work, "as Englisshed" by J. Healey, was published in 1610.

3

eye to be smoked up with the fumes of vain words, concerning kingdoms, provinces, nations, or so. No, let us take two men, let us imagine the one to be poor, or but of a mean estate, the other potent and wealthy; but withal, let my wealthy man take with him fears, sorrows, covetousness, suspicion, disquiet, contentions,—let these be the books for him to hold in the augmentation of his estate, and with all the increase of those cares, together with his estate; and let my poor man take with him, sufficiency with little, love of kindred, neighbors, friends, joyous peace, peaceful religion, soundness of body, sincereness of heart, abstinence of diet, chastity of carriage, and security of conscience.

Where should a man find any one so sottish as would make a doubt which of these to prefer in his choice? Well, then, even as we have done with these two men, so let us do with two families, two nations, or two kingdoms. Lay them both to the line of equity; which done, and duly considered, when it is done, here doth vanity lie bare to the view, and there shines felicity. Wherefore it is more convenient that such as fear and follow the law of the true God should have the swaying of such empires; not so much for themselves, their piety and their honesty (God's admired gifts) will suffice them, both to the enjoying of true felicity in this life and the attaining of that eternal and true felicity in the next. So that here upon earth, the rule and regality that is given to the good man does not return him so much good as it does to those that are under this his rule and regality. But, contrariwise, the government of the wicked harms themselves far more than their subjects, for it gives themselves the greater liberty to exercise their lusts; but for their subjects, they have none but their own iniquities to answer for; for what injury soever the unrighteous master does to the righteous servant, it is no scourge for his guilt, but a trial of his virtue. And therefore he that is good is free, tho he be a slave; and he that is evil, a slave tho he be king. Nor is he slave to one man, but that which is worst of all, unto as many masters as he affects vices; according to the Scriptures, speaking thus hereof: "Of whatsoever a man is overcome, to that he is in bondage."

ANICIUS BOETHIUS

Born in Rome about 475, died about 524; consul in 510 and magister officiorum in the court of Theodoric the Goth; put to death by Theodoric without trial on the charge of treason and magic; his famous work "De Consolatione Philosophiæ" probably written while in prison in Pavia; parts of that work translated by Alfred the Great and Chaucer; secured much influence for the works of Aristotle by his translations and commentaries.

THE HIGHEST HAPPINESS [1]

WHEN Wisdom had sung this lay he ceased the song and was silent a while. Then he began to think deeply in his mind's thought, and spoke thus: Every mortal man troubles himself with various and manifold anxieties, and yet all desire, through various paths, to come to one end; that is, they desire, by different means, to arrive at one happiness; that is, to know God! He is the beginning and the end of every good, and He is the highest happiness.

Then said the Mind: This, methinks, must be the highest good, so that man should need no

[1] From "The Consolations of Philosophy." The translation of Alfred the Great, modernized. Boethius is not usually classed as a Roman author, altho Gibbon said of him that he was "the last Roman whom Cato or Cicero could have recognized as his countryman." Chaucer made a translation of Boethius, which was printed by Caxton. John Walton made a version in 1410, which was printed at a monastery in 1525. Another early version made by George Coluile was published in 1556. Several others appeared in the sixteenth century.

other good, nor moreover be solicitous beyond that—since he possesses that which is the roof of all other goods; for it includes all other goods, and has all of them within it. It would not be the highest good if any good were external to it, because it would then have to desire some good which itself had not.

Then answered Reason, and said: It is very evident that this is the highest happiness, for it is both the roof and floor of all good. What is that, then, but the best happiness, which gathers the other felicities all within it, and includes, and holds them within it; and to it there is a deficiency of none, neither has it need of any; but they all come from it, and again all return to it; as all waters come from the sea, and again all come to the sea? There is none in the little fountain which does not seek the sea, and again, from the sea it arrives at the earth, and so it flows gradually through the earth, till it again comes to the same fountain that it before flowed from, and so again to the sea.

Now this is an example of the true goods, which all mortal men desire to obtain, tho they by various ways think to arrive at them. For every man has natural good in himself, because every man desires to obtain the true good; but it is hindered by the transitory goods, because it is more prone thereto. For some men think that it is the best happiness that a man be so rich that he have need of nothing more; and they choose life accordingly. Some men think that this is the highest good, that he be among his fellows the most honorable of his fellows, and they with all energy seek this. Some think that

7

the supreme good is in the highest power. These desire, either for themselves to rule, or else to associate themselves in friendship with their rulers. Some persuade themselves that it is the best that a man be illustrious and celebrated, and have good fame; they therefore seek this both in peace and in war. Many reckon it for the greatest good and for the greatest happiness, that a man be always blithe in this present life, and fulfil all his lusts. Some, indeed, who desire these riches, are desirous thereof, because they would have the greater power, that they may the more securely enjoy these worldly lusts, and also the riches. Many there are of those who desire power because they would gather overmuch money; or, again, they are desirous to spread the celebrity of their name.

On account of such and other like frail and perishable advantages, the thought of every human mind is troubled with solicitude and with anxiety. It then imagines that it has obtained some exalted goods when it has won the flattery of the people; and methinks that it has bought a very false greatness. Some with much anxiety seek wives, that thereby they may, above all things, have children, and also live happily. True friends, then, I say, are the most precious things of all these worldly felicities. They are not, indeed, to be reckoned as worldly goods, but as divine; for deceitful fortune does not produce them, but God, who naturally formed them as relations. For of every other thing in this world man is desirous, either that he may through it attain to power, or else some worldly lust; except of the true friend, whom he loves sometimes for affection and for fidelity, tho he expect to himself no other rewards. Nature joins and cements friends together with inseparable love. But with these worldly goods, and with this present wealth, men make oftener enemies than friends. By these and by many such things it may be evident to all men that all the bodily goods are inferior to the faculties of the soul.

We indeed think that a man is the stronger because he is great in his body. The fairness, moreover, and the vigor of the body, rejoices and delights the man, and health makes him cheerful. In all these bodily felicities, men seek simple happiness, as it seems to them. For whatsoever every man chiefly loves above all other things, that he persuades himself is best for him, and that is his highest good. When, therefore, he has acquired that, he imagines that he may be very happy. I do not deny that these goods and this happiness are the highest good of this present life. For every man considers that thing best which he chiefly loves above other things; and therefore he persuades himself that he is very happy if he can obtain what he then most desires. Is not now clearly enough shown to thee the form of the false goods, that is, then, possessions, dignity, and power, and glory, and pleasure? Concerning pleasure Epicurus the philosopher said, when he inquired concerning all those other goods which we before mentioned; then said he that pleasure was the highest good, because all the other goods which we before mentioned gratify the mind and delight it, but pleasure alone chiefly gratifies the body.

But we will still speak concerning the **nature**

of men, and concerning their pursuits. Tho, then, their mind and their nature be now dimmed, and they are by that fall sunk down to evil, and thither inclined, yet they are desirous, so far as they can and may, of the highest good. As a drunken man knows that he should go to his house and to his rest, and yet is not able to find the way thither, so is it also with the mind when it is weighed down by the anxieties of this world. It is sometimes intoxicated and misled by them, so far that it can not rightly find out good. Nor yet does it appear to those men that they at all err, who are desirous to obtain this, that they need labor after nothing more. But they think that they are able to collect together all these goods, so that none may be excluded from the number. They therefore know no other good than the collecting of all the most precious things into their power that they may have need of nothing besides them. But there is no one that has not need of some addition, except God alone. He has of His own enough, nor has He need of anything but that which He has in Himself.

Dost thou think, however, that they foolishly imagine that that thing is best deserving of all estimation which they may consider most desirable? No, no. I know that it is not to be despised. How can that be evil which the mind of every man considers to be good, and strives after, and desires to obtain? No, it is not evil; it is the highest good. Why is not power to be reckoned one of the highest goods of this present life? Is that to be esteemed vain and useless which is the most useful of all those worldly things, that is, power? Is good fame and renown to be accounted nothing? No, no. It is not fit that any one account it nothing; for every man thinks that best which he most loves. Do we not know that no anxiety, or difficulties, or trouble, or pain, or sorrow, is happiness? What more, then, need we say about these felicities? Does not every man know what they are, and also know that they are the highest good? And yet almost every man seeks in very little things the best felicities; because he thinks that he may have them all if he have that which he then chiefly wishes to obtain. This is, then, what they chiefly wish to obtain, wealth, and dignity, and authority, and this world's glory, and ostentation, and worldly lust. Of all this they are desirous because they think that, through these things, they may obtain: that there be not to them a deficiency of anything wished; neither of dignity, nor of power, nor of renown, nor of bliss. They wish for all this, and they do well that they desire it, tho they seek it variously. By these things we may clearly perceive that every man is desirous of this, that he may obtain the highest good, if they were able to discover it, or knew how to seek it rightly. But they do not seek it in the most right way. It is not of this world.

ST. THOMAS AQUINAS

Born near Aquino, Italy, probably in 1225, died in 1274;
entered the Dominican order; studied at Cologne under Al-
bertus Magnus; taught at Cologne, Paris, Rome and Bologna;
his chief work the "Summa Theologiæ"; his complete writings
collected in 1787.

A DEFINITION OF HAPPINESS [1]

THE word end has two meanings. In one
meaning it stands for the thing itself which
we desire to gain: thus the miser's end is money.
In another meaning it stands for the near attainment, or possession, or use, or enjoyment of
the thing desired, as if one should say that the
possession of money is the miser's end, or the
enjoyment of something pleasant the end of the
sensualist. In the first meaning of the word,
therefore, the end of man is the Uncreated Good,
namely God, who alone of His infinite goodness
can perfectly satisfy the will of man. But according to the second meaning, the last end of
man is something created, existing in himself,
which is nothing else than the attainment or
enjoyment of the last end. Now the last end
is called happiness. If therefore the happiness
of a man is considered in its cause or object,

[1] From the "Ethics." The complete works of Aquinas
were published in 1787; but a new and notable edition was
compiled in 1883 under the intimate patronage of Pope Leo
XIII, to whom is given credit for a modern revival of interest
in his writings.

in that way it is something uncreated; but if it is considered in essence, in that way happiness is a created thing.

Happiness is said to be the sovereign good of man, because it is the attainment or enjoyment of the sovereign good. So far as the happiness of man is something created, existing in the man himself, we must say that the happiness of man is an act. For happiness is the last perfection of man. But everything is perfect so far as it is in act; for potentiality without actuality is imperfect. Happiness, therefore, must consist in the last and crowning act of man. But it is manifest that activity is the last and crowning act of an active being; whence also it is called by the philosopher "the second act." And hence it is that each thing is said to be for the sake of its activity. It needs must be therefore that the happiness of man is a certain activity.

Life has two meanings. One way it means the very being of the living, and in that way happiness is not life; for of God alone can it be said that His own being is His happiness. In another way life is taken to mean the activity on the part of the living thing by which activity the principle of life is reduced to act. Thus we speak of an active or contemplative life, or of a life of pleasure; and in this way the last end is called life everlasting, as is clear from the text: "This is life everlasting, that they know Thee, the only true God."

By the definition of Boethius, that happiness is "a state made perfect by the aggregate sum of all things good," nothing else is meant than that the happy man is in a state of perfect good.

13

But Aristotle has exprest the proper essence of happiness, showing by what it is that man is constituted in such a state, namely, by a certain activity.

Action is twofold. There is one variety that proceeds from the agent to exterior matter, as the action of cutting and burning, and such an activity can not be happiness, for such activity is not an act and perfection of the agent, but rather of the patient. There is another action immanent, or remaining in the agent himself, as feeling, understanding, and willing. Such action is a perfection and act of the agent, and an activity of this sort may possibly be happiness.

Since happiness means some manner of final perfection, happiness must have different meanings according to the different grades of perfection that there are attainable by different beings capable of happiness. In God is happiness by essence, because His very being is His activity, because He does not enjoy any other thing than Himself. In the angels final perfection is by way of a certain activity, whereby they are united to the uncreated good; and this activity is in them one and everlasting. In men, in the state of the present life, final perfection is by way of an actiivty whereby they are united to God. But this activity can not be everlasting or continuous, and by consequence it is not one, because an act is multiplied by interruption; and therefore, in this state of the present life, perfect happiness is not to be had by man.

Hence the philosopher, placing the happiness of man in this life, says that it is imperfect and after much discussion he comes to this con clusion: "We call them happy, so far as happiness can be predicated of men." But we have a promise from God of perfect happiness, when we shall be "like the angels in heaven." As regards this perfect happiness, the objection drops, because in this state of happiness the mind of man is united to God by one continuous and everlasting activity. But in the present life, so far as we fall short of the unity and continuity of such an activity, so much do we lose of the perfection of happiness. There is, however, granted us a certain participation in happiness, and the more continuous and undivided the activity can be the more will it come up to the idea of happiness. And therefore in the active life, which is busied with many things, there is less of the essence of happiness than in the contemplative life, which is busy with the one occupation of the contemplation of truth.

THOMAS À KEMPIS

Born in Rhenish Prussia about 1380, died in the Netherlands in 1471; his real name Thomas Hammerken; entered an Augustinian convent near Zwolle in 1407; became subprior of the convent in 1423 and again in 1447; generally accepted as the author of "The Imitation of Christ."

OF ETERNAL LIFE AND OF STRIVING FOR IT[1]

SON, when thou perceivest the desire of eternal bliss to be infused into thee from above, and thou wouldst fain go out of the tabernacle of this body, that thou mightest contemplate My brightness without any shadow of change—enlarge thy heart, and receive this holy inspiration with thy whole desire.

Return the greatest thanks to the Supreme Goodness, which dealeth so condescendingly with thee, mercifully visiteth thee, ardently inciteth

[1] From "The Imitation of Christ." Altho commonly ascribed to Thomas à Kempis, there has been much controversy as to the real authorship of this famous work. Many early editions bear the name of Thomas, including one of the year 1471, which is sometimes thought to be the first. As against his authorship it is contended that he was a professional copyist, and that the use of his name in the first edition conformed to a custom that belonged more to a transcriber than to an author. One of the earliest English versions of Thomas à Kempis was made by Wyllyam Atkynson and printed by Wykyns de Worde in 1502. A translation by Edward Hake appeared in 1567. Many other early English editions are known.

thee, and powerfully raiseth thee up, lest by thy own weight thou fall down to the things of earth.

For it is not by thy own thoughtfulness or endeavor that thou receivest this, but by the mere condescension of heavenly grace and divine regard; that so thou mayest advance in virtues and greater humility, and prepare thyself for future conflicts, and labor with the whole affection of thy heart to keep close to Me, and serve Me with a fervent will.

Son, the fire often burneth, but the flame ascendeth not without smoke.

And so the desires of some are on fire after heavenly things, and yet they are not free from the temptation of carnal affection.

Therefore is it not altogether purely for God's honor that they act, when they so earnestly petition Him.

Such also is oftentimes thy desire, which thou hast profest to be so importunate.

For that is not pure and perfect which is alloyed with self-interest.

Ask not that which is pleasant and convenient, but that which is acceptable to Me and My honor; for if thou judgest rightly, thou oughtest to prefer and to follow My appointment rather than thine own desire or any other desirable thing.

I know thy desire, and I have often heard thy groanings.

Thou wouldst wish to be already in the liberty of the glory of the children of God.

Now doth the eternal dwelling, and the heavenly country full of festivity, delight thee.

But that hour is not yet come; for there is

yet another time, a time of war, a time of labor and of probation.

Thou desirest to be filled with the Sovereign Good, but thou canst not at present attain to it.

I am He: wait for Me, saith the Lord, until the kingdom of God come.

Thou hast yet to be tried upon earth and exercised in many things.

Consolation shall sometimes be given thee, but abundant satiety shall not be granted thee.

Take courage, therefore, and be valiant, as well in doing as in suffering things repugnant to nature.

Thou must put on the new man, and be changed into another person.

That which thou wouldst not, thou must oftentimes do; and that which thou wouldst, thou must leave undone.

What pleaseth others shall prosper, what is pleasing to thee shall not succeed.

What others say shall be harkened to; what thou sayest shall be reckoned as naught.

Others shall ask, and shall receive; thou shalt ask, and not obtain.

Others shall be great in the esteem of men; about thee nothing shall be said.

To others this or that shall be committed; but thou shalt be accounted as of no use.

At this nature will sometimes repine, and it will be a great matter if thou bear it with silence.

In these, and many such-like things, the faithful servant of the Lord is wont to be tried how far he can deny and break himself in all things.

There is scarce anything in which thou standest so much in need of dying to thyself as in seeing and suffering things that are contrary to thy will, and more especially when those things are commanded which seem to thee inconvenient and of little use.

And because, being under authority, thou darest not resist the higher power, therefore it seemeth to thee hard to walk at the beck of another, and wholly to give up thy own opinion.

But consider, son, the fruit of these labors, their speedy termination, and their reward exceeding great; and thou wilt not hence derive affliction, but the most strengthening consolation in thy suffering.

For in regard to that little of thy will which thou now willingly forsakest, thou shalt forever have thy will in heaven.

For there thou shalt find all that thou willest, all that thou canst desire.

There shall be to thee the possession of every good, without fear of losing it.

There thy will, always one with Me, shall not covet any extraneous or private thing. There no one shall resist thee, no one complain of thee, no one obstruct thee, nothing shall stand in thy way; but every desirable good shall be present at the same moment, shall replenish all thy affections and satiate them to the full.

There I will give thee glory for the contumely thou hast suffered; a garment of praise for thy sorrow; and for having been seated here in the lowest place, the throne of My kingdom forever.

There will the fruit of obedience appear, there will the labor of penance rejoice, and humble subjection shall be gloriously crowned.

Now, therefore, bow thyself down humbly under the hands of all, and heed not who it was that said or commanded this.

But let it be thy great care, that whether thy superior or inferior or equal require anything of thee, or hint at anything, thou take all in good part, and labor with a sincere will to perform it.

Let one seek this, another that; let this man glory in this thing, another in that, and be praised a thousand thousand times: but thou, for thy part, rejoice neither in this nor in that, but in the contempt of thyself, and in My good pleasure and honor alone.

This is what thou hast to wish for, that whether in life or in death, God may be always glorified in thee.

FRANCE

TWELFTH CENTURY—1885

GEOFFREY DE VILLE-HARDOUIN

Born between 1150 and 1165, died in 1212; marshal of Champagne in 1191; joined the Crusade in 1199 under Theobault III; negotiated successfully with Venice for the transfer of the Crusaders by sea to the Holy Land; followed the Crusade and chronicled all its events from 1198 to 1207.

THE SACK OF CONSTANTINOPLE[1]
(1204)

THIS night passed and the day came which was Thursday morning (13 April, 1204), and then every one in the camp armed themselves, the knights and the soldiers, and each one joined his battle corps. The Marquis of Montferrat advanced toward the palace of Bucoleon; and having occupied it, determined to spare the lives of all those he found therein. There were found there women of the highest rank, and of the most honorable character; the sister of the King of France who had been an empress; and the sister

---

[1] From the "Chronicles." This work is important; first, as a record, generally accepted as eminently trustworthy, and second, for its literary excellence, in which sense it has been held in peculiar esteem. George Saintsbury remarks that these chronicles "are by universal consent among the most attractive works of the Middle Ages." They comprize one of the oldest extant examples of French prose. The passage here given was translated for this collection from the old French by Eric Arthur Bell. A translation by T. Smith was published in 1829.

This sack of Constantinople followed what is known as

23

of the King of Hungary, and other women of quality. Of the treasure that there was in the palace, I can not speak; for there was so much that it was without end or measure. Besides this palace which was surrendered to the Marquis Boniface of Montferrat, that of Blachem was surrendered to Henry, brother of Count Baldwin of Flanders.

The booty that was found here was so great that it can only be compared to that which was found in Bucoleon.[2] Each soldier filled the room that was assigned to him with plunder and had the treasure guarded; and the others who were scattered through the city also had their share of spoil. And the booty obtained was so great that it is impossible for me to estimate it,—gold and silver and plate and precious stones,—rich altar cloths and vestments of silk and robes of ermine, and treasure that had been buried under the ground. And truly doth testify Goeffrey of Ville-Hardouin, Marshal of Champagne, when he says that never in the whole of history had a city yielded so much plunder. Every man took as

the Latin Conquest. More than thirty sieges of the city have occurred. After the conquest here referred to Constantinople was occupied by the Latins. It was finally wrested from them by Michael Palæologus. The conquest of 1204 was achieved during the Fourth Crusade. By Latin Conquest is meant a conquest by Western Christians as against its long-time Greek rulers. This conquest was also inspired by the commercial ambition of the Venetians, who had long coveted what were believed to be the fabulous riches of the city. The Latin Empire survived for fifty-six years in a state of almost constant weakness. The conquest had no direct relation to the original purpose of the Crusades, which was the recovery of Jerusalem from the hands of the infidels.

[2] One of the districts into which the city was divided.

much as he could carry, and there was enough for every one.

Thus fared the Crusaders and the Venetians, and so great was the joy and the honor of the victory that God had given them, that those who had been in poverty were rich and living in luxury. Thus was passed Palm Sunday and Easter Sunday in the honor and joy which God had granted them. And they had good cause to be grateful to our Lord, for they had no more than twenty thousand armed men among them all, and by the grace of God they had captured four hundred thousand or more, and that in the strongest city in the world (that is to say, city of any size), and the best fortified.

Then it was announced throughout the whole army by the Marquis Boniface of Montferrat, who was head of the army, and by the barons and the Doge of Venice, that all the booty should be collected and assessed under pain of excommunication. And the places were chosen in three churches; and they put over them as guards French and Venetians, the most loyal that they could find, and then each man began to bring his booty and put it together. Some acted uprightly and others not, for covetousness which is the root of all evil, prevented them; but the covetous began from this moment to keep things back and our Lord began to like them less. Oh God, how loyally they had behaved up to that moment, and the Lord God had shown them that in everything He had honored and favored them above all other people, and now the righteous began to suffer for the wicked.

The plunder and the booty were collected; and

you must know that it was not all equally divided, for there were a number of those who retained a share in spite of the dread of Papal excommunication. Whatever was brought to the churches was collected and divided between the French and Venetians equally as had been arranged. And you must know that the Crusaders, when they had divided, paid on their part fifty thousand marks of silver to the Venetians, and as for themselves they divided a good hundred thousand among their own people. And do you know how it was divided? Each horseman received double the share of a foot soldier, and each knight double the share of a horseman. And you must know that never did a man, either through his rank and prowess receive anything more than had been arranged, unless it was stolen.

As for the thefts, those who were convicted of guilt, you must know were dealt with summarily and there were enough people hung. The Count of St. Paul hung one of his knights with his horse collar round his neck, because he had kept something back, and there were a number who kept things back, much and little, but this is not known for certain.

You may be assured that the booty was great, for not counting what was stolen and the share that fell to the Venetians, a good four hundred thousand marks of silver were brought back, and as many as ten thousand animals of one kind and another. The plunder of Constantinople was divided thus as you have heard.

JEAN DE JOINVILLE

Born about 1224; died in 1317; attended Louis IX in the
Seventh Crusade, spending six years in the East; his "Memoirs of Louis IX," presented by him in 1309 to the great
grandson of Louis, and first published in 1547.

GREEK FIRE IN BATTLE[1]

NOT long after this, the chief of the Turks, before named, crost with his army into the island
that lies between the Rexi and Damietta branches,
where our army was encamped, and formed a line
of battle, extending from one bank of the river
to the other. The Count d'Anjou, who was on the
spot, attacked the Turks, and defeated them so
completely that they took to flight, and numbers
were drowned in each of the branches of the
Nile.

A large body, however, kept their ground, whom
we dared not attack, on account of their numerous
machines, by which they did us great injury with
the divers things cast from them. During the
attack on the Turks by the Count d'Anjou, the
Count Guy de Ferrois, who was in his company
galloped through the Turkish force, attended by

[1] From the "Memoirs of Louis IX, King of France," commonly called St. Louis. The passage here given is from Joinville's account of a battle between Christians and Saracens,
fought near the Damietta branch of the Nile in 1240. Mr.
Saintsbury remarks that Joinville's work "is one of the most
circumstantial records we have of medieval life and thought."
It was translated by Thomas Johnes, of Hafod, and is now
printed in Bohn's library.

his knights, until they came to another battalion of Saracens, where they performed wonders. But at last he was thrown to the ground with a broken leg, and was led back by two of his knights, supporting him by the arms.

You must know there was difficulty in withdrawing the Count d'Anjou from this attack, wherein he was frequently in the utmost danger, and was ever after greatly honored for it.

Another large body of Turks made an attack on the Count de Poitiers and me; but be assured they were very well received, and served in like manner. It was well for them that they found their way back by which they had come; but they left behind great numbers of slain. We returned safely to our camp scarcely having lost any of our men.

One night the Turks brought forward an engine, called by them La Perriere, a terrible engine to do mischief, and placed it opposite to the chaschateils, which Sir Walter De Curel and I were guarding by night. From this engine they flung such quantities of Greek fire, that it was the most horrible sight ever witnessed. When my companion, the good Sir Walter, saw this shower of fire, he cried out, "Gentlemen, we are all lost without remedy; for should they set fire to our chaschateils we must be burnt; and if we quit our post we are for ever dishonored; from which I conclude, that no one can possibly save us from this peril but God, our benignant Creator; I therefore advise all of you, whenever they throw any of this Greek fire, to cast yourselves on your hands and knees, and cry for mercy to our Lord, in whom alone resides all power."

As soon, therefore, as the Turks threw their fires, we flung ourselves on our hands and knees, as the wise man had advised; and this time they fell between our two cats into a hole in front, which our people had made to extinguish them; and they were instantly put out by a man appointed for that purpose. This Greek fire, in appearance, was like a large tun, and its tail was of the length of a long spear; the noise which it made was like to thunder; and it seemed a great dragon of fire flying through the air, giving so great a light with its flame, that we saw in our camp as clearly as in broad day. Thrice this night did they throw the fire from La Perriere, and four times from cross-bows.

Each time that our good King St. Louis heard them make these discharges of fire, he cast himself on the ground, and with extended arms and eyes turned to the heavens, cried with a loud voice to our Lord, and shedding heavy tears, said "Good Lord God Jesus Christ, preserve thou me, and all my people"; and believe me, his sincere prayers were of great service to us. At every time the fire fell near us, he sent one of his knights to know how we were, and if the fire had hurt us. One of the discharges from the Turks fell beside a chas-chateil, guarded by the men of the Lord Courtenay, struck the bank of the river in front, and ran on the ground toward them, burning with flame. One of the knights of this guard instantly came to me, crying out, "Help us, my lord, or we are burnt; for there is a long train of Greek fire, which the Saracens have discharged, that is running straight for our castle."

AUCASSIN AND NICOLETTE

"Aucassin and Nicolette" is the title of a French romance of the thirteenth century, the name of the author being unknown. The only extant manuscript of the story is preserved in the National Library of France. Several translations into English are well known, among them those by Augustus R. MacDonough, F. W. Bourdillon and Andrew Lang.

How the Count Bougart of Valence made war on Count Garin of Beaucaire,—war so great, so marvelous, and so mortal that never a day dawned but always he was there, by the gates and walls and barriers of the town, with a hundred knights, and ten thousand men-at-arms, horsemen and footmen: so burned he the count's land, and spoiled his country, and slew his men. Now, the Count Garin de Beaucaire was old and frail, and his good days were gone over. No heir had he, neither son nor daughter, save one young man only; such an one as I shall tell you. Aucassin was the name of the damoiseau: fair was he, goodly, and great, and featly fashioned of his body and limbs. His hair was yellow, in little curls, his eyes blue-gray and laughing, his face beautiful and shapely, his nose high and well set, and so richly seen was he in all things good, that in him was none evil at all. But so suddenly was he overtaken of Love, who is a great master, that he would not, of his will, be a knight, nor take arms, nor follow tourneys, nor do whatsoever him beseemed. Therefore his father and mother said to him:

"Son, go take thine arms, mount thine horse, and hold thy land, and help thy men, for if they see thee among them, more stoutly will they keep in battle their lives and lands, and thine and mine."

"Father," answered Aucassin, "what are you saying now? Never may God give me aught of my desire, if I be a knight, or mount my horse, or face stour and battle wherein knights smite and are smitten again, unless thou give me Nicolette, my true love, that I love so well."

"Son," said the father, "this may not be. Let Nicolette go. A slave-girl is she, out of a strange land, and the viscount of this town bought her of the Saracens, and carried her hither, and hath reared her and had her christened, and made her his god-daughter, and one day will find a young man for her, to win her bread honorably. Herein hast thou naught to make nor mend; but if a wife thou wilt have, I will give thee the daughter of a king, or a count. There is no man so rich in France, but if thou desire his daughter, thou shall have her."

"Faith! my father," said Aucassin, "tell me where is the place so high in all the world, that Nicolette, my sweet lady and love, would not grace it well? If she were Empress of Constantinople or of Germany, or Queen of France or England, it were little enough for her; so gentle is she and courteous, and debonnaire, and compact of all good qualities."

When Count Garin de Beaucaire knew that he would not avail to withdraw Aucassin, his son, from the love of Nicolette, he went to the viscount of the city, who was his man, and spake

31

to him saying: "Sir Count: away with Nicolette, thy daughter in God; curst be the land whence she was brought into this country, for by reason of her do I lose Aucassin, that will neither be a knight, nor do aught of the things that fall to him to be done. And wit ye well," he said, "that if I might have her at my will, I would burn her in a fire, and yourself might well be sore adread."

"Sir," said the viscount, "this is grievous to me that he comes and goes and hath speech with her. I had bought the maid at mine own charges, and nourished her, and baptized, and made her my daughter in God. Yea, I would have given her to a young man that should win her bread honorably. With this had Aucassin, thy son, naught to make or mend. But sith it is thy will and thy pleasure, I will send her into that land and that country where never will he see her with his eyes."

"Have a heed to thyself," said the Count Garin: "thence might great evil come on thee."

So parted they each from the other. Now the viscount was a right rich man: so had he a rich palace with a garden in face of it; in an upper chamber thereof he had Nicolette placed, with one old woman to keep her company, and in that chamber put bread and meat and wine and such things as were needful. Then he had the door sealed, that none might come in or go forth, save that there was one window, over against the garden, and quite strait, through which came to them a little air. . . .

Aucassin was cast into prison as ye have heard tell, and Nicolette, of her part, was in the cham-

ber. Now it was summer-time, the month of
May, when days are warm, and long, and clear,
and the nights still and serene. Nicolette lay one
night on her bed, and saw the moon shine clear
through a window, and heard the nightingale sing
in the garden, and she minded her of Aucassin
her friend, whom she loved so well. Then fell
she to thoughts of Count Garin of Beaucaire, that
he hated her to death; and therefore deemed she
that there she would no longer abide, for that, if
she were told of, and the count knew where she
lay, an ill death he would make her die. She saw
that the old woman was sleeping, who held her
company. Then she arose, and clad her in a
mantle of silk she had by her, very goodly, and
took sheets of the bed and towels and knotted one
to the other, and made therewith a cord as long
as she might, and knotted it to a pillar in the
window, and let herself slip down into the garden;
then caught up her raiment in both hands, behind
and before, and kilted up her kirtle, because of
the dew that she saw lying deep on the grass, and
so went on her way down through the garden.

Her locks were yellow and curled, her eyes
blue-gray and smiling, her face featly fashioned,
the nose high and fairly set, the lips more red
than cherry or rose in time of summer, her teeth
white and small; and her breasts so firm that they
bore up the folds of her bodice as they had been
two walnuts; so slim was she in the waist that
your two hands might have clipt her; and the
daisy flowers that brake beneath her as she went
tiptoe, and that bent above her instep, seemed
black against her feet and ankles, so white was
the maiden. She came to the postern-gate, and

unbarred it, and went out through the streets of Beaucaire, keeping always on the shadowy side, for the moon was shining right clear, and so wandered she till she came to the tower where her lover lay. The tower was flanked with pillars, and she cowered under one of them, wrapt in her mantle. Then thrust she her head through a crevice of the tower, that was old and worn, and heard Aucassin, who was weeping within, and making dole and lament for the sweet friend he loved so well. And when she had listened to him some time she began to speak. . . .

When Aucassin heard Nicolette say that she would pass into a far country, he was all in wrath.

"Fair, sweet friend," quoth he, "thou shalt not go, for then wouldst thou be my death. And the first man that saw thee and had the might withal, would take thee straightway into his bed to be his leman. And once thou camest into a man's bed, and that bed not mine, wit ye well that I would not tarry till I had found a knife to pierce my heart and slay myself. Nay, verily, wait so long I would not; but would hurl myself so far as I might see a wall, or a black stone, and I would dash my head against it so mightily that the eyes would start and my brain burst. Rather would I die even such a death than know that thou hadst lain in a man's bed, and that bed not mine."

"Aucassin," she said, "I trow thou lovest me not as much as thou sayest, but I love thee more than thou lovest me."

"Ah, fair, sweet friend," said Aucassin, "it may not be that thou shouldest love me even as I love thee. Woman may not love man as man loves woman; for a woman's love lies in her eye, and the bud of her breast, and her foot's tiptoe, but the love of a man is in his heart planted, whence it can never issue forth and pass away.''

Now when Aucassin and Nicolette were holding this parley together, the town's watchmen were coming down a street, with swords drawn beneath their cloaks, for Count Garin had charged them that if they could take her, they should slay her. But the sentinel that was on the tower saw them coming, and heard them speaking of Nicolette as they went, and threatening to slay her.

"God," quoth he, "this were great pity to slay so fair a maid! Right great charity it were if I could say aught to her, and they perceive it not, and she should be on her guard against them, for if they slay her, then were Aucassin, my damoiseau, dead, and that were great pity." . . .

Aucassin fared through the forest from path to path after Nicolette, and his horse bare him furiously. Think ye not that the thorns him spared, nor the briers, nay, not so, but tare his raiment, that scarce a knot might be tied with the soundest part thereof, and the blood spurted from his arms, and flanks, and legs, in forty places, or thirty, so that behind the Childe men might follow on the track of his blood in the grass. But so much he went in thoughts of Nicolette, his lady sweet, that he felt no pain nor torment, and all the day hurled through the forest in this fashion nor heard no word of her. And when he saw vespers draw nigh, he began to weep for that he found her not. All down an old road, and grass-grown, he fared, when anon, looking along the way before him, he saw such an one as I shall tell you. Tall was he, and great of growth, ugly and hideous: his head huge, and blacker than charcoal, and more than the breadth of a hand between his two eyes; and he had great cheeks, and a big nose and flat, big nostrils and wide, and thick lips redder than steak, and great teeth yellow and ugly, and he was shod with hosen and shoon of ox-hide, bound with cords of bark up over the knee, and all about him a great cloak two-fold; and he leaned upon a grievous cudgel, and Aucassin came unto him, and was afraid when he beheld him.

So they parted from each other, and Aucassin rode on; the night was fair and still, and so long he went that he came to the lodge of boughs that Nicolette had builded and woven within and without, over and under, with flowers, and it was the fairest lodge that might be seen. When Aucassin was ware of it, he stopt suddenly, and the light of the moon fell therein.

"Forsooth!" quoth Aucassin, "here was Nicolette, my sweet lady, and this lodge builded she with her fair hands. For the sweetness of it, and for love of her, will I now alight, and rest here this night long."

He drew forth his foot from the stirrup to alight, and the steed was great and tall. He dreamed so much on Nicolette, his right sweet friend, that he fell heavily upon a stone, and drave his shoulder out of its place. Then knew he that he was hurt sore; nathless he bore him with that force he might, and fastened his horse with the other hand to a thorn. Then turned he on his side, and crept backwise into the lodge of boughs. And he looked through a gap in the lodge and saw the stars in heaven, and one that was brighter than the rest; so began he to speak. . . .

When Nicolette heard Aucassin, she came to him, for she was not far away. She passed within the lodge, and threw her arms about his neck, clipt him and kissed him.

"Fair, sweet friend, welcome be thou!"

"And thou, fair, sweet love, be thou welcome!"

So either kissed and clipt the other, and fair joy was them between.

"Ha! sweet love," quoth Aucassin, "but now was I sore hurt, and my shoulder wried, but I take no heed of it, nor have no hurt therefrom, since I have thee."

Right so felt she his shoulder and found it was wried from its place. And she so handled it with her white hands, and so wrought in her surgery, that by God's will who loveth lovers, it went back into its place. Then took she flowers, and fresh grass, and leaves green, and bound them on the hurt with a strip of her smock, and he was all healed. . . .

When all they of the court heard her speak thus, that she was daughter to the King of Carthage, they knew well that she spake truly; so made they great joy of her, and led her to the castle with great honor, as a king's daughter. And they would have given her to her lord a king of Paynim, but she had no mind to marry. There dwelt she three days or four. And she considered by what device she might seek for Aucassin. Then she got her a viol, and learned to play on it; till they would have married her one day to a rich king of Paynim, and she stole forth by night, and came to the seaport, and dwelt with a poor woman thereby. Then took she a certain herb, and therewith smeared her head and her face, till she was all brown and stained. And she had a coat, and mantle, and smock, and breeches made, and attired herself as if she had been a minstrel. So took she the viol and went to a mariner, and so wrought on him that he took her aboard his vessel. Then hoisted they sail, and fared on the high seas even till they came to the land of Provence. And Nicolette went forth and took the viol, and went playing through all the country, even till she came to the castle of Beaucaire, where Aucassin was.

THE BEST OF THE WORLD'S CLASSICS

JEAN FROISSART

Born in France in 1337, died in 1410; went to England in 1360 by invitation of Queen Philippa, a French woman; visited Scotland in 1365 and Italy in 1368, where he met Petrarch and Chaucer; published his "Chronicles," covering events from 1325 until about 1400, at the close of the fifteenth century, the same being one of the first books printed from movable types; the modern edition comprizes twenty-five volumes.

THE BATTLE OF CRÉCY [1]
(1346)

THE Englishmen, who were in three battles lying on the ground to rest them, as soon as they saw the Frenchmen approach, they rose upon their feet fair and easily without any haste, and arranged their battles. The first, which was the Prince's battle, the archers there stood in manner of a herse and the men of arms in the bottom of the battle. The Earl of Northampton and the

[1] The field of Crécy lies about thirty miles northwest of Amiens, in France. The English under Edward III, numbering about 40,000 men, here defeated the French under Philip VI, numbering 80,000 men, the French loss being commonly placed at 30,000.

Of the merits of Froissart, only one opinion has prevailed. He drew a faithful and vivid picture of events which in the main were personally known to him. "No more graphic account exists of any age," says one writer. Froissart was first translated into English in 1525 by Bourchier, Lord Berners. That translation was superseded later by others. In 1802-1805 Thomas Johnes made another translation, which has since been the one chiefly read.

Earl of Arundel with the second battle were on a wing in good order, ready to comfort the Prince's battle, if need were.

The lords and knights of France came not to the assembly together in good order, for some came before and some came after, in such haste and evil order that one of them did trouble another. When the French King saw the Englishmen his blood changed, and said to his marshals, "Make the Genoways go on before, and begin the battle, in the name of God and St. Denis." There were of the Genoways' cross-bows about a fifteen thousand, but they were so weary of going afoot that day a six leagues armed with their cross-bows, that they said to their constables, "We be not well ordered to fight this day, for we be not in the case to do any great deed of arms: we have more need of rest." These words came to the Earl of Alençon, who said, "A man is well at ease to be charged with such a sort of rascals, to be faint and fail now at most need." Also the same season there fell a great rain and a clipse with a terrible thunder, and before the rain there came flying over both battles a great number of crows for fear of the tempest coming.

Then anon the air began to wax clear, and the sun to shine fair and bright, the which was right in the Frenchmen's eyen and on the Englishmen's backs. When the Genoways were assembled together and began to approach, they made a great leap and cry to abash the Englishmen, but they stood still and stirred not for all that; then the Genoways again the second time made another leap and a fell cry, and stept forward a little, and the Englishmen removed not one foot; thirdly,

again they leapt and cried, and went forth till
they came within shot; then they shot fiercely
with their cross-bows. Then the English archers
stept forth one pace and let fly their arrows so
wholly and so thick, that it seemed snow. When
the Genoways felt the arrows piercing through
heads, arms, and breasts, many of them cast down
their cross-bows, and did cut their strings and
returned discomfited. When the French King saw
them fly away, he said, "Slay these rascals, for
they shall let and trouble us without reason."

Then ye should have seen the men of arms dash
in among them and killed a great number of
them; and ever still the Englishmen shot whereas
they saw thickest press the sharp arrows ran
into the men of arms and into their horses, and
many fell, horse and men, among the Genoways,
and when they were down, they could not relieve
again; the press was so thick that one overthrew
another. And also among the Englishmen there
were certain rascals that went afoot with great
knives, and they went in among the men of arms
and slew and murdered many as they lay on the
ground, both earls, barons, knights, and squires;
whereof the King of England was after dis-
pleased, for he had rather they had been taken
prisoners.

The valiant King of Bohemia called Charles of
Luxembourg, son to the noble Emperor Henry of
Luxembourg, for all that he was nigh blind, when
he understood the order of the battle, he said to
them about him, "Where is the Lord Charles my
son?" His men said, "Sir, we can not tell; we
think he be fighting." Then he said, "Sirs, ye
are my men, my companions and friends in this

journey: I require you bring me so far forward that I may strike one stroke with my sword.'' They said they would do his commandment, and to the intent that they should not lose him in the press, they tied all their reins of their bridles each to other and set the King before to accomplish his desire, and so they went on their enemies. The Lord Charles of Bohemia his son, who wrote himself King of Almaine and bare the arms, he came in good order tu the battle; but when he saw that the matter went awry on their party, he departed, I can not tell you which way. The King his father was so far forward that he strake a stroke with his sword, yea, and more than four, and fought valiantly, and so did his company; and they adventured themselves so forward that they were there all slain, and the next day they were found in the place about the King, and all their horses tied each to other.

The Earl of Alençon came to the battle right ordinately and fought with the Englishmen, and the Earl of Flanders also on his part. These two lords with their companies coasted the English archers and came to the Prince's battle, and there fought valiantly long. The French King would fain have come thither, when he saw their banners, but there was a great hedge of archers before him. The same day the French King had given a great black courser to Sir John of Hainault, and he made the Lord Thierry of Senzeille to ride on him and to bear his banner. The same horse took the bridle in the teeth and brought him through all the currours of the Englishmen, and as he would have returned again, he fell in a great dike and was sore hurt, and had been there dead, and his page had not been, who followed him through all the battles and saw where his master lay in the dike, and had none other let but for his horse; for the Englishmen would not issue out of their battle for taking of any prisoner. Then the page alighted and relieved his master: then he went not back again the same way that they came; there was too many in his way.

This battle between Broye and Crécy this Saturday was right cruel and fell, and many a feat of arms done that came not to my knowledge. In the night divers knights and squires lost their masters, and sometime came on the Englishmen, who received them in such wise that they were ever nigh slain; for there was none taken to mercy nor to ransom, for so the Englishmen were determined.

In the morning the day of the battle certain Frenchmen and Almains perforce opened the archers of the Prince's battle, and came and fought with the men of arms hand to hand. Then the second battle of the Englishmen came to succor the Prince's battle, the which was time, for they had as then much ado; and they with the Prince sent a messenger to the King, who was on a little windmill hill. Then the knight said to the King, "Sir, the Earl of Warwick and the Earl of Oxford, Sir Raynold Cobham and other, such as be about the Prince your son, are fiercely fought withal and are sore handled; wherefore they desire you that you and your battle will come and aid them; for if the Frenchmen increase, as they doubt they will, your son and they shall have much ado." Then the King said, "Is my son dead, or hurt, or on the earth felled?"

"No, sir," quoth the knight, "but he is hardly matched; wherefore he hath need of your aid." "Well," said the King, "return to him and to them that sent you hither, and say to them that they send no more to me for any adventure that falleth, as long as my son is alive: and also say to them that they suffer him this day to win his spurs; for if God be pleased, I will this journey be his and the honor thereof, and to them that be about him." Then the knight returned again to them and shewed the King's words, the which greatly encouraged them, and repined in that they had sent to the King as they did.

Sir Godfrey of Harcourt would gladly that the Earl of Harcourt, his brother, might have been saved; for he heard say by them that saw his banner how that he was there in the field on the French party: but Sir Godfrey could not come to him betimes, for he was slain or he could come at him, and so was also the Earl of Aumale his nephew. In another place the Earl of Alençon and the Earl of Flanders fought valiantly, every lord under his own banner; but finally they could not resist against the puissance of the Englishmen, and so there they were also slain, and divers other knights and squires. Also the Earl Louis of Blois, nephew to the French King, and the Duke of Lorraine, fought under their banners; but at last they were closed in among a company of Englishmen and Welshmen, and there were slain for all their prowess. Also there was slain the Earl of Auxerre, the Earl of Saint-Pol, and many other.

In the evening the French King, who had left about him no more than a threescore persons, one and other, whereof Sir John of Hainault was one, who had remounted once the King, for his horse was slain with an arrow, then he said to the King, "Sir, depart hence, for it is time; lose not yourself willfully: if ye have loss at this time, ye shall recover it again another season." And so he took the King's horse by the bridle and led him away in a manner perforce. Then the King rode till he came to the castle of Broye. The gate was closed, because it was by that time dark: then the King called the captain, who came to the walls and said, "Who is that calleth there this time of night?" Then the King said, "Open your gate quickly, for this is the fortune of France." The captain knew then it was the King, and opened the gate and let down the bridge. Then the King entered, and he had with him but five barons, Sir John of Hainault, Sir Charles of Montmorency, the Lord of Beaujeu, the Lord d'Aubigny, and the Lord of Montsault. The King would not tarry there, but drank and departed thence about midnight, and so rode by such guides as knew the country till he came in the morning to Amiens, and there he rested.

This Saturday the Englishmen never departed from their battles for chasing of any man, but kept still their field, and ever defended themselves against all such as came to assail them. This battle ended about evensong time.

PHILIPPE DE COMINES

Born in France about 1445, died in 1511; after serving
Charles the Bold, went over to Louis XI, in whose household he was a confidant and adviser; arrested on political
charges in 1486 and imprisoned more than two years; arrested later by Charles VIII and exiled for ten years; returning to court, he fell into disgrace, went into retirement
and wrote his "Memoirs," the first series covering the history of France between 1464 and 1483, the second, the
period from 1494 to 1498.

OF THE CHARACTER OF LOUIS XI [1]

I HAVE seen many deceptions in this world,
especially in servants toward their masters; and
I have always found that proud and stately
princes who will hear but few, are more liable to
be imposed upon than those who are open and
accessible: but of all the princes that I ever knew,
the wisest and most dexterous to extricate himself out of any danger or difficulty in time of adversity was our master King Louis XI. He was
the humblest in his conversation and habit, and

---

[1] From the "Memoirs." Louis reigned from 1461 to 1483.
It was he, more than any other king, who represt the power
of the feudal princes and consolidated their territories under
the French monarchy.

Comines has been called "the father of modern history."
Hallam says his work "almost makes an epoch in historical
literature"; while Sainte-Beuve has declared that from it "all
political history takes its rise." Comines was translated into
English by T. Banett in 1596. The best-known modern
translation is the one in Bohn's Library, made by Andrew R.
Scoble.

the most painful and indefatigable to win over
any man to his side that he thought capable of
doing him either mischief or service: tho he was
often refused, he would never give over a man
that he wished to gain, but still prest and continued his insinuations, promising him largely, and
presenting him with such sums and honors as he
knew would gratify his ambition; and for such
as he had discarded in time of peace and prosperity, he paid dear (when he had occasion for
them) to recover them again; but when he had
once reconciled them, he retained no enmity toward them for what has passed, but employed
them freely for the future. He was naturally
kind and indulgent to persons of mean estate, and
hostile to all great men who had no need of him.

Never prince was so conversable nor so inquisi-
tive as he, for his desire was to know everybody
he could; and indeed he knew all persons of any
authority or worth in England, Spain, Portugal,
and Italy, in the territories of the Dukes of Burgundy and Bretagne, and among his own subjects: and by those qualities he preserved the
crown upon his head, which was in much danger
by the enemies he had created to himself upon his
accession to the throne.

But above all, his great bounty and liberality
did him the greatest service: and yet, as he behaved himself wisely in time of distress, so when
he thought himself a little out of danger, tho it
were but by a truce, he would disoblige the servants
and officers of his court by mean and petty ways
which were little to his advantage; and as for
peace, he could hardly endure the thoughts of it.
He spoke slightingly of most people, and rather

before their faces than behind their backs; unless he was afraid of them, and of that sort there were a great many, for he was naturally somewhat timorous. When he had done himself any prejudice by his talk, or was apprehensive he should do so, and wished to make amends, he would say to the person whom he had disobliged "I am sensible my tongue has done me a good deal of mischief; but on the other hand, it has sometimes done me much good: however, it is but reason I should make some reparation for the injury." And he never used this kind of apologies to any person but he granted some favor to the person to whom he made it, and it was always of considerable amount.

It is certainly a great blessing from God upon any prince to have experienced adversity as well as prosperity, good as well as evil, and especially if the good outweighs the evil, as it did in the King our master. I am of opinion that the troubles he was involved in in his youth, when he fled from his father and resided six years together with Philip, Duke of Burgundy, were of great service to him; for there he learned to be complaisant to such as he had occasion to use, which was no slight advantage of adversity. As soon as he found himself a powerful and crowned king his mind was wholly bent upon revenge; but he quickly found the inconvenience of this, repented by degrees of his indiscretion, and made sufficient reparation for his folly and error by regaining those he had injured. Besides, I am very confident that if his education had not been different from the usual education of such nobles as I have seen in France, he could not so easily have worked himself out of his troubles: for they are brought up to nothing but to make themselves ridiculous, both in their clothes and discourse; they have no knowledge of letters; no wise man is suffered to come near them, to improve their understandings; they have governors who manage their business, but they do nothing themselves: nay, there are some nobles who tho they have an income of thirteen livres, will take pride to bid you "Go to my servants and let them answer you," thinking by such speeches to imitate the state and grandeur of a prince; and I have seen their servants take great advantage of them, giving them to understand they were fools; and if afterward they came to apply their minds to business and attempted to manage their own affairs, they began so late they could make nothing of it. And it is certain that all those who have performed any great or memorable action worthy to be recorded in history, began always in their youth; and this is to be attributed to the method of their education, or some particular blessing of God. . . .

Of all diversions he loved hunting and hawking in their seasons; but his chief delight was in dogs. In hunting, his eagerness and pain were equal to his pleasure, for his chase was the stag, which he always ran down. He rose very early in the morning, rode sometimes a great distance, and would not leave his sport, let the weather be never so bad; and when he came home at night he was often very weary, and generally in a violent passion with some of his courtiers or huntsmen; for hunting is a sport not always to be managed according to the master's direction; yet in the opinion of most people, he understood it as well as any prince of his time. He was continually at these sports, lodging in the country villages to which his recreations led him, till he was interrupted by business; for during the most part of the summer there was constantly war between him and Charles, Duke of Burgundy, and in the winter they made truces; so that he had but a little time during the whole year to spend in pleasure, and even then the fatigues he underwent were excessive. When his body was at rest his mind was at work, for he had affairs in several places at once, and would concern himself as much in those of his neighbors as in his own; putting officers of his own over all the great families, and endeavoring to divide their authority as much as possible. When he was at war he labored for a peace or a truce, and when he had obtained it he was impatient for war again. He troubled himself with many trifles in his government which he had better have left alone: but it was his temper, and he could not help it; besides, he had a prodigious memory, and he forgot nothing, but knew everybody, as well in other countries as in his own.

And in truth he seemed better fitted to rule a world than to govern a single kingdom. I speak not of his minority, for then I was not with him; but when he was eleven years he was, by the advice of some of the nobility and others of his kingdom, embroiled in a war with his father, Charles VII, which lasted not long, and was called the Praguerie. When he was arrived at man's estate he was married, much against his inclination, to the King of Scotland's daughter; and he regretted her existence during the whole course of her life. Afterward, by reason of the broils and factions in his father's court, he retired into Dauphiny (which was his own), whither many persons of quality followed him, and indeed more than he could entertain. During his residence in Dauphiny he married the Duke of Savoy's daughter, and not long after he had great disputes with his father-in-law, and a terrible war was begun between them.

His father, King Charles VII, seeing his son attended by so many good officers and raising men at his pleasure, resolved to go in person against him with a considerable body of forces, in order to disperse them. While he was upon his march I put out proclamations, requiring them all as his subjects, under great penalties, to repair to him; and many obeyed, to the great displeasure of the Dauphin, who finding his father incensed, tho he was strong enough to resist, resolved to retire and leave that country to him; and accordingly he removed with but a slender retinue into Burgundy to Duke Philip's court, who received him honorably, furnished him nobly, and maintained him and his principal servants by way of pensions; and to the rest he gave presents as he saw occasion during the whole time of their residence there. However, the Dauphin entertained so many at his own expense that his money often failed, to his great disgust and mortification; for he was forced to borrow, or his people would have forsaken him; which is certainly a great affliction to a prince who was utterly unaccustomed to those straits. So that during his residence at the court of Burgundy he had his anxieties, for he was constrained to cajole the duke and his ministers,

lest they should think he was too burdensome
and had laid too long upon their hands; for he
had been with them six years, and his father,
King Charles, was constantly pressing and solicit-
ing the Duke of Burgundy, by his ambassadors,
either to deliver him up to him or to banish him
out of his dominions. And this, you may believe,
gave the Dauphin some uneasy thoughts and
would not suffer him to be idle. In which season
of his life, then, was it that he may be said to
have enjoyed himself? I believe from his infancy
and innocence to his death, his whole life was
nothing but one continued scene of troubles and
fatigues; and I am of opinion that if all the days
of his life were computed in which his joys and
pleasures outweighed his pain and trouble, they
would be found so few that there would be twenty
mournful ones to one pleasant.

MARGUERITE D'ANGOU-LÊME

Born in France in 1492, died in 1549; sister of Francis I; married in 1509 Duc d' Alençon, and later Henri d'Albret, King of Navarre; assumed the direction of government after the death of the King in 1554; wrote poems and letters, the latter published in 1841-42; her "Heptameron" modeled on the "Decameron" of Boccaccio, published in 1558 after her death, its authorship perhaps collaborative.

OF HUSBANDS WHO ARE UNFAITHFUL [1]

A LITTLE company of five ladies and five noble gentlemen have been interrupted in their travels by heavy rains and great floods, and find themselves together in a hospitable abbey. They while away the time as best they can, and the second day Parlamente says to the old Lady Oisille, "Madame, I wonder that you who have so much experience do not think of some pastime to sweeten the gloom that our long delay here causes us." The other ladies echo her wishes, and all the gentlemen agree with them, and beg the Lady Oisille to be pleased to direct how they shall amuse themselves. She answers them:

"My children, you ask of me something that I find very difficult,—to teach you a pastime that can deliver you from your sadness; for having sought some such remedy all my life I have never found but one—the reading of Holy Writ; in

[1] From the "Heptameron," of which a translation by R. Codrington appeared in London in 1654.

which is found the true and perfect joy of the mind, from which proceed the comfort and health of the body. And if you ask me what keeps me so joyous and so healthy in my old age, it is that as soon as I rise I take and read the Holy Scriptures, seeing and contemplating the will of God, who for our sakes sent His son on earth to announce this holy word and good news, by which He promises remission of sins, satisfaction for all duties by the gifts He makes us of His love, passion and merits. This consideration gives me so much joy that I take my Psalter and as humbly as I can I sing with my heart and pronounce with my tongue the beautiful psalms and canticles that the Holy Spirit wrote in the heart of David and of other authors. And this contentment that I have in them does me so much good that the ills that every day may happen to me seem to me to be blessings, seeing that I have in my heart, by faith, Him who has borne them for me. Likewise, before supper, I retire, to pasture my soul in reading; and then, in the evening, I call to mind what I have done in the past day, in order to ask pardon for my faults, and to thank Him for His kindnesses, and in His love, fear and peace I repose, assured against all ills. Wherefore, my children, this is the pastime in which I have long stayed my steps, after having searched all things, where I found no content for my spirit. It seems to me that if every morning you will give an hour to reading, and then, during mass, devoutly say your prayers, you will find in this desert the same beauty as in cities; for he who knows God, sees all beautiful things in Him, and without Him all is ugliness. . . .

"I beg you, ladies," continues the narrator, "if God give you such husbands,[2] not to despair till you have long tried every means to reclaim them; for there are twenty-four hours in a day in which a man may change his way of thinking, and a woman should deem herself happier to have won her husband by patience and long effort than if fortune and her parents had given her a more perfect one." "Yes," said Oisille, "this is an example for all married women."—"Let her follow this example who will," said Parlamente: "but as for me, it would not be possible for me to have such long patience; for, however true it may be that in all estates patience is a fine virtue, it's my opinion that in marriage it brings about at last unfriendliness; because, suffering unkindness from a fellow being, one is forced to separate from him as far as possible, and from this separation arises a contempt for the fault of the disloyal one, and in this contempt little by little love diminishes; for it is what is valued that is loved." —"But there is danger," said Ennarsuite, "that the impatient wife may find a furious husband, who would give her pain in lieu of patience."— "But what could a husband do," said Parlamente, "save what has been recounted in this story?"—"What could he do?" said Ennarsuite, "he could beat his wife." . . .

"I think," said Parlamente, "that a good woman would not be so grieved in being beaten out of anger, as in being contemptuously treated by a man who does not care for her, and after having endured the suffering of the loss of his friendship, nothing the husband might do would

[2] That is, unfaithful husbands.

cause her much concern. And besides, the story says that the trouble she took to draw him back to her was because of her love for her children, and I believe it.''—''And do you think it was so very patient of her,'' said Nomerfide, ''to set fire to the bed in which her husband was sleeping?'' —''Yes,'' said Longarine, ''for when she saw the smoke she awoke him; and that was just the thing where she was most in fault, for of such husbands as those the ashes are good to make lye for the washtub.''—''You are cruel, Longarine,'' said Oisille, ''and you did not live in such fashion with your husband.''—''No,'' said Longarine, ''for, God be thanked, he never gave me such occasion, but reason to regret him all my life, instead of to complain of him.''—''And if he had treated you in this way,'' said Nomerfide, ''what would you have done?''—''I loved him so much,'' said Longarine, ''that I think I should have killed him and then killed myself; for to die after such vengeance would be pleasanter to me than to live faithfully with a faithless husband.''

''As far as I see,'' said Hircan, ''you love your husbands only for yourselves. If they are good after your own heart, you love them well; if they commit toward you the least fault in the world, they have lost their week's work by a Saturday. The long and the short is that you want to be mistresses; for my part I am of your mind, provided all the husbands also agree to it.''—''It is reasonable,'' said Parlamente, ''that the man rule us as our head, but not that he desert us or ill-treat us.''—''God,'' said Oisille, ''has set in such due order the man and the woman that if the marriage estate is not abused, I hold it to be one of the most beautiful and stable conditions in the world; and I am sure that all those here present, whatever air they assume, think no less highly of it. And forasmuch as men say they are wiser than women, they should be more sharply punished when the fault is on their side. But we have talked enough on this subject.''

FRANÇOIS RABELAIS

Born in Touraine in 1495, died in Paris in 1553; educated
at an abbey and spent fifteen or more years as a monk;
studied medicine in 1530 and practised in Lyons; traveled
in Italy; in charge of a parish at Meudon in 1550-52; com-
posed almanacs and edited old medical books; published
"Pantagruel" in 1533 and "Gargantua" in 1535, the success
of which led to several sequels, the last appearing in the
year of his death.

I

GARGANTUA IN HIS CHILDHOOD[1]

GARGANTUA, from three years to five, was nourished and instructed in all proper discipline by
the commandment of his father, and spent that
time like the other little children of the country,
—that is, in drinking, eating, and sleeping; in eating, sleeping, and drinking; and in sleeping, drinking, and eating. Still he wallowed in the mire,

[1] From Book I, Chapter XI, of "The Inestimable Life of
the Great Gargantua, Father of Pantagruel." The basis of all
English translations of Rabelais is the work begun by Sir
Thomas Urquhart and completed by Peter A. Motteux.
Urquhart was a Scotchman, who was born in 1611 and died
in 1660. Motteux was a Frenchman, who settled in England after the revocation of the Edict of Nantes, and was
the author of several plays. This translation has been called
'one of the most perfect that ever man accomplished." Other
and later versions have usually been based on Urquhart and
Motteux, but have been expurgated, as is the case with the
passages given here. An earlier version of "Pantagruel,"
published in London in 1620, was ascribed to "Democritus
Pseudomantio."

blackened his face, trod down his shoes at heel; at the flies he did oftentimes yawn, and willingly ran after the butterflies, the empire whereof belonged to his father. He sharpened his teeth with a slipper, washed his hands with his broth, combed his head with a bowl, sat down between two stools and came to the ground, covered himself with a wet sack, drank while eating his soup, ate his cake without bread, would bite in laughing, laugh in biting, hide himself in the water for fear of rain, go cross, fall into dumps, look demure, skin the fox, say the ape's *paternoster*, return to his sheep, turn the sows into the hay, beat the dog before the lion, put the cart before the horse, scratch where he did not itch, shoe the grasshopper, tickle himself to make himself laugh, know flies in milk, scrape paper, blur parchment, then run away, pull at the kid's leather, reckon without his host, beat the bushes without catching the birds, and thought that bladders were lanterns. He always looked a gift-horse in the mouth, hoped to catch larks if ever the heavens should fall, and made a virtue of necessity. Every morning his father's puppies ate out of the dish with him, and he with them. He would bite their

Rabelais, by common consent, has a place among the greatest prose writers of the world. In his knowledge of human nature and his literary excellence, he is often ranked as inferior only to Shakespeare. As an exponent of the sentiments and atmosphere of his own time, we find in him what is found only in a few of the world's greatest writers. That he has not been more widely read in modern times, is attributed chiefly to the extraordinary coarseness of language which he constantly introduces into his pages. This coarseness is, in fact, so pervasive that expurgation is made extremely difficult to any one who would preserve some fair remnant of the original.

ears, and they would scratch his nose. The good man Grangousier said to Gargantua's governesses:

"Philip, King of Macedon, knew the wit of his son Alexander, by his skilful managing of a horse;[2] for the said horse was so fierce and unruly that none durst adventure to ride him, because he gave a fall to all his riders, breaking the neck of this man, the leg of that, the brain of one, and the jawbone of another. This by Alexander being considered, one day in the hippodrome (which was a place appointed for the walking and running of horses), he perceived that the fury of the horse proceeded merely from the fear he had of his own shadow; whereupon, getting on his back he ran him against the sun, so that the shadow fell behind, and by that means tamed the horse and brought him to his hand. Whereby his father recognized the divine judgment that was in him, and caused him most carefully to be instructed by Aristotle, who at that time was highly renowned above all the philosophers of Greece. After the same manner I tell you, that as regards my son Gargantua, I know that his understanding doth participate of some divinity, —so keen, subtle, profound, and clear do I find him; and if he be well taught, he will attain to a sovereign degree of wisdom. Therefore will I commit him to some learned man, to have him indoctrinated according to his capacity, and will spare no cost."

Whereupon they appointed him a great sophister-doctor, called Maître Tubal Holophernes, who taught him his A B C so well that he could

[2] The famous horse Bucephalus is here referred to.

say it by heart backward; and about this he was five years and three months. Then read he to him Donat, Facet, Theodolet, and Alanus *in parabolis*. About this he was thirteen years, six months, and two weeks. But you must remark that in the mean time he did learn to write in Gothic characters, and that he wrote all his books, —for the art of printing was not then in use. After that he read unto him the book "De Modis Significandi," with the commentaries of Hurtebise, of Fasquin, of Tropditeux, of Gaulehaut, of John le Veau, of Billonio, of Brelingandus, and a rabble of others; and herein he spent more than eighteen years and eleven months, and was so well versed in it that at the examination he would recite it by heart backward, and did sometimes prove on his fingers to his mother *quod de modis significandi non erat scientia*. Then did he read to him the "Compost," on which he spent sixteen years and two months, and that justly at the time his said preceptor died, which was in the year one thousand four hundred and twenty.

Afterward he got another old fellow with a cough to teach him, named Maître Jobelin Bridé, who read unto him Hugutio, Hebrard's "Grécisme," the "Doctrinal," the "Parts," the "Quid Est," the "Supplementum"; Marmoquet "De Moribus in Mensa Servandis"; Seneca "De Quatour Virtutibus Cardinalibus"; Passavantus "Cum Commento" and "Dormi Securé," for the holidays; and some other of such-like stuff, by reading whereof he became as wise as any we have ever baked in an oven.

At the last his father perceived that indeed he studied hard, and that altho he spent all his time in it, he did nevertheless profit nothing, but which is worse, grew thereby foolish, simple, doted, and blockish: whereof making a heavy regret to Don Philip des Marays, Viceroy of Papeligose, he found that it were better for him to learn nothing at all than to be taught such-like books under such schoolmasters; because their knowledge was nothing but brutishness, and their wisdom but toys, bastardizing good and noble spirits and corrupting the flower of youth. "That it is so, take," said he, "any young boy of the present time, who hath only studied two years: if he have not a better judgment, a better discourse, and that exprest in better terms, than your son, with a completer carriage and civility to all manner of persons, account me forever a chawbacon of La Brène."

This pleased Grangousier very well, and he commanded that it should be done. At night at supper, the said Des Marays brought in a young page of his from Ville-gouges, called Eudemon, so well combed, so well drest, so well brushed, so sweet in his behavior, that he resembled a little angel more than a human creature. Then he said to Grangousier, "Do you see this child? He is not as yet full twelve years old. Let us try, if it pleaseth you, what difference there is betwixt the knowledge of the doting dreamers of old time and the young lads that are now."

The trial pleased Grangousier, and he commanded the page to begin. Then Eudemon, asking leave of the viceroy, his master, so to do, with his cap in his hand, a clear and open countenance, ruddy lips, his eyes steady, and his looks fixt upon Gargantua, with a youthful modesty, stood up

straight on his feet and began to commend and
magnify him, first, for his virtue and good manners; secondly, for his knowledge; thirdly, for
his nobility; fourthly, for his bodily beauty; and
in the fifth place, sweetly exhorted him to reverence his father with all observancy, who was
so careful to have him well brought up. In the
end he prayed him that he would vouchsafe to
admit of him amongst the least of his servants;
for other favor at that time desired he none of
heaven but that he might do him some grateful
and acceptable service.

All this was by him delivered with gestures so
proper, pronunciation so distinct, a voice so elo-
quent, language so well turned, and in such good
Latin, that he seemed rather a Gracchus, a Cicero, an Æmilius of the time past than a youth
of his age. But all the countenance that Gargantua kept was that he fell to crying like a
cow, and cast down his face, hiding it with his
cap; nor could they possibly draw one word
from him. Whereat his father was so grievously
vexed that he would have killed Maître Jobelin;
but the said Des Marays withheld him from it
by fair persuasions, so that at length he pacified
his wrath. The Grangousier commanded he
should be paid his wages, that they should make
him drink theologically, after which he was to
go to all the devils. "At least," said he, "today shall it not cost his host much, if by chance
he should die as drunk as an Englishman."

II

GARGANTUA'S EDUCATION [3]

Maître Jobelin being gone out of the house, Grangousier consulted with the viceroy what tutor they should choose for Gargantua; and it was betwixt them resolved that Ponocrates, the tutor of Eudemon, should have the charge, and that they should all go together to Paris to know what was the study of the young men of France at that time. . . .

Ponocrates appointed that for the beginning he should do as he had been accustomed; to the end he might understand by what means, for so long a time, his old masters had made him so foolish, simple, and ignorant. He disposed, therefore, of his time in such fashion that ordinarily he did awake between eight and nine o'clock, whether it was day or not; for so had his ancient governors ordained, alleging that which David saith, *Vanum est vobis ante lucem surgere.* Then did he tumble and wallow in the bed some time, the better to stir up his vital spirits, and appareled himself according to the season; but willingly he would wear a great long gown of thick frieze, lined with fox fur. Afterward he combed his head with the German comb, which is the four fingers and the thumb; for his preceptors said that to comb himself other-

[3] From Book I of "The Inestimable Life of the Great Gargantua, Father of Pantagruel." The Urquhart-Motteux translation.

wise, to wash and make himself neat was to lose time in this world. Then to suppress the dew and bad air, he breakfasted on fair fried tripe, fair grilled meats, fair hams, fair hashed capon, and store of sipped brewis.

Ponocrates showed him that he ought not to eat so soon after rising out of his bed, unless he had performed some exercise beforehand. Gargantua answered: "What! have not I sufficiently well exercised myself? I rolled myself six or seven turns in my bed before I rose. Is not that enough? Pope Alexander did so, by the advice of a Jew, his physician; and lived till his dying day in despite of the envious. My first masters have used me to it, saying that breakfast makes a good memory; wherefore they drank first. I am very well after it, and dine but the better. And Maître Tubal, who was the first licentiate at Paris, told me that it is not everything to run a pace, but to set forth well betimes: so doth not the total welfare of our humanity depend upon perpetual drinking *atas, atas*, like ducks, but on drinking well in the morning; whence the verse—

" 'To rise betimes is no good hour,
To drink betimes is better sure.' "

After he had thoroughly broken his fast, he went to church; and they carried for him, in a great basket, a huge breviary. There he heard six-and-twenty or thirty masses. This while, to the same place came his sayer of hours, lapped up about the chin like a tufted whoop, and his breath perfumed with good store of sirup. With him he mumbled all his kyriels, which he so curiously picked that there fell not so much as one grain to the ground. As he went from the church, they brought him, upon a dray drawn by oxen, a heap of paternosters of Sanct Claude, every one of them being of the bigness of a hat-block; and thus walking through the cloisters, galleries, or garden, he said more in turning them over than sixteen hermits would have done. Then did he study for some paltry half-hour with his eyes fixt upon his book; but as the comic saith, his mind was in the kitchen. Then he sat down at table; and because he was naturally phlegmatic, he began his meal with some dozens of hams, dried neats' tongues, mullet's roe, chitterlings, and such other forerunners of wine.

In the meanwhile, four of his folks did cast into his mouth, one after another continually, mustard by whole shovelfuls. Immediately after that he drank a horrific draft of white wine for the ease of his kidneys. When that was done, he ate according to the season meat agreeable to his appetite, and then left off eating when he was like to crack for fulness. As for his drinking, he had neither end nor rule. For he was wont to say, that the limits and bounds of drinking were when the cork of the shoes of him that drinketh swelleth up half a foot high.

Then heavily mumbling a scurvy grace, he washed his hands in fresh wine, picked his teeth with the foot of a pig, and talked jovially with his attendants. Then the carpet being spread, they brought great store of cards, dice, and chessboards.

After having well played, reveled, passed and spent his time, it was proper to drink a little, and that was eleven goblets the man; and immediately after making good cheer again, he would stretch himself upon a fair bench, or a good large bed, and there sleep two or three hours together without thinking or speaking any hurt. After he was awakened he would shake his ears a little. In the mean time they brought him fresh wine. Then he drank better than ever. Ponocrates showed him that it was an ill diet to drink so after sleeping. "It is," answered Gargantua, "the very life of the Fathers; for naturally I sleep salt, and my sleep hath been to me instead of so much ham."

Then began he to study a little, and the paternosters first, which the better and more formally to dispatch, he got up on an old mule which had served nine kings; and so mumbling with his mouth, doddling his head, would go see a coney caught in a net. At his return he went into the kitchen to know what roast meat was on the spit; and supped very well, upon my conscience, and commonly did invite some of his neighbors that were good drinkers; with whom carousing, they told stories of all sorts, from the old to the new. After supper were brought in upon the place the fair wooden gospels—that is to say, many pairs of tables and cards—with little small banquets, intermined with collations and reer-suppers. Then did he sleep without unbridling until eight o'clock in the next morning.

When Ponocrates knew Gargantua's vicious manner of living, he resolved to bring him up in another kind; but for a while he bore with him, considering that nature does not endure sudden changes without great violence. Therefore, to begin his work the better, he requested a learned physician of that time, called Maître Theodorus, seriously to perpend, if it were possible, how to bring Gargantua unto a better course. The said physician purged him canonically with Anticyran hellebore, by which medicine he cleansed all the alteration and perverse habitude of his brain. By this means also Ponocrates made him forget all that he had learned under his ancient preceptors. To do this better, they brought him into the company of learned men who were there, in emulation of whom a great desire and affection came to him to study otherwise, and to improve his parts. Afterward he put himself into such a train of study that he lost not any hour in the day, but employed all his time in learning and honest knowledge. Gargantua awaked then about four o'clock in the morning.

While they were rubbing him, there was read unto him some chapter of the Holy Scripture aloud and clearly, with a pronunciation fit for the matter; and hereunto was appointed a young page born in Basché, named Anagnostes. According to the purpose and argument of that lesson, he oftentimes gave himself to revere, adore, pray, and send up his supplications to that good God whose word did show His majesty and marvelous judgments. Then his master repeated what had been read, expounding unto him the most obscure and difficult points. They then considered the face of the sky, if it was such as they had observed it the night before, and into what signs the sun was entering, as also the moon for that day. This done, he was appareled, combed, curled, trimmed, and perfumed, during which time they repeated to him the lessons of the day before. He himself said them by heart, and upon them grounded practical cases concerning the estate of man; which he would prosecute sometimes two or three hours, but ordinarily they ceased as soon as he was fully clothed. Then for three good hours there was reading. This done, they went forth, still conferring of the substance of the reading, and disported themselves at ball, tennis, or the *pile trigone;* gallantly exercising their bodies, as before they had done their minds. All their play was but in liberty, for they left off when they pleased; and that was commonly when they did sweat, or were otherwise weary. Then were they very well dried and rubbed, shifted their shirts, and walking soberly, went to see if dinner was ready. While they stayed for that, they did clearly and eloquently recite some sentences that they had retained of the lecture.

In the mean time Master Appetite came, and then very orderly sat they down at table. At the beginning of the meal there was read some pleasant history of ancient prowess, until he had taken his wine. Then if they thought good, they continued reading, or began to discourse merrily together; speaking first of the virtue, propriety, efficacy, and nature of all that was served in at that table; of bread, of wine, of water, of salt, of flesh, fish, fruits, herbs, roots, and of their dressing. By means whereof, he learned in a little time all the passages that on these subject are to be found in Pliny, Athenæus, Dioscorides, Julius Pollux, Gallen, Porphyrius,

Oppian, Polybius, Heliodorus, Aristotle, Ælian, and others. While they talked of these things, many times, to be more the certain, they caused the very books to be brought to the table; and so well and perfectly did he in his memory retain the things above said, that in that time there was not a physician that knew half so much as he did. Afterward they conferred of the lessons read in the morning; and ending their repast with some conserve of quince, he washed his hands and eyes with fair fresh water, and gave thanks unto God in some fine canticle, made in praise of the divine bounty and munificence.

This done, they brought in cards, not to play, but to learn a thousand pretty tricks and new inventions, which were all grounded upon arithmetic. By this means he fell in love with that numerical science; and every day after dinner and supper he passed his time in it as pleasantly as he was wont to do at cards and dice: so that at last he understood so well both the theory and practise thereof, that Tonstal the Englishman, who had written very largely of that purpose, confest that verily in comparison of him he understood nothing but double Dutch; and not only in that, but in the other mathematical sciences, as geometry, astronomy, music. For while waiting for the digestion of his food, they made a thousand joyous instruments and geometrical figures, and at the same time practised the astronomical canons.

After this they recreated themselves with singing musically, in four or five parts, or upon a set theme, as it best pleased them. In matter of musical instruments, he learned to play the lute, the spinet, the harp, the German flute, the flute with nine holes, the violin, and the sackbut. This hour thus spent, he betook himself to his principal study for three hours together, or more, as well to repeat his matutinal lectures as to proceed in the book wherein he was; as also to write handsomely, to draw and form the antique and Roman letters. This being done, they went out of their house, and with them a young gentleman of Touraine, named Gymnast, who taught him the art of riding.

Changing then his clothes, he mounted on any kind of a horse, which he made to bound in the air, to jump the ditch, to leap the palisade, and to turn short in a ring both to the right and left hand. There he broke not his lance; for it is the greatest foolishness in the world to say, I have broken ten lances at tilts or in fight. A carpenter can do even as much. But it is a glorious and praiseworthy action with one lance to break and overthrow ten enemies. Therefore with a sharp, strong, and stiff lance would he usually force a door, pierce a harness, uproot a tree, carry away the ring, lift up a saddle, with the mail-coat and gantlet. All this he did in complete arms from head to foot. He was singularly skilful in leaping nimbly from one horse to another without putting foot to ground. He could likewise from either side, with a lance in his hand, leap on horseback without stirrups, and rule the horse at his pleasure without a bridle; for such things are useful in military engagements. Another day he exercised the battle-ax, which he so dextrously wielded that he was passed knight of arms in the field.

Then tossed he the pike, played with the two-handed sword, with the back sword, with the Spanish tuck, the dagger, poniard, armed, unarmed, with a buckler, with a cloak, with a target. Then would he hunt the hart, the roebuck, the bear, the fallow deer, the wild boar, the hare, the pheasant, the partridge, and the bustard. He played at the great ball, and made it bound in the air, both with fist and foot. He wrestled, ran, jumped, not at three steps and a leap, nor a hopping, nor yet at the German jump; "for," said Gymnast, "these jumps are for the wars altogether unprofitable, and of no use": but at one leap he would skip over a ditch, spring over a hedge, mount six paces upon a wall, climb after this fashion up against a window, the height of a lance.

He did swim in deep waters on his face, on his back, sidewise, with all his body, with his feet only, with one hand in the air, wherein he held a book, crossing thus the breadth of the river Seine without wetting, and dragging along his cloak with his teeth, as did Julius Cæsar; then with the help of one hand he entered forcibly into a boat, from whence he cast himself again headlong into the water, sounded the depths, hollowed the rocks, and plunged into the pits and gulfs. Then turned he the boat about, governed it, led it swiftly or slowly with the stream and against the stream, stopt it in its course, guided it with one hand, and with the other laid hard about him with a huge great oar, hoisted the sail, hied up along the mast by the shrouds, ran upon the bulwarks, set the compass, tackled the bowlines, and steered the helm. Coming out of the water, he ran furiously up against a hill, and with the same alacrity and swiftness ran down again. He climbed up trees like a cat, leaped from the one to the other like a squirrel. He did pull down the great boughs and branches, like another Milo: then with two sharp well-steeled daggers, and two tried bodkins, would he run up by the wall to the very top of a house like a rat; then suddenly come down from the top to the bottom, with such an even disposal of members that by the fall he would catch no harm.

He did cast the dart, throw the bar, put the stone, practise the javelin, the boar-spear or partizan, and the halbert. He broke the strongest bows in drawing, bended against his breast the greatest cross-bows of steel, took his aim by the eye with the hand-gun, traversed the cannon; shot at the butts, at the pape-gay, before him, sidewise, and behind him, like the Parthians. They tied a cable-rope to the top of a high tower, by one end whereof hanging near the ground he wrought himself with his hands to the very top; then came down again so sturdily and firmly that you could not on a plain meadow have run with more assurance. They set up a great pole fixt upon two trees. There would he hang by his hands, and with them alone, his feet touching at nothing, would go back and fore along the aforesaid rope with so great swiftness, that hardly could one overtake him with running.

III

OF THE FOUNDING OF AN IDEAL ABBEY[4]

THERE was left only the monk to provide for; whom Gargantua would have made Abbot of Seuillé, but he refused it. He would have given him the Abbey of Bourgueil, or of Sanct Florent, which was better, or both if it pleased him; but the monk gave him a very peremptory answer, that he would never take upon him the charge nor government of monks. "For how shall I be able," said he, "to rule over others, that have not full power and command of myself? If you think I have done you, or may hereafter do you any acceptable service, give me leave to found an abbey after my own mind and fancy." The motion pleased Gargantua very well; who thereupon offered him all the country of Thelema by the river Loire, till within two leagues of the great forest of Port-Huaut. The monk then requested Gargantua to institute his religious order contrary to all others.

"First, then," said Gargantua, "you must not build a wall about your convent, for all other abbeys are strongly walled and mured about."

Moreover, seeing there are certain convents in the world whereof the custom is, if any women come in—I mean honorable and honest women—they immediately sweep the ground which they have trod upon; therefore was it ordained that

[4] From Book I of "The Inestimable Life of the Great Gargantua, Father of Pantagruel." The Urquhart-Motteux translation.

if any man or woman, entered into religious orders, should by chance come within this new abbey, all the rooms should be thoroughly washed and cleansed through which they had passed.

And because in other monasteries all is compassed, limited, and regulated by hours, it was decreed that in this new structure there should be neither clock nor dial, but that according to the opportunities, and incident occasions, all their works should be disposed of; "for," said Gargantua, "the greatest loss of time that I know is to count the hours. What good comes of it? Nor can there be any greater folly in the world than for one to guide and direct his courses by the sound of a bell, and not by his own judgment and discretion."

Item, Because at that time they put no women into nunneries but such as were either one-eyed, lame, humpbacked, ill-favored, misshapen, foolish, senseless, spoiled, or corrupt; nor encloistered any men but those that were either sickly, ill-bred, clownish, and the trouble of the house:

("Apropos," said the monk—"a woman that is neither fair nor good, to what use serves she?" "To make a nun of," said Gargantua. "Yes," said the monk, "and to make shirts.")

Therefore, Gargantua said, was it ordained, that into this religious order should be admitted no women that were not fair, well-featured, and of a sweet disposition; nor men that were not comely, personable, and also of a sweet disposition.

Item, Because in the convents of women men come not but underhand, privily, and by stealth, it was therefore enacted that in this house there shall be no women in case there be not men, nor men in case there be not women.

Item, Because both men and women that are received into religious orders after the year of their novitiates were constrained and forced perpetually to stay there all the days of their life: it was ordered that all of whatever kind, men or women, admitted within this abbey, should have full leave to depart with peace and contentment whensoever it should seem good to them so to do.

Item, For that the religious men and women did ordinarily make three vows—to wit, those of chastity, poverty, and obedience: it was therefore constituted and appointed that in this convent they might be honorably married, that they might be rich, and live at liberty. In regard to the legitimate age, the women were to be admitted from ten till fifteen, and the men from twelve till eighteen.

For the fabric and furniture of the abbey, Gargantua caused to be delivered out in ready money twenty-seven hundred thousand eight hundred and one-and-thirty of those long-wooled rams; and for every year until the whole work was completed he allotted threescore nine thousand gold crowns, and as many of the seven stars, to be charged all upon the receipt of the river Dive. For the foundation and maintenance thereof he settled in perpetuity three-and-twenty hundred threescore and nine thousand five hundred and fourteen rose nobles, taxes exempted from all in landed rents, and payable every year at the gate of the abbey; and for this gave them fair letters patent.

The building was hexagonal, and in such a
fashion that in every one of the six corners there
was built a great round tower, sixty paces in
diameter, and were all of a like form and bigness. Upon the north side ran the river Loire,
on the bank whereof was situated the tower called
Arctic. Going toward the east there was another
called Calær, the next following Anatole, the next
Mesembrine, the next Hesperia, and the last
Criere. Between each two towers was the space
of three hundred and twelve paces. The whole
edifice was built in six stories, reckoning the
cellars underground for one. The second was
vaulted after the fashion of a basket-handle;
the rest were coated with Flanders plaster, in
the form of a lamp foot. It was roofed with
fine slates of lead, carrying figures of baskets
and animals; the ridge gilt, together with the
gutters, which issued without the wall between
the windows, painted diagonally in gold and
blue down to the ground, where they ended in
great canals, which carried away the water below
the house into the river.

This same building was a hundred times more
sumptuous and magnificent than ever was Boni-
vet; for there were in it nine thousand three
hundred and two-and-thirty chambers, every one
whereof had a withdrawing-room, a closet, a
wardrobe, a chapel, and a passage into a great
hall. Between every tower, in the midst of
the said body of building, there was a winding
stair, whereof the steps were part of porphyry,
which is a dark-red marble spotted with white,
part of Numidian stone, and part of serpentine
marble; each of those steps being two-and-twenty

feet in length and three fingers thick, and the just number of twelve betwixt every landing place. On every landing were two fair antique arcades where the light came in; and by those they went into a cabinet, made even with, and of the breadth of the said winding, and they mounted above the roof and ended in a pavilion By this winding they entered on every side into a great hall, and from the halls into the chambers. From the Arctic tower unto the Crier were fair great libraries in Greek, Latin, Hebrew French, Italian, and Spanish, respectively distributed on different stories, according to their languages. In the midst there was a wonderful winding stair, the entry whereof was without the house, in an arch six fathoms broad. It was made in such symmetry and largeness that six men-at-arms, lance on thigh, might ride abreast all up to the very top of all the palace. From the tower Anatole to the Mesembrine were fair great galleries, all painted with the ancien prowess, histories, and descriptions of the world In the midst thereof there was likewise such another ascent and gate as we said there was on the river-side.

In the middle of the lower court there was a stately fountain of fair alabaster. Upon the top thereof stood the three Graces, with horns of abundance, and did jet out the water at their breasts, mouth, ears, and eyes. The inside of the buildings in this lower court stood upon great pillars of Cassydonian stone, and porphyry in fair ancient arches. Within these were spacious galleries, long and large, adorned with curious pictures—the horns of bucks and unicorns

f the rhinoceros and the hippopotamus; the
teeth and tusks of elephants, and other things
well worth the beholding. The lodging of the
ladies took up all from the tower Arctic unto the
gate Mesembrine. The men possess the rest. Before the said lodging of the ladies, that they
might have their recreation, between the two
first towers, on the outside, were placed the tiltyard, the hippodrome, the theater, the swimming-bath, with most admirable baths in three stages,
well furnished with all necessary accommodation,
and store of myrtle-water. By the river-side was
the fair garden of pleasure, and in the midst
of that a fair labyrinth. Between the two other
towers were the tennis and fives courts. Toward
the tower Criere stood the orchard full of all
fruit-trees, set and ranged in a quincunx. At
the end of that was the great park, abounding
with all sort of game. Betwixt the third couple
of towers were the butts for arquebus, crossbow,
and arbalist. The stables were beyond the offices,
and before them stood the falconry, managed
by falconers very expert in the art; and it was
yearly supplied by the Candians, Venetians, Sarmatians, with all sorts of excellent birds, eagles,
gerfalcons, goshawks, falcons, sparrow-hawks,
merlins, and other kinds of them, so gentle and
perfectly well trained that, flying from the castle
for their own disport, they would not fail to
catch whatever they encountered. The venery
was a little further off, drawing toward the park.
All the halls, chambers, and cabinets were hung
with tapestry of divers sorts, according to the
seasons of the year. All the pavements were
covered with green cloth. The beds were em-

broidered. In every back chamber there was a looking-glass of pure crystal, set in a frame of fine gold garnished with pearls, and of such greatness that it would represent to the full the whole person. At the going out of the halls belonging to the ladies' lodgings were the perfumers and hair-dressers, through whose hands the gallants passed when they were to visit the ladies. These did every morning furnish the ladies' chambers with rose-water, musk, and angelica; and to each of them gave a little smelling bottle breathing the choicest aromatical scents.

The ladies on the foundation of this order were appareled after their own pleasure and liking. But since, of their own free will, they were reformed in manner as followeth:

They wore stockings of scarlet which reached just three inches above the knee, having the border beautified with embroideries and trimming. Their garters were of the color of their bracelets and circled the knee both over and under. Their shoes and slippers were either of red, violet, or crimson velvet, cut *à barbe d'écrévisse.*

Next to their smock they put on a fair corset of pure silk camblet; above that went the petticoat of white, red tawny, or gray taffeta. Above this was the *cotte* in cloth of silver, with needlework either (according to the temperature and disposition of the weather) of satin, damask, velvet, orange, tawny, green, ash-colored, blue, yellow, crimson, cloth of gold, cloth of silver, or some other choice stuff, according to the day.

Their gowns, correspondent to the season, were either of cloth of gold with silver edging, of red satin covered with gold purl, of taffeta, white blue, black, or tawny, of silk serge, silk camblet, velvet, cloth of silver, silver tissue, cloth of gold, or figured satin with golden threads.

In the summer, some days, instead of gowns, they wore fair mantles of the above-named stuff, or capes of violet velvet with edging of gold, or with knotted cordwork of gold embroidery, garnished with little Indian pearls. They always carried a fair plume of feathers, of the color of their muff, bravely adorned with spangles of gold. In the winter-time they had their taffeta gowns of all colors, as above named, and those lined with the rich furrings of wolves, weasels, Calabrian martlet, sables, and other costly furs. Their beads, rings, bracelets, and collars were of precious stones, such as carbuncles, rubies, diamonds, sapphires, emerald, turquoises, garnets, agates, beryls, and pearls.

Their head-dressing varied with the season of the year. In winter it was of the French fashion; in the spring of the Spanish; in summer of the fashion of Tuscany, except only upon the holidays and Sundays, at which times they were accoutered in the French mode, because they accounted it more honorable, better befitting the modesty of a matron.

The men were appareled after their fashion. Their stockings were of worsted or of serge, of white, black, or scarlet. Their breeches were of velvet, of the same color with their stockings, or very near, embroidered and cut according to their fancy. Their doublet was of cloth of gold, cloth of silver, velvet, satin, damask, or taffeta, of the same colors, cut embroidered, and trimmed up in the same manner. The points were of silk of the same colors, the tags were of gold enameled. Their coats and jerkins were of cloth of gold, cloth of silver, gold tissue, or velvet embroidered, as they thought fit. Their gowns were every whit as costly as those of the ladies. Their girdles were of silk, of the color of their doublets. Every one had a gallant sword by his side, the hilt and handle whereof were gilt, and the scabbard of velvet, of the color of his breeches, the end in gold, and goldsmith's work. The dagger of the same. Their caps were of black velvet, adorned with jewels and buttons of gold. Upon that they wore a white plume, most prettily and minion-like parted by so many rows of gold spangles, at the end whereof hung dangling fair rubies, emeralds, etc.

But so great was the sympathy between the gallants and the ladies, that every day they were appareled in the same livery. And that they might not miss, there were certain gentlemen appointed to tell the youths every morning what colors the ladies would on that day wear; for all was done according to the pleasure of the ladies. In these so handsome clothes, and habiliments so rich, think not that either one or other of either sex did waste any time at all; for the masters of the wardrobes had all their raiments and apparel so ready for every morning, and the chamber-ladies were so well skilled, that in a trice they would be drest, and completely in their clothes from head to foot. And to have these accouterments with the more conveniency, there was about the wood of Thelema a row of houses half a league long, very neat and cleanly, wherein dwelt the goldsmiths, lapidaries, embroiderers, tailors, gold-drawers, velvet-weavers, tapestry-makers, and upholsterers, who wrought there every one in his own trade, and all for the aforesaid friars and nuns. They were furnished with matter and stuff from the hands of Lord Nausiclete, who every year brought them seven ships from the Perlas and Cannibal Islands, laden with ingots of gold, with raw silk, with pearls and precious stones. And if any pearls began to grow old, and lose somewhat of their natural whiteness and luster, those by their art they did renew by tendering them to cocks to be eaten, as they used to give casting unto hawks.

All their life was spent not in laws, statutes, or rules, but according to their own free will and pleasure. They rose out of their beds when they thought good; they did eat, drink, labor, sleep, when they had a mind to it, and were disposed for it. None did awake them, none did constrain them to eat, drink, nor do any other thing; for so had Gargantua established it. In all their rule, and strictest tie of their order, there was but this one clause to be observed: *Fay ce que vouldras*.

Because men that are free, well born, well bred, and conversant in honest companies, have naturally an instinct and spur that prompteth them unto virtuous actions and withdraws them from vice, which is called honor. Those same men, when by base subjection and constraint they are brought under and kept down, turn aside from that noble disposition by which they formerly were inclined to virtue, to shake off the bond of servitude; for it is agreeable with the nature of man to long after things forbidden.

JOHN CALVIN

Born in France in 1509, died in Geneva in 1564; studied in Paris and Orleans; became identified with the Reformation about 1528; banished from Paris in 1533; published his "Institutes," his most famous work, in Latin at Basel in 1536, and in French in 1540; settled at Geneva in 1536; banished from Geneva in 1538; returned to Geneva in 1541; had a memorable controversy with Servetus in 1553; founded the Academy of Geneva in 1559.

OF FREEDOM FOR THE WILL [1]

GOD has provided the soul of man with intellect, by which he might discern good from evil, just from unjust, and might know what to follow or to shun, Reason going before with her lamp; whence philosophers, in reference to her directing power have called τὸ ἡγεμονιχόν. To this he has joined will, to which choice belongs. Man excelled in these noble endowments in his primitive condition, when reason, intelligence, prudence, and judgment not only sufficed for the government of his earthly life, but also enabled him to rise up to God and eternal happiness. Thereafter choice was added to direct the appetites and temper all the organic motions; the will being thus perfectly submissive to the authority of reason.

[1] From "The Institutes." Calvin's work was translated into English by Thomas Norton and published in 1561. An abridgment, translated by Christopher Fetherstone, was published in Edinburgh in 1585, and another abridgment by H. Holland in London in 1596. Many other translations of Calvin's writings appeared in the sixteenth century. John Allen issued a version of the "Institutes" in 1830, which has been held in esteem.

In this upright state, man possest freedom of will, by which if he chose he was able to obtain eternal life.

It were here unseasonable to introduce the question concerning the secret predestination of God, because we are not considering what might or might not happen, but what the nature of man truly was. Adam, therefore, might have stood if he chose, since it was only by his own will that he fell; but it was because his will was pliable in either direction, and he had not received constancy to persevere, that he so easily fell. Still he had a free choice of good and evil; and not only so, but in the mind and will there was the highest rectitude, and all the organic parts were duly framed to obedience, until man corrupted its good properties, and destroyed himself. Hence the great darkness of philosophers who have looked for a complete building in a ruin, and fit arrangement in disorder. The principle they set out with was, that man could not be a rational animal unless he had a free choice of good and evil. They also imagined that the distinction between virtue and vice was destroyed, if man did not of his own counsel arrange his life. So far well, had there been no change in man. This being unknown to them, it is not surprizing that they throw everything into confusion. But those who, while they profess to be the disciples of Christ, still seek for free-will in man, notwithstanding of his being lost and drowned in spiritual destruction, labor under manifold delusion, making a heterogeneous mixture of inspired doctrine and philosophical opinions, and so erring as to both.

But it will be better to leave these things to their own place. At present it is necessary only to remember that man at his first creation was very different from all his posterity; who, deriving their origin from him after he was corrupted, received a hereditary taint. At first every part of the soul was formed to rectitude. There was soundness of mind and freedom of will to choose the good. If any one objects that it was placed, as it were, in a slippery position because its power was weak, I answer, that the degree conferred was sufficient to take away every excuse. For surely the Deity could not be tied down to this condition,—to make man such that he either could not or would not sin. Such a nature might have been more excellent; but to expostulate with God as if he had been bound to confer this nature on man, is more than unjust, seeing he had full right to determine how much or how little he would give. Why he did not sustain him by the virtue of perseverance is hidden in his counsel; it is ours to keep within the bounds of soberness. Man had received the power, if he had the will, but he had not the will which would have given the power; for this will would have been followed by perseverance. Still, after he had received so much, there is no excuse for his having spontaneously brought death upon himself. No necessity was laid upon God to give him more than that intermediate and even transient will, that out of man's fall he might extract materials for his own glory.

JOACHIM DU BELLAY

Born about 1524, died in 1560; surnamed "The French
Ovid" and "The Apollo of the Pléiade"; noted as poet and
prose writer; a cousin of Cardinal du Bellay and for a time
his secretary; wrote forty-seven sonnets on the antiquities of
Rome; his most notable work in prose is his "Défense et
Illustration de la Langue Françoise."

WHY OLD FRENCH WAS NOT AS RICH AS GREEK AND LATIN [1]

IF our language is not as copious or rich as the
Greek or Latin, this must not be laid to their
charge, assuming that our language is not capable
in itself of being barren and sterile; but it should
rather be attributed to the ignorance of our an-
cestors, who, having (as some one says, speaking
of the ancient Romans) held good doing in
greater estimation than good talking and pre-
ferred to leave to their posterity examples of
virtue rather than precepts, have deprived themselves of the glory of their great deeds, and us

[1] From the "Défence et Illustration de la Langue Françoise." Translated for this collection by Eric Arthur Bell.
Du Bellay belonged to a group of sixteenth-century writers
known as the Pléiade, who took upon themselves the mission
of reducing the French language, in its literary forms, to
something comparable to Greek and Latin. Mr. Saintsbury
says they "made modern French—made it, we may say, twice
over"; by which he means that French, in their time, was
revolutionized, and that, in the Romantic movement of 1830,
Hugo and his associates were armed by the work of the
Pléiade for their revolt against the restraints of rule and
language that had been imposed by the eighteenth century.

of their imitation; and by the same means have left our tongue so poor and bare that it has need of ornament and (if we may be allowed the phrase) of borrowed plumage.

But who is willing to admit that the Greek and Roman tongues have always possest that excellence which characterized them at the time of Homer, Demosthenes, Virgil, and Cicero? And if these authors were of the opinion that a little diligence and culture were incapable of producing greater fruit, why did they make such efforts to bring it to the pitch of perfection it is in to-day? I can say the same thing of our language, which is now beginning to bloom without bearing fruit, like a plant which has not yet flowered, waiting till it can produce all the fruit possible. This is certainly not the fault of nature who has rendered it more sterile than the others, but the fault of those who have tended it, and have not cultivated it sufficiently. Like a wild plant which grows in the desert, without ever being watered or pruned or protected by the trees and shrubs which give it shade, it fades and almost dies.

If the ancient Romans had been so negligent of the culture of their language when first they began to develop it, it is certain that they could not have become so great in so short a time. But they, in the guise of good agriculturists, first of all transplanted it from a wild locality to a cultivated one, and then in order that it might bear fruit earlier and better, cut away several useless shoots and substituted exotic and domestic ones, mostly drawn from the Greek language, which have grafted so well on to the trunk that they appear no longer adopted but natural. Out of these have sprung, from the Latin tongue, flowers and colored fruits in great number and of much eloquence, all of which things, not so much from its own nature but artificially, every tongue is wont to produce. And if the Greeks and Romans, more diligent in the culture of their tongue than we are in ours, found an eloquence in their language only after much labor and industry, are we for this reason, even if our vernacular is not as rich as it might be, to condemn it as something vile and of little value?

The time will come perhaps, and I hope it will be for the good of the French, when the language of this noble and powerful kingdom (unless with France the whole French language is to be buried),[2] which is already beginning to throw out its roots, will shoot out of the ground and rise to such a height and size that it will even emulate that of the Greeks and the Romans, producing like them, Homers, Demostheneses, Virgils, and Ciceros, in the same way that France has already produced her Pericles, Alcibiades, Themistocles, and Scipio.

---

[2] Du Bellay here refers to the unhappy political state of France during his short life of thirty-six years. He was born one year before the defeat of Francis I at Pavia. When twenty years old, Henry VIII in league with Charles V had invaded France. Fourteen years later the country was distracted by disastrous religious wars which led up to the massacre of St. Bartholomew a few years after his death.

MICHEL DE MONTAIGNE

Born in France in 1533, died in 1592; educated at a college in Bordeaux; studied law; attached to the court of Francis II in 1559, and to the person of Henry III in 1571; traveled in Germany, Italy and Switzerland in 1580; made mayor of Bordeaux in 1581; published his "Essays" in 1580, the first English translation, made by Florio, appearing in 1603.

I

A WORD TO HIS READERS[1]

READER, loe here a well-meaning Booke. It doth at the first entrance forewarne thee, that in contriving the same, I have proposed unto my selfe no other than a familiar and private end: I have no respect or consideration at all, either to thy service, or to my glory; my forces are not capable of any such desseigne. I have vowed the same to the particular commodity of my kinsfolks and friends: to the end, that losing me (which

---

[1] From the preface to the "Essays," as translated by John Florio. A copy of Florio's "Montaigne" is known to have been in the library of Shakespeare, one of the few extant autographs of the poet being in a copy of this translation now preserved in the library of the British Museum.

Montaigne is usually linked with Rabelais as to his important place in the history of French prose. The two have come down to us very much as Chaucer has come down in English literature—as a "well undefiled." Montaigne secured in his own lifetime a popularity which he has never lost, if, indeed, it has not been increased.

they are likely to do ere long) they may therein find some lineaments of my conditions and humors, and by that meanes reserve more whole, and more lively foster, the knowledge and acquaintance they have had of me. Had my intention beene to forestal and purchase the worlds opinion and favor, I would surely have adorned my selfe more quaintly, or kept a more grave and solemne march. I desire therein to be delineated in mine owne genuine, simple and ordinarie fashion, without contention, art or study; for it is my selfe I pourtray. My imperfections shall therein be read to the life, and my naturall forme discerned, so farre-forth as publike reverence hath permitted me. For if my fortune had beene to have lived among those nations, which yet are said to live under the sweet liberty of Natures first and uncorrupted lawes, I assure thee, I would most willingly have pourtrayed my selfe fully and naked. Thus, gentle Reader, my selfe am the groundworke of my booke: It is then no reason thou shouldest employ thy time about so frivolous and vaine a Subject. Therefore farewell.

II

OF SOCIETY AND SOLITUDE [2]

THERE are some particular natures that are private and retired: my natural way is proper for communication, and apt to lay me open; I am all without and in sight, born for society and friendship. The solitude that I love myself and recommend to others, is chiefly no other than to withdraw my thoughts and affections into myself; to restrain and check, not my steps, but my own cares and desires, resigning all foreign solicitude, and mortally avoiding servitude and obligation, and not so much the crowd of men, as the crowd of business. Local solitude, to say the truth, rather gives me more room, and sets me more at large; I more readily throw myself upon the affairs of state and the world, when I am alone; at the Louvre, and in the bustle of the court, I fold myself within my own skin; the crowd thrusts me upon myself; and I never entertain myself so wantonly, with so much license, or so especially, as in places of respect and ceremonious prudence: our follies do not make me laugh, but our wisdom does. I am naturally no enemy to a court life; I have therein passed a good part of my own, and am of a humor cheerfully to frequent great company, provided it be by intervals and at my own time: but this softness of judg-

[2] From the Essay entitled "Of Three Commerces," in Book III, Chapter III; translated by Charles Cotton, as revised by William Carew Hazlitt.

ment whereof I speak, ties me perforce to solitude. Even at home, amidst a numerous family, and in a house sufficiently frequented, I see people enough, but rarely such with whom I delight to converse; and I there reserve both for myself and others an unusual liberty: there is in my house no such thing as ceremony, ushering, or waiting upon people down to the coach, and such other troublesome ceremonies as our courtesy enjoins (O servile and importunate custom!) Every one there governs himself according to his own method; let who will speak his thoughts, I sit mute, meditating and shut up in my closet, without any offense to my guests.

The men, whose society and familiarity I covet, are those they call sincere and able men; and the image of these makes me disrelish the rest. It is, if rightly taken, the rarest of our forms, and a form that we chiefly owe to nature. The end of this commerce is simply privacy, frequentation and conference, the exercise of souls, without other fruit. In our discourse, all subjects are alike to me; let there be neither weight, nor depth, 'tis all one: there is yet grace and pertinency; all there is tinted with a mature and constant judgment, and mixt with goodness, freedom, gaiety, and friendship. 'Tis not only in talking of the affairs of kings and state, that our wits discover their force and beauty, but every whit as much in private conferences. I understand my men even by their silence and smiles; and better discover them, perhaps, at table, than in the council. Hippomachus said very well, "that he could know the good wrestlers by only seeing them walk in the street." If learning please to step into our talk, it shall not be rejected, not magisterial, imperious, and importunate, as it commonly is, but suffragan and docile itself; we there only seek to pass away our time; when we have a mind to be instructed and preached to, we will go seek this in its throne; please let it humble itself to us for the nonce; for, useful and profitable as it is, I imagine that, at need, we may manage well enough without it, and do our business without its assistance. A well-descended soul, and practised in the conversation of men, will of herself render herself sufficiently agreeable; art is nothing but the counterpart and register of what such souls produce.

III

OF HIS OWN LIBRARY[3]

It goes side by side with me in my whole course, and everywhere is assisting me: it comforts me in my old age and solitude; it eases me of a troublesome weight of idleness, and delivers me at all hours from company that I dislike: it blunts the point of griefs, if they are not extreme, and have not got an entire possession of my soul. To divert myself from a troublesome fancy, 'tis but to run to my books; they presently fix me to them and drive the other out of my thoughts; and do

[3] From the essay entitled "Of Three Commerces," Book III, Chapter III. The translation of Charles Cotton, as revised by William Carew Hazlitt.

not mutiny at seeing that I have only recourse to them for want of other more real, natural, and lively commodities; they always receive me with the same kindness. He may well go afoot, they say, who leads his horse in his hand; and our James, King of Naples and Sicily, who, handsome, young and healthful, caused himself to be carried about on a barrow, extended upon a pitiful mattress in a poor robe of gray cloth, and a cap of the same, but attended withal by a royal train of litters, led horses of all sorts, gentlemen and officers, did yet herein represent a tender and unsteady authority: "The sick man is not to be pitied, who has his cure in his sleeve." In the experience and practise of this maxim, which is a very true one, consists all the benefit I reap from books; and yet I make as little use of them, almost, as those who know them not: I enjoy them as a miser does his money, in knowing that I may enjoy them when I please: my mind is satisfied with this right of possession. I never travel without books, either in peace or war; and yet sometimes I pass over several days, and sometimes months, without looking on them: I will read by and by, say I to myself, or to-morrow, or when I please; and in the interim, time steals away without any inconvenience. For it is not to be imagined to what degree I please myself and rest content in this consideration, that I have them by me to divert myself with them when I am disposed, and to call to mind what a refreshment they are to my life. 'Tis the best viaticum I have yet found out for this human journey, and I very much pity those men of understanding who are unprovided of it. I the rather accept of any other sort of diversion, how light soever, because this can never fail me.

When at home, I a little more frequent my library, whence I overlook at once all the concerns of my family. 'Tis situated at the entrance into my house, and I thence see under me my garden, court, and base-court, and almost all parts of the building. There I turn over now one book, and then another, on various subjects without method or design. One while I meditate, another I record and dictate, as I walk to and fro, such whimsies as these I present to you here. 'Tis in the third story of a tower, of which the ground room is my chapel, the second story a chamber with a withdrawing-room and closet, where I often lie, to be more retired; and above is a great wardrobe. This formerly was the most useless part of the house. I there pass away both most of the days of my life and most of the hours of those days. In the night I am never there. There is by the side of it a cabinet handsome enough, with a fireplace very commodiously contrived, and plenty of light: and were I not more afraid of the trouble than the expense—the trouble that frights me from all business, I could very easily adjoin on either side, and on the same floor, a gallery of an hundred paces long, and twelve broad, having found walls already raised for some other design, to the requisite height.

Every place of retirement requires a walk: my thoughts sleep if I sit still; my fancy does not go by itself, as when my legs move it: and all those who study without a book are in the same condition. The figure of my study is round, and there is no more open wall than what is taken up by my table and my chair, so that the remaining parts of the circle present me a view of all my books at once, ranged upon five rows of shelves around about me. It has three noble and free prospects, and is sixteen paces in diameter. I am not so continually there in winter; for my house is built upon an eminence, as its name imports, and no part of it is so much exposed to the wind and weather as this, which pleases me the better, as being of more difficult access and a little remote, as well upon the account of exercise, as also being there more retired from the crowd. 'Tis there that I am in my kingdom, and there I endeavor to make myself an absolute monarch, and to sequester this one corner from all society, conjugal, filial, and civil; elsewhere I have but verbal authority only, and of a confused essence. That man, in my opinion, is very miserable, who has not a home where to be by himself, where to entertain himself alone, or to conceal himself from others. Ambition sufficiently plagues her proselytes, by keeping them always in show, like the statue of a public square: "Magna servitus est magna fortuna." They can not so much as be private in the water-closet. I have thought nothing so severe in the austerity of life that our monks affect, as what I have observed in some of their communities; namely, by rule to have a perpetual society of place, and numerous persons present in every action whatever; and think it much more supportable to be always alone, than never to be so.

If any one shall tell me that it is to undervalue the muses, to make use of them only for sport and to pass away the time, I shall tell him, that he does not know, so well as I, the value of the sport, the pleasure, and the pastime; I can hardly forbear to add that all other end is ridiculous. I live from hand to mouth, and, with reverence be it spoken, I only live for myself; there all my designs terminate. I studied, when young, for ostentation; since, to make myself a little wiser; and now for my diversion, but never for any profit. A vain and prodigal humor I had after this sort of furniture, not only for the supplying my own need, but, moreover, for ornament and outward show, I have since quite cured myself of.

Books have many charming qualities to such as know how to choose them; but every good has its ill; 'tis a pleasure that is not pure and clean, no more than others: it has its inconveniences, and great ones too. The soul indeed is exercised therein; but the body, the care of which I must withal never neglect, remains in the mean time without action, and grows heavy and somber. I know no excess more prejudicial to me, nor more to be avoided in this my declining age.

IV

THAT THE SOUL DISCHARGES HER PASSIONS UPON FALSE OBJECTS WHERE TRUE ONES ARE WANTING [4]

A GENTLEMAN of my country, who was very often tormented with the gout, being importun'd by his physicians totally to reclaim his appetite from all manner of salt meats, was wont presently to reply that he must needs have something to quarrel with in the extremity of his fits, and that he fancy'd that railing at and cursing one while the Bologna sausages, and another the dry'd tongues and the hams, was some mitigation to his pain. And in good earnest, as the arm when it is advanced to strike, if it fail of meeting with that upon which it was design'd to discharge the blow, and spends itself in vain, does offend the striker himself; and as also, that to make a pleasant prospect the sight should not be lost and dilated in a vast extent of empty air, but have some bounds to limit and circumscribe it at a reasonable distance:

"As winds do lose their strength, unless withstood
    By some dark grove of strong opposing wood."

So it appears that the soul, being transported and discompos'd, turns its violence upon itself, if not supply'd with something to oppose it, and

[4] The translation of Cotton before it was revised by Hazlitt.

99

therefore always requires an enemy as an object on which to discharge its fury and resentment. Plutarch says very well of those who are delighted with little dogs and monkeys, that the amorous part which is in us, for want of a legitimate object, rather than lie idle, does after that manner forge, and create one frivolous and false; as we see that the soul in the exercise of its passions inclines rather to deceive itself, by creating a false and fantastical subject, even contrary to its own relief, than not to have something to work upon. And after this manner brute beasts direct their fury to fall upon the stone or weapon that has hurt them, and with their teeth even execute their revenge upon themselves, for the injury they have receiv'd from another.

> So the fierce bear, made fiercer by the smart
> Of the bold Lybian's mortal guided dart,
> Turns round upon the wound, and the tough spear
> Contorted o'er her breast does flying bear
> Down. . . . —*Claudian.*

What causes of the misadventures that befall us do we not invent? What is it that we do not lay the fault to right or wrong, that we may have something to quarrel with? Those beautiful tresses, young lady, you may so liberally tear off, are no way guilty, nor is it the whiteness of those delicate breasts you so unmercifully beat, that with an unlucky bullet has slain your beloved brother: quarrel with something else. Livy, Dec. 3, l. 5., speaking of the Roman army in Spain, says that for the loss of two brothers, who were both great captains, "*Flere omnes repente et offensare capita,*" that they all wept, and tore their hair. 'Tis the common practise of affliction. And the philosopher Bion said pleasantly of the king, who by handfuls pull'd his hair off his head for sorrow, "Does this man think that baldness is a remedy for grief?" Who has not seen peevish gamesters worry the cards with their teeth, and swallow whole bales of dice in revenge for the loss of their money? Xerxes whipt the sea, and wrote a challenge to Mount Athos; Cyrus employ'd a whole army several days at work, to revenge himself of the river Gnidus, for the fright it had put him into in passing over; and Caligula demolish'd a very beautiful palace for the pleasure his mother had once enjoy'd there. I remember there was a story current, when I was a boy, that one of our neighboring kings, having receiv'd a blow from the hand of God, swore he would be reveng'd, and in order to it, made proclamation that for ten years to come no one should pray to him, or so much as mention him throughout his dominions; by which we are not so much to take measure of the folly, as the vainglory of the nation of which this tale was told. They are vices that, indeed, always go together; but such actions as these have in them more of presumption than want of wit. Augustus Cæsar, having been tost with a tempest at sea, fell to defying Neptune, and in the pomp of the Circensian games, to be reveng'd, depos'd his statue from the place it had amongst the other deities. Wherein he was less excusable than the former, and less than he was afterward, when having lost a battle under Quintilius Varus in Germany, in rage and despair he went running his head against the walls, and crying out, O Varus! give me my men again! for this exceeds all folly, for as much as impiety is joined with it, invading God himself, or at least Fortune, as if she had ears that were subject to our batteries; like the Thracians, who, when it thunders, or lightens, fall to shooting against heaven with Titanian madness, as if by flights of arrows they intended to reduce God Almighty to reason. Tho the ancient poet in Plutarch tells us,

"We must not quarrel heaven in our affairs."

But we can never enough decry nor sufficiently condemn the senseless and ridiculous sallies of our unruly passions.

V

THAT MEN ARE NOT TO JUDGE OF OUR HAPPINESS TILL AFTER DEATH[5]

EVERY one is acquainted with the story of King Crœsus to this purpose, who being taken prisoner by Cyrus, and by him condemn'd to die, as he was going to execution, cry'd out, "O Solon, Solon!" which being presently reported to Cyrus, and he sending to inquire what it meant, Crœsus gave him to understand that he now found the advertisement Solon had formerly given him true to his cost, which was, "That men, however fortune may smile upon them, could never be said

[5] The translation of Cotton, before it was revised by Hazlitt.

to be happy, till they had been seen to pass over the last day of their lives, by reason of the uncertainty and mutability of human things, which upon very light and trivial occasions are subject to be totally chang'd into a quite contrary condition.''

And therefore it was, that Agesilaus made answer to one that was saying, ''What a happy young man the King of Persia was to come so young to so mighty a kingdom.'' ''Tis true [said he], but neither was Priam unhappy at his years.'' In a short time, of kings of Macedon, successors to that mighty Alexander, were made joyners and scriveners at Rome; of a tyrant of Sicily, a pedant at Corinth; of a conqueror of one-half of the world, and general of so many armies, a miserable suppliant to the rascally officers of a king of Egypt. So much the prolongation of five or six months of life cost the great and noble Pompey, and no longer since than our fathers' days, Ludovico Sforza, the tenth duke of Milan, whom all Italy had so long truckled under, was seen to die a wretched prisoner at Loches, but not till he had lived ten years in captivity, which was the worst part of his fortune. The fairest of all queens (Mary, Queen of Scots), widow to the greatest king in Europe,[6] did she not come to die by the hand of an executioner? Unworthy and barbarous cruelty! and a thousand more examples there are of the same kind; for it seems that as storms and tempests have a malice to the proud and overtow'ring heights of our lofty buildings, there are also

---

[6] Francis II of France, to whom she was married in 1558 and who died two years afterward.

spirits above that are envious of the grandeurs here below.

> *Usque adeo res humanas vis abdita quædam*
> *Obterit, et pulchros fasces, sævasque secures*
> *Proculcare ac ludibrio sibi habere videtur.*
> —*Lucret.*, 1. 5.

And it should seem also that Fortune sometimes lies in wait to surprize the last hour of our lives, to show the power she has in a moment to overthrow what she was so many years in building, making us cry out with Laborius, *"Nimirum hac die una plus vixi mihi quam vivendum fuit."*—Macrob., 1. 2., c. 2. "I have liv'd longer by this one day than I ought to have done." And in this sense, this good advice of Solon may reasonably be taken; but he being a philosopher, with which sort of men the favors and disgraces of fortune stand for nothing, either to the making a man happy or unhappy, and with whom grandeurs and powers, accidents of quality, are upon the matter indifferent: I am apt to think that he had some further aim, and that his meaning was that the very felicity of life itself, which depends upon the tranquillity and contentment of a well-descended spirit, and the resolution and assurance of a well-order'd soul, ought never to be attributed to any man, till he has first been seen to play the last, and doubtless the hardest act of his part, because there may be disguise and dissimulation in all the rest, where these fine philosophical discourses are only put on; and where accidents do not touch us to the quick, they give us leisure to maintain the same sober gravity; but in this last scene of death, there is no more counterfeiting; we must speak plain, and must discover what there is of pure and clean in the bottom.

Nam veræ voces tum demum pectore ab imo
Ejiciuntur, et eripitur persona manet res.

—*Lucret., l. 3.*

"Then that at last truth issues from the heart,
The vizor's gone, we act our own true part."

Wherefore at this last all the other actions of our life ought to be try'd and sifted. 'Tis the master-day, 'tis the day that is judge of all the rest, 'tis the day (says one of the ancients) that ought to judge of all my foregoing years. To death do I refer the essay of the fruit of all my studies. We shall then see whether my discourses came only from my mouth or from my heart. I have seen many by their death give a good or an ill repute to their whole life. Scipio, the father-in-law of Pompey the Great, in dying well, wip'd away the ill opinion that till then every one had conceived of him. Epaminondas being ask'd which of the three he had in the greatest esteem, Chabrias, Iphicrates, or himself; "You must first see us die (said he) before that question can be resolv'd": and, in truth, he would infinitely wrong that great man, who would weigh him without the honor and grandeur of his end.

God Almightly had order'd all things as it has best pleased Him; but I have in my time seen three of the most execrable persons that ever I knew in all manners of abominable living, and the most infamous to boot, who all dy'd a very regular death, and in all circumstances compos'd even to perfection. There are brave, and fortunate deaths. I have seen death cut the thread of the progress of a prodigious advancement, and in the height and flower of its increase of a certain person, with so glorious an end, that in my opinion his ambitious and generous designs had nothing in them so high and great as their interruption; and he arrived without completing his course, at the place to which his ambition pretended with greater glory than he could himself either hope or desire, and anticipated by his fall the name and power to which he aspir'd, by perfecting his career. In the judgment I make of another man's life, I always observe how he carried himself at his death; and the principal concern I have for my own is that I may die handsomely; that is, patiently and without noise.

RENÉ DESCARTES

Born in Touraine in 1596, died in Stockholm in 1650; founder of modern general philosophy; educated at a Jesuit college in France; lived in Paris in 1613-18; at the siege of La Rochelle in 1628; in retirement in Holland in 1629-49; defending his philosophical ideas; his first famous work, "Discours de la Methode," published in Leyden in 1637; published "Meditations of Philosophy" in 1641; a treatise on the passion of love in 1649; other works published after his death; famous as a mathematician as well as philosopher, his geometry being still standard in Europe.

OF MATERIAL THINGS AND OF THE EXISTENCE OF GOD[1]

SEVERAL questions remain for consideration respecting the attributes of God and my own nature or mind. I will, however, on some other occasion perhaps resume the investigation of these. Meanwhile, as I have discovered what must be done and what avoided to arrive at the knowledge of truth, what I have chiefly to do is to essay to emerge from the state of doubt in which I have for some time been, and to discover whether anything can be known with certainty regarding material objects. But before considering whether such objects as I conceive exist without me, I must examine their ideas in so far as these are to be found in my consciousness, and discover which of them are distinct and which confused.

[1] From the "Meditations," translated by John Veitch.

In the first place, I distinctly imagine that quantity which the philosophers commonly call continuous, or the extension in length, breadth, and depth that is in this quantity, or rather in the object to which it is attributed. Further, I can enumerate in it many diverse parts, and attribute to each of these all sorts of sizes, figures, situations, and local motions; and, in fine, I can assign to each of these motions all degrees of duration. And I not only distinctly know these things when I thus consider them in general; but besides, by a little attention, I discover innumerable particulars respecting figures, numbers, motion, and the like, which are so evidently true, and so accordant with my nature, that when I now discover them I do not so much appear to learn anything new as to call to remembrance what I before knew, or for the first time to remark what was before in my mind, but to which I had not hitherto directed my attention. And what I here find of most importance is, that I discover in my mind innumerable ideas of certain objects, which can not be esteemed pure negations, altho perhaps they possess no reality beyond my thought, and which are not framed by me, tho it may be in my power to think, or not to think them, but possess true and immutable natures of their own.

As, for example, when I imagine a triangle, altho there is not perhaps and never was in any place in the universe apart from my thought one such figure, it remains true, nevertheless, that this figure possesses a certain determinate nature, form, or essence, which is immutable and eternal, and not framed by me, nor in any degree dependent on my thought; as appears from the circumstance, that diverse properties of the triangle may be demonstrated, viz., that its three angles are equal to two right, that its greatest side is subtended by its greatest angle, and the like, which, whether I will or not, I now clearly discern to belong to it, altho before I did not at all think of them, when, for the first time, I imagined a triangle, and which accordingly can not be said to have been invented by me.

Nor is it a valid objection to allege that perhaps this idea of a triangle came into my mind by the medium of the senses, through my having seen bodies of a triangular figure; for I am able to form in thought an innumerable variety of figures with regard to which it can not be supposed that they were ever objects of sense, and I can nevertheless demonstrate diverse properties of their nature no less than of the triangle, all of which are assuredly true since I clearly conceive them: and they are therefore something, and not mere negations; for it is highly evident that all that is true is something (truth being identical with existence); and I have already fully shown the truth of the principle, that whatever is clearly and distinctly known is true. And altho this had not been demonstrated, yet the nature of my mind is such as to compel me to assent to what I clearly conceive while I so conceive it; and I recollect that even when I still strongly adhered to the objects of sense, I reckoned among the number of the most certain truths those I clearly conceived relating to figures, numbers, and other matters that pertain to arithmetic and geometry, and in general to the pure mathematics.

But now if because I can draw from my thought the idea of an object it follows that all I clearly and distinctly apprehend to pertain to this object does in truth belong to it, may I not from this derive an argument for the existence of God? It is certain that I no less find the idea of a God in my consciousness, that is, the idea of a being supremely perfect, than that of any figure or number whatever: and I know with not less clearness and distinctness that an (actual and eternal) existence pertains to his nature than that all which is demonstrable of any figure or number really belongs to the nature of that figure or number; and, therefore, altho all the conclusions of the preceding "Meditations" were false, the existence of God would pass with me for a truth at least as certain as I ever judged any truth of mathematics to be, altho indeed such a doctrine may at first sight appear to contain more sophistry than truth. For, as I have been accustomed in every other matter to distinguish between existence and essence, I easily believe that the existence can be separated from the essence of God, and that thus God may be conceived as not actually existing. But, nevertheless, when I think of it more attentively, it appears that the existence can no more be separated from the essence of God than the idea of a mountain from that of a valley, or the equality of its three angles to two right angles, from the essence of a (rectilineal) triangle; so that it is not less impossible to conceive a God, that is, a being supremely perfect, to whom existence is wanting, or who is devoid of a certain perfection, than to conceive a mountain without a valley.

But tho, in truth, I can not conceive a God unless as existing, any more than I can a mountain without a valley, yet, just as it does not follow that there is any mountain in the world merely because I conceive a mountain with a valley, so likewise, tho I conceive God as existing, it does not seem to follow on that account that God exists; for my thought imposes no necessity on things; and as I may imagine a winged horse, tho there be none such, so I could perhaps attribute existence to God, tho no God existed. But the cases are not analogous, and a fallacy lurks under the semblance of this objection: for because I can not conceive a mountain without a valley, it does not follow that there is any mountain or valley in existence, but simply that the mountain or valley, whether they do or do not exist, are inseparable from each other; whereas, on the other hand, because I can not conceive God unless as existing, it follows that existence is inseparable from Him, and therefore that He really exists: not that this is brought about by my thought, or that it imposes any necessity on things, but, on the contrary, the necessity which lies in the thing itself, that is, the necessity of the existence of God, determines me to think in this way: for it is not in my power to conceive a God without existence, that is, a being supremely perfect, and yet devoid of an absolute perfection, as I am free to imagine a horse with or without wings.

DUC DE LA ROCHE-FOUCAULD

Born in 1613, died in 1680; a duke and prince of distinction in his own day, but now known through his "Maxims," "Memoirs" and "Letters"; his "Maxims" first issued anonymously in 1665; a sixth edition, published in 1693, contains fifty additional maxims; his Letters not published until 1818.

A SELECTION FROM THE "MAXIMS" [1]

THE contempt of riches in philosophers was only a hidden desire to avenge their merit upon the injustice of fortune, by despising the very goods of which fortune had deprived them; it was a secret to guard themselves against the degradation of poverty; it was a back way by which to arrive at that distinction which they could not gain by riches.

Perfect valor is to do without witnesses what one would do before all the world.

As it is the mark of great minds to say many

[1] From the translation by J. W. Willis Bund and J. Hain Friswell. At least eight English translations of La Rochefoucauld had appeared before 1870—including the years 1689, 1694, 1706, 1749, 1799 and 1815. Besides these, Swedish, Spanish and Italian translations have been made. The first English version (1689), appears to have been made by Mrs. Aphra Behn, the barber's daughter, upon whom has been conferred the distinction of being "the first female writer who lived by her pen in England." One of the later translations is by A. S. Bolton. The translation by Messrs. Bund and Friswell includes fifty additional maxims attributed to La Rochefoucauld.

things in a few words, so it is that of little minds to use many words to say nothing.

Who lives without folly is not so wise as he thinks.

There is no disguise which can long hide love where it exists, nor feign it where it does not.

The gratitude of most men is but a secret desire of receiving greater benefits.

Almost all the world takes pleasure in paying small debts; many people show gratitude for trifling, but there is hardly one who does not show ingratitude for great favors.

Nothing is rarer than true good nature; those who think they have it are generally only pliant or weak.

There is no less eloquence in the voice, in the eyes and in the air of a speaker than in his choice of words.

True eloquence consists in saying all that should be, not all that could be said.

There are people whose faults become them, others whose very virtues disgrace them.

We are never so happy or so unhappy as we suppose.

Our enemies come nearer the truth in the opinions they form of us than we do in our opinion of ourselves.

Most people judge men only by success or by fortune.

Love of glory, fear of shame, greed of fortune, the desire to make life agreeable and comfortable, and the wish to depreciate others are often causes of that bravery so vaunted among men.

The fame of great men ought always to be estimated by the means used to acquire it.

If we never flattered ourselves the flattery of others would not hurt us.

When great men permit themselves to be cast down by the continuance of misfortune, they show us that they were only sustained by ambition, and not by their mind; so that *plus* a great vanity, heroes are made like other men.

We may forgive those who bore us, we can not forgive those whom we bore.

To praise good actions heartily is in some measure to take part in them.

There is a kind of greatness which does not depend upon fortune: it is a certain manner that distinguishes us, and which seems to destine us for great things: it is the value we insensibly set upon ourselves; it is by this quality that we gain the deference of other men, and it is this which commonly raises us more above them than birth, rank, or even merit itself.

The cause why the majority of women are so little given to friendship is, that it is insipid after having felt love.

Women can not be completely severe unless they hate.

The praise we give to new comers into the world arises from the envy we bear to those who are established.

Little minds are too much wounded by little things; great minds see all and are not even hurt.

Most young people think they are natural when they are only boorish and rude.

To establish ourselves in the world we do everything to appear as if we were established.

Why we hate with so much bitterness those who

deceive us is because they think themselves more clever than we are.

Too great a hurry to discharge an obligation is a kind of ingratitude.

The moderation of those who are happy arises from the calm which good fortune bestows upon their temper.

Pride is much the same in all men; the only difference is the method and manner of showing it.

The constancy of the wise is only the talent of concealing the agitation of their hearts.

Whatever difference there appears in our fortunes, there is nevertheless a certain compensation of good and evil which renders them equal.

What we term virtue is often but a mass of various actions and divers interests, which fortune, or our own industry, manage to arrange; and it is not always from valor or from chastity that men are brave, and women chaste.

Most men expose themselves in battle enough to save their honor, few wish to do so more than sufficiently, or than is necessary to make the design for which they expose themselves succeed.

If we never flattered ourselves we should have but scant pleasure.

Sincerity is an openness of heart; we find it in very few people; what we usually see is only an artful dissimulation to win the confidence of others.

We may find women who have never indulged in an intrigue, but it is rare to find those who have intrigued but once.

Every one blames his memory, no one blames his judgment.

In the intercourse of life, we please more by our faults than by our good qualities.

We are easily consoled at the misfortunes of our friends when they enable us to prove our tenderness for them.

Virtue in woman is often the love of reputation and repose.

He is a truly good man who desires always to bear the inspection of good men.

We frequently do good to enable us with impunity to do evil.

Every one praises his heart, none dare praise their understanding.

He is really wise who is nettled at nothing.

Hypocrisy is the homage vice pays to virtue.[2]

In the adversity of our best friends we always find something which is not wholly displeasing to us.[3]

[2] A maxim similar to this has been found in the writings of other men. Thus Massillon, in one of his sermons, said, "Vice pays homage to virtue in doing honor to her appearance"; and Junius, writing to the Duke of Grafton, said, "You have done as much mischief to the community as Machiavel, if Machiavel had not known that an appearance of morals and religion are useful in society." Both, however, lived in a period subsequent to that in which La Rochefoucauld wrote.

[3] This maxim, which more than any other has caused La Rochefoucauld to be criticized severely as a cynic, if not a misanthrope, appeared only in the first two editions of the book. In the others, published in the author's lifetime, it was supprest. In defense of the author, it has been maintained that what he meant by the saying was that the pleasure derived from a friend's misfortunes has its origin in the opportunity thus afforded to give him help. The reader should compare this saying with another that is included in these selections, "We are easily consoled at the misfortunes of our friends when they enable us to prove our tenderness for them."

The confidence we have in ourselves arises in a great measure from that that we have in others.

Women for the most part surrender themselves more from weakness than from passion. Whence it is that bold and pushing men succeed better than others, altho they are not so lovable.

The great ones of the earth can neither command health of body nor repose of mind, and they buy always at too dear a price the good they can acquire.

Few things are needed to make a wise man happy; nothing can make a fool content; that is why most men are miserable.

The harm that others do us is often less than that we do ourselves.

Magnanimity is a noble effort of pride which makes a man master of himself, to make him master of all things.

BLAISE PASCAL

Born in France in 1623, died in 1662; educated in Paris; became celebrated at seventeen for a work on conic sections; became connected with the monastery at Port Royal, whose doctrines he defended against the Jesuits; published "Entretien sur Epictéte et Montaigne" in 1655; wrote his "Provincial Letters" in 1656-57; in his last days engaged on an "Apologie de la Religion Catholique" which, uncompleted, was published in 1670 as his "Pensées."

OF THE PREVALENCE OF SELF-LOVE[1]

SELF is hateful. You, Milton, conceal self, but do not thereby destroy it; therefore you are still hateful. Not so, for in acting as we do, to oblige everybody, we give no reason for hating us. True, if we only hated in self the vexation which it causes us. But if I hate it because it is unjust, and because it makes itself the center of all, I shall always hate it.

In one word, Self has two qualities: it is unjust in its essence, because it makes itself the center of all; it is inconvenient to others, in that it would bring them into subjection, for each "I" is the enemy, and would fain be the tyrant of all

---

[1] From the "Thoughts." Many translations have been made of Pascal's "Thoughts"—one in 1680 by J. Walker, one in 1704 by Basil Kennet, one in 1825 by Edward Craig. A more modern one is by C. Kegan Paul, the London publisher, who was also a man of letters. Early translations from the older French, Italian and other Continental writers have frequently come down to us without mention of translators' names on title-pages or in the prefatory matter.

others. You take away the inconvenience, but not the injustice, and thus you do not render it lovable to those who hate injustice; you render it lovable only to the unjust, who find in it an enemy no longer. Thus you remain unjust and can please none but the unjust.

OF SELF-LOVE.—The nature of self-love and of this human "I" is to love self only, and consider self only. But what can it do? It can not prevent the object it loves from being full of faults and miseries; man would fain be great and sees that he is little; would fain be happy, and sees that he is miserable; would fain be perfect, and sees that he is full of imperfections; would fain be the object of the love and esteem of men, and sees that his faults merit only their aversion and contempt. The embarrassment wherein he finds himself produces in him the most unjust and criminal passion imaginable. For he conceives a mortal hatred against that truth which blames him and convinces him of his faults. Desiring to annihilate it, yet unable to destroy it in its essence, he destroys it as much as he can in his own knowledge, and in that of others; that is to say, he devotes all his care to the concealment of his faults, both from others and from himself, and he can neither bear that others should show them to him, nor that they should see them.

It is no doubt an evil to be full of faults, but it is a greater evil to be full of them, yet unwilling to recognize them, because that is to add the further fault of a voluntary illusion. We do not like others to deceive us, we do not think it just in them to require more esteem from us than they deserve; it is therefore unjust that we should deceive them, desiring more esteem from them than we deserve.

Thus if they discover no more imperfections and vices in us than we really have, it is plain they do us no wrong, since it is not they who cause them; but rather they who do us a service, since they help us to deliver ourselves from an evil, the ignorance of these imperfections. We ought not to be troubled that they know our faults and despise us, since it is but just they should know us as we are, and despise us if we are despicable.

Such are the sentiments which would arise in a heart full of equity and justice. What should we say then of our own heart, finding in it a wholly contrary disposition? For is it not true that we hate truth, and those who tell it us, and that we would wish them to have an erroneously favorable opinion of us, and to esteem us other than indeed we are?

One proof of this fills me with dismay. The Catholic religion does not oblige us to tell out our sins indiscriminately to all; it allows us to remain hidden from men in general; but she excepts one alone, to whom she commands us to open the very depths of our hearts, and to show ourselves to him as we are. There is but this one man in the world whom she orders us to undeceive; she binds him to an inviolable secrecy, so that this knowledge is to him as tho it were not. We can imagine nothing more charitable and more tender. Yet such is the corruption of man, that he finds even this law harsh, and it is one of the main reasons which has set a large portion of Europe in revolt against the Church.

How unjust and unreasonable is the human heart which finds it hard to be obliged to do in regard to one man what in some degree it were just to do to all men. For is it just that we should deceive them?

There are different degrees in this dislike to the truth, but it may be said that all have it in some degree, for it is inseparable from self-love. This false delicacy causes those who must needs reprove others to choose so many windings and modifications in order to avoid shocking them. They must needs lessen our faults, seem to excuse them, mix praises with their blame, give evidences of affection and esteem. Yet this medicine is bitter to self-love, which takes as little as it can, always with disgust, often with a secret anger.

Hence it happens that if any desire our love, they avoid doing us a service which they know to be disagreeable; they treat us as we would wish to be treated: we hate the truth, and they hide it from us; we wish to be flattered, they flatter us; we love to be deceived, they deceive us.

Thus each degree of good fortune which raises us in the world removes us further from truth, because we fear most to wound those whose affection is most useful, and whose dislike is most dangerous. A prince may be the byword of all Europe, yet he alone know nothing of it. I am not surprized; to speak the truth is useful to whom it is spoken, but disadvantageous to those who speak it, since it makes them hated. Now those who live with princes love their own interests more than that of the prince they serve, and thus they take care not to benefit him so as to do themselves a disservice.

This misfortune is, no doubt, greater and more common in the higher classes, but lesser men are not exempt from it, since there is always an interest in making men love us. Thus human life is but a perpetual illusion, an interchange of deceit and flattery. No one speaks of us in our presence as in our absence. The society of men is founded on this universal deceit; few friendships would last if every man knew what his friend said of him behind his back, tho he then spoke in sincerity and without passion.

Man is, then, only disguise, falsehood, and hypocrisy, both in himself and with regard to others. He will not be told the truth; he avoids telling it to others; and all these tendencies, so far removed from justice and reason, have their natural roots in his heart.

MADAME DE SÉVIGNÉ

Born in Paris in 1626, died in 1696; married in 1644 to
the Marquis de Sévigné, who was killed in a duel in 1651;
lived late in life in Brittany; wrote to her married daughter,
Madame de Grigman, the famous letters from which has
proceeded her fame.

I

GREAT NEWS FROM PARIS [1]

I AM going to tell you a thing, the most astonishing, the most surprizing, the most marvelous,
the most miraculous, the most magnificent, the
most confounding, the most unheard-of, the most
singular, the most extraordinary, the most in-
credible, the most unforeseen, the greatest, the
least, the rarest, the most common, the most public, the most private till to-day, the most brilliant, the most inevitable; in short, a thing of
which there is but one example in past ages, and
that not an exact one either; a thing that we can
not believe at Paris; how, then, will it gain
credence at Lyons? a thing which makes everybody cry, "Lord, have mercy upon us!" a thing
which causes the greatest joy to Madame de

[1] From a letter dated Paris, December 15, 1670. George
Saintsbury has described Madame de Sévigné as "the most
charming of all letter-writers in all languages." Translations
of these letters into English were made in 1732, 1745, 1764,
and other years, including a version by Mackie in 1802.

Rohan and Madame de Hauterive; a thing, in fine, which is to happen on Sunday next, when those who are present will doubt the evidence of their senses; a thing which, tho it is to be done on Sunday, yet perhaps will not be finished on Monday.

I can not bring myself to tell you; guess what it is. I give you three times to do it in. What, not a word to throw at a dog? Well, then, I find I must tell you. Monsieur de Lauzun is to be married next Sunday at the Louvre, to—pray guess to whom! I give you four times to do it in,—I give you six,—I give you a hundred. Says Madame de Coulanges: "It is really very hard to guess; perhaps it is Madame de la Vallière."

Indeed madame, it is not. "It is Mademoiselle de Retz, then." No, nor she either; you are extremely provincial. "Lord bless me," say you, "what stupid wretches we are! it is Mademoiselle de Colbert all the while." Nay, now you are still further from the mark. "Why, then, it must certainly be Mademoiselle de Crequy." You have it not yet. Well, I find I must tell you at last. He is to be married next Sunday at the Louvre, with the King's leave, to Mademoiselle—Mademoiselle de — Mademoiselle — guess, pray guess her name; he is to be married to Mademoiselle, the great Mademoiselle; Mademoiselle, daughter of the late Monsieur; Mademoiselle, granddaughter of Henry IV; Mademoiselle d'Eu, Mademoiselle de Dombes, Mademoiselle de Montpensier, Mademoiselle d'Orleans, Mademoiselle, the King's cousin-german — Mademoiselle, destined to the throne—Mademoiselle, the only match in France that was worthy of Monsieur.

What glorious matter for talk! If you should burst forth like a bedlamite, say we have told you a lie, that it is false, that we are making a jest of you, and that a pretty jest it is, without wit or invention; in short, if you abuse us, we shall think you are quite in the right; for we have done just the same things ourselves. Farewell, you will find by the letters you receive this post whether we tell you truth or not.

II

AN IMPOSING FUNERAL DESCRIBED [*]

I MUST return to narration, it is a folly I can never resist. Prepare, therefore, for a description. I was yesterday at a service performed in honor of the Chancellor Segnier at the Oratory. Painting, sculpture, music, rhetoric—in a word, the four liberal arts—were at the expense of it. Nothing could exceed the beauty of the decorations; they were finely imagined, and designed by Le Brun. The mausoleum reached to the top of the dome, adorned with a thousand lamps, and a variety of figures characteristic of him in whose honor it was erected. Beneath were four figures of Death, bearing the marks of his several dignities, as having taken away his honors with his life. One of them held his helmet, another his ducal

[*] From a letter to her daughter, dated Paris, May 6, 1672.

coronet, another the ensigns of his order, another his chancellor's mace. The four sister arts, painting, music, eloquence, and sculpture, were represented in deep distress, bewailing the loss of their protector. The first representation was supported by the four virtues, fortitude, temperance, justice, and religion. Above these, four angels, or genii, received the soul of the deceased, and seemed preening their purple wings to bear their precious charge to heaven. The mausoleum was adorned with a variety of little seraphs who supported an illuminated shrine, which was fixt to the top of the cupola. Nothing so magnificent or so well imagined was ever seen; it is Le Brun's masterpiece. The whole church was adorned with pictures, devices, and emblems, which all bore some relation to the life, or office of the chancellor; and some of his noblest actions were represented in painting. Madame de Verneuil offered to purchase all the decoration at a great price; but it was unanimously resolved by those who had contributed to it to adorn a gallery with it, and to consecrate it as an everlasting monument of their gratitude and magnificence. The assembly was grand and numerous, but without confusion. I sat next to Monsieur de Tulle, Madame Colbert and the Duke of Monmouth, who is as handsome as when we saw him at the *palais royal*. (Let me tell you in a parenthesis that he is going to the army to join the King.) A young father of the Oratory came to speak the funeral oration. I desired Monsieur de Tulle to bid him come down, and to mount the pulpit in his place; since nothing could sustain the beauty of the spectacle, and

he excellence of the music but the force of his
eloquence.

My child, this young man trembled when he began, and we all trembled for him. Our ears were
at first struck with a provincial accent; he is of
Marseilles, and called Lené. But as he recovered
from his confusion, he became so brilliant; established himself so well, gave so just a measure of
praise to the deceased; touched with so much address and delicacy all the passages in his life
where delicacy was required! placed in so true
a light all that was most worthy of admiration;
employed all the charms of expression, all the
masterly strokes of eloquence with so much
propriety and so much grace that every one
present, without exception, burst into applause,
charmed with so perfect, so finished a performance. He is twenty-eight years of age, the
intimate friend of M. de Tulle, who accompanied him when he left the assembly. We were
for naming him the Chevalier Mascaron, and
think he will even surpass his friend. As for
the music, it was fine beyond all description.
Baptiste exerted himself to the utmost, and was
assisted by all the King's musicians. There was
an addition made to that fine "Miserere," and
here was a "Libera" which filled the eyes of
the whole assembly with tears; I do not think
the music in heaven could exceed it. There were
several prelates present. I desired Guitaut to
look for the good Bishop of Marseilles, but we
could not see him. I whispered him that if it
had been the funeral oration of any person living
to whom he might have made his court by it he
would not have failed to have been there. This

little pleasantry made us laugh, in spite of the solemnity of the ceremony. My dear child, what a strange letter is this! I fancy I have almost lost my senses! What is this long account to you? To tell the truth, I have satisfied my love of description.

ALAIN RENÉ LE SAGE

Born in France in 1668, died in 1747; studied philosophy and law in Paris; wrote many novels and plays, some of them borrowed from Spanish originals; published his chief work, "Gil Blas," in 1715-35.

I

IN THE SERVICE OF DR. SANGRADO [1]

I DETERMINED to throw myself in the way of Signor Arias de Londona, and to look out for a new berth in his register; but as I was on my way to No Thoroughfare, who should come across me but Doctor Sangrado, whom I had not seen since the day of my master's death. I took the liberty of touching my hat. He kenned me in a twinkling, tho I had changed my dress; and with as much warmth as his temperament would allow him, "Heyday!" said he, "the very lad I wanted to see; you have never been out of my thought. I have occasion for a clever fellow about me, and pitched upon you as the very thing, if you can read and write." "Sir," replied I, "if that is all you require, I am your man." "In that case," rejoined he, "we need

[1] From "Gil Blas," which is perhaps as well known in English as in French, innumerable translations having been made. The best known is the one by Tobias Smollett, which has survived in favor to the present time. A translation by P. Proctor appeared in 1774, one by Martin Smart in 1807, and one by Benjamin H. Malkin in 1809.

look no further. Come home with me: it will be all comfort; I shall behave to you like a brother. You will have no wages, but everything will be found you. You shall eat and drink according to the true faith, and be taught to cure all diseases. In a word, you shall rather be my young Sangrado than my footman."

I closed in with the doctor's proposal, in the hope of becoming an Esculapius under so inspired a master. He carried me home on the spur of the occasion, to install me in my honorable employment; which honorable employment consisted in writing down the name and residence of the patients who sent for him in his absence. There had indeed been a register for this purpose, kept by an old domestic; but she had not the gift of spelling accurately, and wrote a most perplexing hand. This account I was to keep. It might truly be called a bill of mortality; for my members all went from bad to worse during the short time they continued in this system. I was a sort of bookkeeper for the other world, to take places in the stage, and to see that the first come were the first served. My pen was always in my hand, for Doctor Sangrado had more practise than any physician of his time in Valladolid. He had got into reputation with the public by a certain professional slang, humored by a medical face, and some extraordinary cases more honored by implicit faith than scrupulous investigation.

He was in no want of patients, nor consequently of property. He did not keep the best house in the world: we lived with some little attention to economy. The usual bill of fare consisted of peas, beans, boiled apples or cheese. He considered this food as best suited to the human stomach; that is to say, as most amenable to the grinders, whence it was to encounter the process of digestion. Nevertheless, easy as was their passage, he was not for stopping the way with too much of them; and to be sure, he was in the right. But tho he cautioned the maid and me against repletion in respect of solids, it was made up by free permission to drink as much water as we liked. Far from prescribing us any limits in that direction, he would tell us sometimes: "Drink, my children: health consists in the pliability and moisture of the parts. Drink water by pailfuls: it is a universal dissolvent; water liquefies all the salts. Is the course of the blood a little sluggish? this grand principle sets it forward: too rapid? its career is checked." Our doctor was so orthodox on this head that tho advanced in years, he drank nothing himself but water. He defined old age to be a natural consumption which dries us up and wastes us away: on this principle he deplored the ignorance of those who call wine "old men's milk." He maintained that wine wears them out and corrodes them; and pleaded with all the force of his eloquence against that liquor, fatal in common both to the young and old—that friend with a serpent in its bosom—that pleasure with a dagger under its girdle.

In spite of these fine arguments, at the end of a week a looseness ensued, with some twinges, which I was blasphemous enough to saddle on the universal dissolvent and the new-fangled diet. I stated my symptoms to my master, in the hope that he would relax the rigor of his regimen and qualify my meals with a little wine; but his hostility to that liquor was inflexible. "If you have not philosophy enough," said he, "for pure water, there are innocent infusions to strengthen the stomach against the nausea of aqueous quaffings. Sage, for example, has a very pretty flavor; and if you wish to heighten it into a debauch, it is only mixing rosemary, wild poppy, and other simples with it—but no compounds."

In vain did he crack off his water, and teach me the secret of composing delicious messes. I was so abstemious that, remarking my moderation, he said: "In good sooth, Gil Blas, I marvel not that you are no better than you are: you do not drink enough, my friend. Water taken in a small quantity serves only to separate the particles of bile and set them in action; but our practise is to drown them in a copious drench. Fear not, my good lad, lest a superabundance of liquid should either weaken or chill your stomach; far from thy better judgment be that silly fear of unadulterated drink. I will insure you against all consequences; and if my authority will not serve your turn, read Celsus. That oracle of the ancient makes an admirable panegyric on water; in short, he says in plain terms that those who plead an inconstant stomach in favor of wine, publish a libel on their own viscera, and make their constitution a pretense for their sensuality."

As it would have been ungenteel in me to run riot on my entrance into the career of practise, I affected thorough conviction; indeed, I thought there was something in it. I therefore went on drinking water on the authority of Celsus, or to speak in scientific terms, I began to drown the bile in copious drenches of that unadulterated liquor; and tho I felt myself more out of order from day to day, prejudice won the cause against experience. It is evident therefore that I was in the right road to the practise of physic. Yet I could not always be insensible to the qualms which increased in my frame, to that degree as to determine me on quitting Doctor Sangrado. But he invested me with a new office which changed my tone. ''Hark you, my child,'' said he to me one day: ''I am not one of those hard and ungrateful masters who leave their household to grow gray in service without a suitable reward. I am well pleased with you, I have a regard for you; and without waiting till you have served your time, I will make your fortune. Without more ado, I will initiate you in the healing art, of which I have for so many years been at the head. Other physicians make the science to consist of various unintelligible branches; but I will shorten the road for you, and dispense with the drudgery of studying natural philosophy, pharmacy, botany, and anatomy. Remember, my friend, that bleeding and drinking warm water are the two grand principles—the true secret of curing all the distempers incident to humanity. Yes, this marvelous secret which I reveal to you, and which Nature, beyond the reach of my colleagues, has failed in rescuing from my pen, is comprehended in these two articles; namely, bleeding and drenching. Here you have the sum total of my philosophy; you are thoroughly bottomed in medicine, and may raise yourself to the summit of fame on the shoulders of my long experience. You may enter into partnership at once, by keeping the books in the morning and going out to visit patients in the afternoon. While I dose the nobility and clergy, you shall labor in your vocation among the lower orders; and when you have felt your ground a little, I will get you admitted into our body. You are a philosopher, Gil Blas, tho you have never graduated; the common herd of them, tho they have graduated in due form and order, are likely to run out the length of their tether without knowing their right hand from their left.''

I thanked the doctor for having so speedily enabled me to serve as his deputy; and by way of acknowledging his goodness, promised to follow his system to the end of my career, with a magnanimous indifference about the aphorisms of Hippocrates. But that engagement was not to be taken to the letter. This tender attachment to water went against the grain, and I had a scheme for drinking wine every day snugly among the patients. I left off wearing my own suit a second time, to take up one of my master's and look like an experienced practitioner. After which I brought my medical theories into play, leaving those it might concern to look to the event. I began on an alguazil in a pleurisy; he was condemned to be bled with the utmost rigor of the law, at the same time that the system was to be replenished copiously with water. Next I made a lodgment in the veins of a gouty pastry-cook, who roared like a lion by reason of gouty spasms. I stood on no more ceremony with his blood than with that of the alguazil, and laid no restriction on his taste for simple liquids. My prescriptions brought me in twelve rials: an incident so auspicious in my professional career, that I only wished for the plagues of Egypt on all the hale subjects of Valladolid. . .

II

AS AN ARCHBISHOP'S FAVORITE [2]

I HAD been after dinner to get together my baggage, and take my horse from the inn where I had put up; and afterward returned to supper at the archbishop's palace, where a neatly furnished room was got ready for me, and such a bed as was more likely to pamper than to mortify the flesh. The day following his Grace sent for me quite as soon as I was ready to go to him. It was to give me a homily to transcribe. He made a point of having it copied with all possible accuracy. It was done to please him; for I omitted neither accent, nor comma, nor the minutest tittle of all he had marked down. His satisfaction at observing this was heightened by its being unexpected. "Eternal Father!" exclaimed he in a holy rapture, when he had glanced his eye over all the folios of my copy, "was ever anything seen so correct? You are too good a transcriber not to have some little smattering of the grammarian. Now tell me with

[2] From "Gil Blas."

the freedom of a friend: in writing it over, have you been struck with nothing that grated upon your feelings? Some little careless idiom, or some word used in an improper sense?" "Oh, may it please your Grace," answered I with a modest air, "it is not for me, with my confined education and coarse taste, to aim at making critical remarks. And tho ever so well qualified, I am satisfied that your Grace's works would come out pure from the essay." The successor of the apostles smiled at my answer. He made no observation on it; but it was easy to see through all his piety that he was an arrant author at the bottom: there is something in that dye that not heaven itself can wash out.

I seemed to have purchased the fee simple of his good graces by my flattery. Day after day did I get a step farther in his esteem; and Don Ferdinand, who came to see him very often, told me my footing was so firm that there could not be a doubt but my fortune was made. Of this my master himself gave me a proof some little time afterward; and the occasion was as follows: One evening in his closet he rehearsed before me, with appropriate emphasis and action, a homily which he was to deliver the next day in the cathedral. He did not content himself with asking me what I thought of it in the gross, but insisted on my telling him what passages struck me most. I had the good fortune to pick out those which were nearest to his own taste—his favorite commonplaces. Thus, as luck would have it, I passed in his estimation for a man who had a quick and natural relish of the real and less obvious beauties in a work. "This indeed," exclaimed he, "is what you may call having discernment and feeling in perfection! Well, well, my friend! it can not be said of you,

> '*Beatum in crasso jurares aëre natum.*'"

In a word, he was so highly pleased with me as to add in a tone of extraordinary emotion, "Never mind, Gil Blas! henceforward take no care about hereafter: I shall make it my business to place you among the favored children of my bounty. You have my best wishes; and to prove to you that you have them, I shall take you into my inmost confidence."

These words were no sooner out of his mouth than I fell at his Grace's feet, quite overwhelmed with gratitude. I embraced his elliptical legs with almost pagan idolatry, and considered myself as a man on the high-road to a very handsome fortune. "Yes, my child," resumed the archbishop, whose speech had been cut short by the rapidity of my prostration, "I mean to make you the receiver-general of all my inmost ruminations. Harken attentively to what I am going to say. I have a great pleasure in preaching. The Lord sheds a blessing on my homilies; they sink deep into the hearts of sinners; set up a glass in which vice sees its own image, and bring back many from the paths of error into the high-road of repentance. What a heavenly sight, when a miser, scared at the hideous picture of his avarice drawn by my eloquence, opens his coffers to the poor and needy, and dispenses the accumulated store with a liberal hand! The voluptuary, too, is snatched from the pleasures of the table; ambition flies at my command to the wholesome discipline of the monastic cell; while female frailty, tottering on the brink of ruin, with one ear open to the siren voice of the seducer and the other to my saintly correctives, is restored to domestic happiness and the approving smile of heaven, by the timely warnings of the pulpit.

"These miraculous conversions, which happen almost every Sunday, ought of themselves to goad me on in the career of saving souls. Nevertheless, to conceal no part of my weakness from my monitor, there is another reward on which my heart is intent—a reward which the seraphic scrupulousness of my virtue to little purpose condemns as too carnal—a literary reputation for a sublime and elegant style. The honor of being handed down to posterity as a perfect pulpit orator has its irresistible attractions. My compositions are generally thought to be equally powerful and persuasive; but I could wish of all things to steer clear of the rock on which good authors split who are too long before the public, and to retire from professional life with my reputation in undiminished luster. To this end, my dear Gil Blas," continued the prelate, "there is one thing requisite from your zeal and friendship. Whenever it shall strike you that my pen begins to contract, as it were, the ossification of old age, whenever you see my genius in its climacteric, do not fail to give me a hint. There is no trusting to one's self in such a case: pride and conceit were the original sin of man. The probe of criticism must be entrusted to an impartial stander-by, of fine talents and unshaken probity. Both those requisites center in you:

you are my choice, and I give myself up to your direction.''

"Heaven be praised, my lord," said I, "there is no need to trouble yourself with any such thoughts yet. Besides, an understanding of your Grace's mold and caliber will last out double the time of a common genius; or to speak with more certainty and truth, it will never be the worse for wear, if you live to the age of Methusaleh. I consider you as a second Cardinal Ximenes, whose powers, superior to decay, instead of flagging with years, seemed to derive new vigor from their approximation with the heavenly regions." "No flattery, my friend!" interrupted he. "I know myself to be in danger of failing all at once. At my age one begins to be sensible of infirmities, and those of the body communicate with the mind. I repeat it to you, Gil Blas, as soon as you shall be of opinion that my head is not so clear as usual, give me warning of it instantly. Do not be afraid of offending by frankness and sincerity: to put me in mind of my own frailty will be the strongest proof of your affection for me. Besides, your very interest is concerned in it; for if it should, by any spite of chance toward you, come to my ears that the people say in town, 'His Grace's sermons produce no longer their accustomed impression; it is time for him to abandon his pulpit to younger candidates'— I do assure you, most seriously and solemnly, you will lose not only my friendship, but the provision for life that I have promised you. Such will be the result of your silly tampering with truth."

Here my patron left off to wait for my answer, which was an echo of his speech, and a promise of obeying him in all things. From that moment there were no secrets from me; I became the prime favorite. All the household, except Melchior de la Ronda, looked at me with an eye of envy. It was curious to observe the manner in which the whole establishment, from the highest to the lowest, thought it necessary to demean themselves toward his Grace's confidential secretary; there was no meanness to which they would not stoop to curry favor with me: I could scarcely believe they were Spaniards. I left no stone unturned to be of service to them, without being taken in by their interested assiduities.

DUC DE SAINT-SIMON

Born in France in 1675, died in 1755; served in the army
in the time of Louis XIV; member of the Council of Regency in the reign of Louis XV; ambassador to Spain in
1721; his "Memoirs," first published in twenty volumes in
1829-30; not to be confounded with the Count of Saint-
Simon, the philosopher and socialist, the memoir writer being
a duke.

I

THE DEATH OF THE DAUPHIN [1]

MONSEIGNEUR LE DAUPHIN, ill and agitated by
the most bitter grief, kept his chamber; but on
Saturday morning of the 13th, being prest to go
to Marly to avoid the horror of the noise where
the Dauphine was lying dead, he set out for that
place at seven o'clock in the morning. Shortly
after arriving he heard mass in the chapel, and
thence was carried in a chair to the window
of one of his rooms. Madame de Maintenon
came to see him there afterward. The anguish
of the interview was speedily too much for her,
and she went away. Early in the morning I
went uninvited to see M. le Dauphin. He showed
me that he perceived this with an air of gentleness and of affection which penetrated me. But
I was terrified with his looks, constrained, fixt

[1] From the "Memoirs on the Reign of Louis XIV and the
Regency." Translated by Bayle St. John, traveler and
author, his "Village Life in Egypt" appearing in 1853.

and with something wild about them; with the
change of his looks and with the marks there,
livid rather than red, that I observed in good
number and large; marks observed by the others
also.

The Dauphin was standing. In a few moments
he was apprized that the King had awaked. The
tears that he had restrained now rolled from
his eyes; he turned round at the news, but said
nothing, remaining stock still. His three attendants proposed to him once or twice that he
should go to the King. He neither spoke nor
stirred. I approached and made signs to him
to go, then softly spoke to the same effect. Seeing that he still remained speechless and motionless, I made bold to take his arm, representing
to him that sooner or later he must see the King
who expected him, and assuredly with the desire
to see and embrace him. He cast upon me a
look that pierced my soul and went away. I
followed him some few steps and then withdrew
to recover breath. I never saw him again. May
I, by the mercy of God, see him eternally where
God's goodness doubtless has placed him!

The Dauphin reached the chamber of the King,
full just then of company. As soon as he appeared the King called him and embraced him
tenderly again and again. These first moments,
so touching, passed in words broken by sobs and
tears. Shortly afterward the King, looking at
the Dauphin, was terrified by the same things
that had previously struck me with affright. Everybody around was so also, the doctors more
than the others. The King ordered them to feel
his pulse, that they found bad, so they said after-

ward; for the time they contented themselves with saying that it was not regular, and that the Dauphin would do wisely to go to bed. The King embraced him again, recommended him very tenderly to take care of himself, and ordered him to go to bed. He obeyed and rose no more!

It was now late in the morning. The King had passed a cruel night and had a bad headache; he saw at his dinner the few courtiers who presented themselves, and then after dinner went to the Dauphin. The fever had augmented, the pulse was worse than before. The King passed into the apartment of Madame de Maintenon, and the Dauphin was left with attendants and his doctors. He spent the day in prayers and holy reading.

On the morrow, Sunday, the uneasiness felt on account of the Dauphin augmented. He himself did not conceal his belief that he would never rise again, and that the plot Pondin had warned him of had been executed. He explained himself to this effect more than once and always with a disdain of earthly grandeur and an incomparable submission and love of God. It is impossible to describe the general consternation. On Monday the 15th the King was bled. The Dauphin was no better than before. The King and Madame de Maintenon saw him separately several times during the day, which was passed in prayers and reading.

On Tuesday, the 16th, the Dauphin was worse. He felt himself devoured by a consuming fire, which the external fever did not seem to justify, but the pulse was very extraordinary and exceedingly menacing. This was a deceptive day.

The marks in the Dauphin's face extended all over the body. They were regarded as the marks of measles. Hope arose thereon, but the doctors and the most clear-sighted of the court could not forget that these same marks had shown themselves on the body of the Dauphine, a fact unknown out of her chamber until after death.

On Wednesday, the 17th, the malady considerably increased. I had news at all times of the Dauphin's state from Cheverney, an excellent apothecary of the King and of my family. He hid nothing from us. He had told us what he thought of the Dauphine's illness; he told us now what he thought of the Dauphin's. I no longer hoped therefore, or rather I hoped to the end against all hope.

On Wednesday the pains increased. They were like a devouring fire, but more violent than ever. Very late into the evening the Dauphin sent to the King for permission to receive the communion early the next morning and without display at the mass performed in his chamber. Nobody heard of this that evening; it was not known until the following morning. I was in extreme desolation. I scarcely saw the King once a day. I did nothing but go in quest of news several times a day, and to the house of M. de Chevreuse, where I was completely free. M. de Chevreuse—always calm, always sanguine—endeavored to prove to us by his medical reasonings that there was more reason to hope than to fear; but he did so with a tranquillity that roused my impatience. I returned home to pass a cruel night.

On Thursday morning, the 18th February, I learned that the Dauphin, who had waited for midnight with impatience, had heard mass immediately after the communion, had passed two hours in devout communication with God, and that his reason then became embarrassed. Madame de Saint-Simon told me afterward that he had received extreme unction; in fine that he had died at half-past eight.

These memoirs are not written to describe my private sentiments. But in reading them—if long after me they shall ever appear—my state and that of Madame de Saint-Simon will only too keenly be felt. I will content myself with saying that the first days after the Dauphin's death scarcely appeared to us more than moments; that I wished to quit all, to withdraw from the court and the world, and that I was only hindered by the wisdom, conduct and power over me of Madame de Saint-Simon, who yet had some trouble to subdue my sorrowful desire.

II

THE PUBLIC WATCHING THE KING AND MADAME [2]

THE King wished to show the court all the maneuvers of war; the siege of Compiègne was therefore undertaken, according to due form, with lines, trenches, batteries, mines, etc. On Saturday, the 13th of September, the assault took place. To witness it, the King, Madame de

[2] From the "Memoirs."

Maintenon,[3] all the ladies of the court, and a number of gentlemen, stationed themselves upon an old rampart, from which the plain and all the disposition of the troops could be seen. I was in the half-circle very close to the King. It was the most beautiful sight that can be imagined to see all that army, and the prodigious number of spectators on horse and foot, and that game of attack and defense so cleverly conducted.

But a spectacle of another sort—that I could paint forty years hence as well as to-day, so strongly did it strike me—was that which from the summit of this rampart the King gave to all his army, and to the innumerable crowd of spectators of all kinds in the plain below. Madame de Maintenon faced the plain and the troops in her sedan-chair, alone, between its three windows drawn up; her porters having retired to a distance. On the left pole in front

[3] At the period of which Saint-Simon here writes, Madame de Maintenon had acquired that ascendency over Louis XIV which resulted in her marriage to him. She had been born in a prison, and was three years the senior of the King. Her first husband was the poet Scarron, at whose death, after a marriage of nine years, she had found herself in poverty. She secured a pension from Anne of Austria, the mother of the King, but at the queen-mother's death the pension was discontinued. She was placed in charge of the King's natural son, to whom she became much devoted, and was advanced through the King's favor to various positions at court, receiving in 1678 the title of marquise. Five years later the queen of Louis XIV died, and Louis married Madame de Maintenon, whose influence over him in matters of church and state became thereafter very great. She was a patroness of art and literature, intensely orthodox in religion, and has been held largely responsible for the King's revocation of the Edict of Nantes, which occurred during the year of their marriage, tho she opposed the violent persecutions which followed.

sat Madame la Duchesse de Bourgogne; and on the same side, in a semicircle, standing, were Madame la Duchesse, Madame la Princesse de Conti, and all the ladies—and behind them again, many men. At the right window was the King, standing, and a little in the rear a semicircle of the most distinguished men of the court. The King was nearly always uncovered; and every now and then stooped to speak to Madame de Maintenon, and explain to her what she saw, and the reason of each movement.

Each time that he did so she was obliging enough to open the window four or five inches, but never half-way; for I noticed particularly, and I admit that I was more attentive to this spectacle than to that of the troops. Sometimes she opened of her own accord to ask some question of him: but generally it was he who, without waiting for her, stooped down to instruct her of what was passing; and sometimes, if she did not notice him, he tapped at the glass to make her open it. He never spoke save to her, except when he gave a few brief orders, or just answered Madame la Duchesse de Bourgogne, who wanted to make him speak, and with whom Madame de Maintenon carried on a conversation by signs, without opening the front window, through which the young princess screamed to her from time to time. I watched the countenance of every one carefully: all exprest surprize, tempered with prudence, and shame that was, as it were, ashamed of itself; every one behind the chair and in the semicircle watched this scene more than what was going on in the army. The King often put his hat on the top of the chair in order to get his head in to speak; and this continual exercise tired his loins very much. Monseigneur was on horseback in the plain with the young princes. It was about five o'clock in the afternoon, and the weather was as brilliant as could be desired.

Opposite the sedan-chair was an opening with some steps cut through the wall, and communicating with the plain below. It had been made for the purpose of fetching orders from the King, should they be necessary. The case happened. Crenan, who commanded, sent Conillac, an officer in one of the defending regiments, to ask for some instructions from the King. Conillac had been stationed at the foot of the rampart, where what was passing above could not be seen. He mounted the steps; and as soon as his head and shoulders were at the top, caught sight of the chair, the King, and all the assembled company. He was not prepared for such a scene; and it struck him with such astonishment that he stopt short, with mouth and eyes wide open—surprize painted upon every feature. I see him now as distinctly as I did then. The King, as well as the rest of the company, remarked the agitation of Conillac, and said to him with emotion, "Well, Conillac! come up." Conillac remained motionless, and the King continued, "Come up. What is the matter?" Conillac, thus addrest, finished his ascent, and came toward the King with slow and trembling steps, rolling his eyes from right to left like one deranged. Then he stammered something, but in a tone so low that it could not be heard. "What do you say?" cried the King. "Speak up." But Conillac was unable; and the King, finding he could get nothing out of him, told him to go away. He did not need to be told twice, but disappeared at once. As soon as he was gone, the King looking round said, "I don't know what is the matter with Conillac. He has lost his wits: he did not remember what he had to say to me." No one answered.

Toward the moment of the capitulation, Madame de Maintenon apparently asked permission to go away; for the King cried, "The chairmen of madame!" They came and took her away; in less than a quarter of an hour afterward the King retired also, and nearly everybody else. There was much interchange of glances, nudging with elbows, and then whisperings in the ear. Everybody was full of what had taken place on the ramparts between the King and Madame de Maintenon. Even the soldiers asked what meant that sedan-chair, and the King every moment stooping to put his head inside of it. It became necessary gently to silence these questions of the troops. What effect this sight had upon foreigners present, and what they said of it, may be imagined. All over Europe it was as much talked of as the camp of Compiègne itself, with all its pomp and prodigious splendor.

BARON DE MONTESQUIEU

Born near Bordeaux in 1689, died in Paris in 1755; studied law and became a councilor in 1716; president of the Bordeaux Parliament; devoted himself to a study of literature and jurisprudence; published "Persian Letters" in 1721, which secured him an election to the Academy in 1728; traveled in Austria, Italy, Germany, Holland and England; published "Grandeur and Decadence of the Romans" in 1734, and "Spirit of the Laws" in 1748.[1]

I

OF THE CAUSES WHICH DESTROYED ROME [2]

WHILE the sovereignty of Rome was confined to Italy, it was easy for the commonwealth to subsist: every soldier was at the same time a citizen; every Consul raised an army, and other citizens marched into the field under his successor: as their forces were not very numerous, such persons only were received among the troops as had possessions considerable enough to make them interested in the preservation of the city; the Senate kept a watchful eye over the conduct of the generals, and did not give them an oppor-

[1] Montesquieu is declared by Mr. Saintsbury to deserve the title of "the greatest man of letters of the French eighteenth century." He places him above Voltaire because "of his far greater originality and depth of thought."

[2] From the "Grandeur and Decadence of the Romans," of which an English translation was issued as early as 1751.

tunity of machinating anything to the prejudice of their country.

But after the legions had passed the Alps and crossed the sea, the soldiers whom the Romans had been obliged to leave during several campaigns in the countries they were subduing, lost insensibly that genius and turn of mind which characterized a Roman citizen; and the generals having armies and kingdoms at their disposal were sensible of their own strength, and would no longer obey.

The soldiers therefore began to acknowledge no superior but their general; to found their hopes on him only, and to view the city as from a great distance: they were no longer the soldiers of the republic, but of Sulla, of Marius, of Pompey, and of Cæsar. The Romans could no longer tell whether the person who headed an army in a province was their general or their enemy.

So long as the people of Rome were corrupted by their tribunes only, on whom they could bestow nothing but their power, the Senate could easily defend themselves, because they acted consistently and with one regular tenor, whereas the common people were continually shifting from the extremes of fury to the extremes of cowardice; but when they were enabled to invest their favorites with a formidable exterior authority, the whole wisdom of the Senate was baffled, and the commonwealth was undone.

The reason why free states are not so permanent as other forms of government is because the misfortunes and successes which happen to them generally occasion the loss of liberty; whereas the successes and misfortunes of an arbitrary government contribute equally to the enslaving of the people. A wise republic ought not to run any hazard which may expose it to good or ill fortune; the only happiness the several individuals of it should aspire after is to give perpetuity to their state.

If the unbounded extent of the Roman empire proved the ruin of the republic, the vast compass of the city was no less fatal to it.

The Romans had subdued the whole universe by the assistance of the nations of Italy, on whom they had bestowed various privileges at different times. Most of those nations did not at first set any great value on the freedom of the city of Rome, and some chose rather to preserve their ancient usages; but when this privilege became that of universal sovereignty—when a man who was not a Roman citizen was considered as nothing, and with this title was everything—the people of Italy resolved either to be Romans or die: not being able to obtain this by cabals and entreaties, they had recourse to arms; and rising in all that part of Italy opposite to the Ionian sea, the rest of the allies were going to follow their example. Rome, being now forced to combat against those who were, if I may be allowed the figure, the hands with which they shackled the universe, was upon the brink of ruin; the Romans were going to be confined merely to their walls: they therefore granted this so much wished-for privilege to the allies who had not yet been wanting in fidelity; and they indulged it, by insensible degrees, to all other nations.

But now Rome was no longer that city the

inhabitants of which had breathed one and the
same spirit, the same love for liberty, the same
hatred of tyranny; a city in which a jealousy
of the power of the Senate and of the preroga-
tives of the great (ever accompanied with respect) was only a love of equality. The nations
of Italy being made citizens of Rome, every city
brought thither its genius, its particular interests,
and its dependence on some mighty protector:
Rome, being now rent and divided, no longer
f·rmed one entire body, and men were no longer
citizens of it but in a kind of fictitious way;
as there were no longer the same magistrates,
the same walls, the same gods, the same temples,
the same burying-places, Rome was no longer
beheld with the same eyes; the citizens were no
longer fired with the same love for their country,
and the Roman sentiments were obliterated.

Cities and nations were now invited to Rome
by the ambitious, to disconcert the suffrages, or
influence them in their own favor; the public
assemblies were so many conspiracies against the
state, and a tumultuous crowd of seditious
wretches was dignified with the title of Comitia.
The authority of the people and their laws—
nay, that people themselves—were no more than
so many chimeras; and so universal was the
anarchy of those times that it was not possible
to determine whether the people had made a law
or not.

Authors enlarge very copiously on the divisions
which proved the destruction of Rome; but their
readers seldom discover those divisions to have
been always necessary and inevitable. The grandeur of the republic was the only source of that

calamity, and exasperated popular tumults into civil wars. Dissensions were not to be prevented; and those martial spirits which were so fierce and formidable abroad could not be habituated to any considerable moderation at home. Those who expect in a free state to see the people undaunted in war and pusillanimous in peace, are certainly desirous of impossibilities; and it may be advanced as a general rule that whenever a perfect calm is visible, in a state that calls itself a republic, the spirit of liberty no longer subsists.

Union, in a body politic, is a very equivocal term: true union is such a harmony as makes all the particular parts, as opposite as they may seem to us, concur to the general welfare of the society, in the same manner as discords in music contribute to the general melody of sound. Union may prevail in a state full of seeming commotions; or in other words, there may be a harmony from whence results prosperity, which alone is true peace; and may be considered in the same view as the various parts of this universe, which are eternally connected by the action of some and the reaction of others.

In a despotic state, indeed, which is every government where the power is immoderately exerted, a real division is perpetually kindled. The peasant, the soldier, the merchant, the magistrate, and the grandee, have no other conjunction than what arises from the ability of the one to oppress the other without resistance; and if at any time a union happens to be introduced, citizens are not then united, but dead bodies are laid in the grave contiguous to each other.

It must be acknowledged that the Roman laws were too weak to govern the republic; but experience has proved it to be an invariable fact that good laws, which raise the reputation and power of a small republic, become incommodious to it when once its grandeur is established, because it was their natural effect to make a great people but not to govern them.

The difference is very considerable between good laws and those which may be called convenient; between such laws as give a people dominion over others, and such as continue tnem in the possession of power when they have once acquired it.

There is at this time a republic in the world (the Canton of Berne), of which few persons have any knowledge, and which, by plans accomplished in silence and secrecy, is daily enlarging its power. And certain it is that if it ever rises to that height of grandeur for which it seems preordained by its wisdom, it must inevitably change its laws; and the necessary innovations will not be eff..cted by any legislator, but must spring from corruption itself.

Rome was founded for grandeur, and her laws had an admirable tendency to bestow it; for which reason, in all the variations of her government, whether monarchy, aristocracy, or popular, she constantly engaged in enterprises which required conduct to accomplish them, and always succeeded. The experience of a day did not furnish her with more wisdom than all other nations, but she obtained it by a long succession of events. She sustained a small, a moderate, and an immense fortune with the same superiority, derived true welfare from the whole train of her prosperities, and refined every instance of calamity into beneficial instructions.

She lost her liberty because she completed her work too soon.

II

OF THE RELATION OF LAWS TO DIFFERENT HUMAN BEINGS [3]

LAWS, in their most general signification, are the necessary relations arising from the nature of things. In this sense all beings have their laws; the Deity His laws, the material world its laws, the intelligences superior to man their laws, the beasts their laws, man his laws.

They who assert that a blind fatality produced the various effects we behold in this world talk very absurdly; for can anything be more unreasonable than to pretend that a blind fatality could be productive of intelligent beings?

There is, then, a primitive reason; and laws are the relations subsisting between it and different beings, and the relations of these to one another.

God is related to the universe, as Creator and Preserver; the laws by which He created all things are those by which He preserves them. He acts according to these rules, because He knows them; He knows them, because He made

[3] From "The Spirit of Laws." The translation of Thomas Nugent was published in 1756.

hem; and He made them, because they are rela-
ive to His wisdom and power.

Since we observe that the world, tho formed
by the motion of matter, and void of understanding, subsists through so long a succession
of ages, its motions must certainly be directed
by invariable laws; and could we imagine another world, it must also have constant rules,
or it would inevitably perish.

Thus the creation, which seems an arbitrary
act, supposes laws as invariable as those of the
fatality of the atheists. It would be absurd to
say that the Creator might govern the world
without those rules, since without them it could
not subsist.

These rules are a fixt and variable relation.
In bodies moved, the motion is received, increased, diminished, lost, according to the rela-
ions of the quantity of matter and velocity;
each diversity is uniformity, each change is constancy.

Particular intelligent beings may have laws of
their own making, but they have some likewise
which they never made. Before they were intel-
igent beings, they were possible; they had therefore possible relations, and consequently possible
laws. Before laws were made, there were rela-
ions of possible justice. To say that there is
nothing just or unjust but what is commanded
or forbidden by positive laws is the same as
saying that before the describing of a circle all
the radii were not equal.

We must therefore acknowledge relations of
justice antecedent to the positive law by which
they are established: as for instance, that if

human societies existed it would be right to
conform to their laws; if there were intelligent
beings that had received a benefit of another
being, they ought to show their gratitude; if
one intelligent being had created another intelligent being, the latter ought to continue in its
original state of dependence; if one intelligent
being injures another, it deserves a retaliation
and so on.

But the intelligent world is far from being so
well governed as the physical. For tho the former has also its laws, which of their own nature
are invariable, it does not conform to them so
exactly as the physical world. This is because
on the one hand, particular intelligent beings
are of a finite nature, and consequently liable
to error; and on the other, their nature requires
them to be free agents. Hence they do not steadily conform to their primitive laws; and even
those of their own instituting they frequently
infringe.

Whether brutes be governed by the general
laws of motion or by a particular movement we
can not determine. Be that as it may, they have
not a more intimate relation to God than the rest
of the material world; and sensation is of no
other use to them than in the relation they have
either to other particular beings or to themselves.

By the allurements of pleasure they preserve
the individual, and by the same allurements they
preserve their species. They have natural laws
because they are united by sensation; positive
laws they have none, because they are not connected by knowledge. And yet they do not inva-
riably conform to their natural laws; these are

better observed by vegetables, that have neither understanding nor sense.

Brutes are deprived of the high advantages which we have; but they have some which we have not. They have not our hopes, but they are without our fears; they are subject like us to death, but without knowing it; even most of them are more attentive than we to self-preservation, and do not make so bad a use of their passions.

Man, as a physical being, is like other bodies, governed by invariable laws. As an intelligent being, he incessantly transgresses the laws established by God, and changes those of his own instituting. He is left to his private direction, tho a limited being, and subject, like all finite intelligences, to ignorance and error; even his imperfect knowledge he loses; and as a sensible creature, he is hurried away by a thousand impetuous passions. Such a being might every instant forget his Creator; God has therefore reminded him of his duty by the laws of religion. Such a being is liable every moment to forget himself; philosophy has provided against this by the laws of morality. Formed to live in society, he might forget his fellow creatures; legislators have therefore by political and civil laws confined him to his duty.

FRANÇOIS AROUET VOLTAIRE

Born in Paris in 1694, died in 1778; his original name Arouet; educated at the College of Louis-le-Grand; exiled because of his freedom of speech; twice imprisoned in the Bastille; resided in England in 1726-29; went to Prussia at the invitation of Frederick the Great in 1750, remaining three years, the friendship ending in bitter enmity; wrote in Prussia his "Le Siècle de Louis XIV"; settled at Geneva in 1756, and two years later at Ferney, where he lived until his death in 1778; visited Paris in 1778, being received with great honors; his works very numerous, one edition comprising seventy-two volumes.

I

OF BACON'S GREATNESS [1]

Not long since the trite and frivolous question following was debated in a very polite and learned company, viz., Who was the greatest man, Cæsar, Alexander, Tamerlane, Cromwell, etc.?

Somebody answered that Sir Isaac Newton excelled them all. The gentleman's assertion was very just; for if true greatness consists in having received from heaven a mighty genius, and in

[1] From the "Letters on England." Voltaire's visit to England followed immediately upon his release from imprisonment in the Bastille. During the two years he spent there, he acquired an intimate knowledge of English life, and came to know most of the eminent Englishmen of the time.

An English version of Voltaire's writings, in thirty-five volumes, was published in 1761-69, with notes by Smollett and others. The "Letters from England" seem to have first appeared in English in 1734.

having employed it to enlighten our own mind and that of others, a man like Sir Isaac Newton, whose equal is hardly found in a thousand years, is the truly great man. And those politicians and conquerors (and all ages produce some) were generally so many illustrious wicked men. That man claims our respect who commands over the minds of the rest of the world by the force of truth, not those who enslave their fellow creatures; he who is acquainted with the universe, not they who deface it.

The most singular and the best of all his pieces is that which, at this time, is the most useless and the least read. I mean his "Novum Scientiarum Organum." This is the scaffold with which the new philosophy was raised; and when the edifice was built, part of it, at least the scaffold was no longer of service.

Lord Bacon was not yet acquainted with nature, but then he knew, and pointed out the several paths that lead to it. He had despised in his younger years the thing called philosophy in the universities, and did all that lay in his power to prevent those societies of men instituted to improve human reason from depraving it by their quiddities, their horrors of the vacuum, their substantial forms, and all those impertinent terms which not only ignorance had rendered venerable, but which had been made sacred by their being ridiculously blended with religion.

He is the father of experimental philosophy. It must, indeed, be confest that very surprizing secrets had been found out before his time—the sea compass, printing, engraving on copper plates, oil painting, looking-glasses; the art of restoring, in some measure, old men to their sight by spectacles; gunpowder, etc., had been discovered. A new world had been fought for, found, and conquered. Would not one suppose that these sublime discoveries had been made by the greatest philosophers, and in ages much more enlightened than the present? But it was far otherwise; all these great changes happened in the most stupid and barbarous times. Chance only gave birth to most of those inventions; and it is very probable that what is called chance contributed very much to the discovery of America; at least it has been always thought that Christopher Columbus undertook his voyage merely on the relation of a captain of a ship which a storm had driven as far westward as the Caribbean Island. Be this as it will, men had sailed round the world, and could destroy cities by an artificial thunder more dreadful than the real one; but, then, they were not acquainted with the circulation of the blood, the weight of the air, the laws of motions, light, the number of our planets, etc. And a man who maintained a thesis on Aristotle's "Categories," on the universals *a parte rei*, or such-like nonsense, was looked upon as a prodigy.

The most astonishing, the most useful inventions, are not those which reflect the greatest honor on the human mind. It is to a mechanical instinct, which is found in many men, and not to true philosophy that most arts owe their origin.

The discovery of fire, the art of making bread, of melting and preparing metals, of building houses, and the invention of the shuttle are infinitely more beneficial to mankind than printing or the sea compass; and yet these arts were invented by uncultivated, savage men.

What a prodigious use the Greeks and Romans made afterward of mechanics! Nevertheless, they believed that there were crystal heavens, that the stars were small lamps which sometimes fell into the sea, and one of their greatest philosophers, after long researches, found that the stars were so many flints which had been detached from the earth.

In a word, no one before Lord Bacon was acquainted with experimental philosophy, nor with the several physical experiments which have been made since his time. Scarce one of them but is hinted at in his work, and he himself had made several. He made a kind of pneumatic engine, by which he guessed the elasticity of the air. He approached on all sides, as it were, to the discovery of its weight, and had very near attained it, but some time after Torricelli seized upon this truth. In a little time experimental philosophy began to be cultivated on a sudden in most parts of Europe. It was a hidden treasure which Lord Bacon had some notion of, and which all the philosophers, encouraged by his promises, endeavored to dig up.

But that which surprized me most was to read in his work, in express terms, the new attraction, the invention of which is ascribed to Sir Isaac Newton.

We must search, says Lord Bacon, whether there may not be a kind of magnetic power which operates between the earth and heavy bodies, between the moon and the ocean, between the planets, etc. In another place he says, either heavy bodies must be carried toward the center of the earth, or must be reciprocally attracted by it; and in the latter case it is evident that the nearer bodies in their falling, draw toward the earth, the stronger they will attract one another. We must, says he, make an experiment to see whether the same clock will go faster on the top of a mountain or at the bottom of a mine; whether the strength of the weights decreases on the mountain and increases in the mine. It is probable that the earth has a true attractive power.

This forerunner in philosophy was also an elegant writer, a historian, and a wit.

His moral essays are greatly esteemed, but they were drawn up in the view of instructing rather than of pleasing; and, as they are not a satire upon mankind, like Rochefoucauld's "Maxims," nor written upon a skeptical plan, like Montaigne's "Essays," they are not so much read as those two ingenious authors.

II

ENGLAND'S REGARD FOR MEN OF LETTERS [2]

NEITHER the English nor any other people have foundations established in favor of the polite arts like those in France. There are universities in most countries, but it is in France only that we

[2] From the "Letters on England."

meet with so beneficial an encouragement for astronomy and all parts of the mathematics, for physic, for reasearches into antiquity, for painting, sculpture, and architecture. Louis XIV has immortalized his name by these several foundations, and this immortality did not cost him two hundred thousand livres a year.

I must confess that one of the things I very much wonder at is that as the Parliament of Great Britain have promised a reward of £20,000 to any person who may discover the longitude, they should never have once thought to imitate Louis XIV in his munificence with regard to the arts and sciences.

Merit, indeed, meets in England with rewards of another kind, which redound more to the honor of the nation. The English have so great a veneration for exalted talents, that a man of merit in their country is always sure of making his fortune. Mr. Addison in France would have been elected a member of one of the academies, and, by the credit of some women, might have obtained a yearly pension of twelve hundred livres, or else might have been imprisoned in the Bastille, upon pretense that certain strokes in his tragedy of Cato had been discovered which glanced at the porter of some man in power. Mr. Addison was raised to the post of Secretary of State in England. Sir Isaac Newton was made Master of the Royal Mint. Mr. Congreve had a considerable employment. Mr. Prior was Plenipotentiary. Dr. Swift is Dean of St. Patrick's in Dublin, and is more revered in Ireland than the Primate himself. The religion which Mr. Pope professes * ex-

* Pope was a Catholic.

cludes him, indeed, from preferments of every kind, but then it did not prevent his gaining two hundred thousand livres by his excellent translation of Homer. I myself saw a long time in France the author of "Rhadamistus"[4] ready to perish for hunger. And the son of one of the greatest men our country ever gave birth to, and who was beginning to run the noble career which his father had set him, would have been reduced to the extremes of misery had he not been patronized by Monsieur Fagon.

But the circumstance which mostly encourages the arts in England is the great veneration which is paid them. The picture of the Prime Minister hangs over the chimney of his own closet, but I have seen that of Mr. Pope in twenty noblemen's houses. Sir Isaac Newton was revered in his lifetime, and had a due respect paid to him after his death,—the greatest men in the nation disputing who should have the honor of holding up his pall. Go into Westminster Abbey, and you will find that what raises the admiration of the spectator is not the mausoleums of the English kings, but the monuments which the gratitude of the nation has erected to perpetuate the memory of those illustrious men who contributed to its glory. We view their statues in that abbey in the same manner as those of Sophocles, Plato, and other immortal personages were viewed in Athens; and I am persuaded that the bare sight of those glorious monuments has fired more than one breast, and been the occasion of their becoming great men.

The English have even been reproached with

---

[4] "Rhadamiste et Zénobia," a tragedy by Crébillon (1711), who long suffered from neglect and want.

paying too extravagant honors to mere merit, and censured for interring the celebrated actress Mrs. Oldfield [5] in Westminster Abbey, with almost the same pomp as Sir Isaac Newton. Some pretend that the English had paid her these great funeral honors purposely to make us more strongly sensible of the barbarity and injustice which they object to in us, for having buried Mademoiselle Le Couvreur ignominiously in the fields.

But be assured from me that the English were prompted by no other principle in burying Mrs. Oldfield in Westminster Abbey than their good sense. They are far from being so ridiculous as to brand with infamy an art which has immortalized a Euripides and a Sophocles; or to exclude from the body of their citizens a set of people whose business is to set off with the utmost grace of speech and action those pieces which the nation is proud of.

Under the reign of Charles I and in the beginning of the civil wars raised by a number of rigid fanatics, who at last were the victims to it, a great many pieces were published against theatrical and other shows, which were attacked with the greater virulence because that monarch and his queen, daughter to Henry I of France, were passionately fond of them.

One Mr. Prynne, a man of most furiously scrupulous principles, who would have thought himself damned had he worn a cassock instead of

[5] Anne, or "Nance" Oldfield was born in 1683, and died in 1730. Her death occurred in the year which followed the close of Voltaire's English visit. At her funeral, the body lay in state in the Jerusalem Chamber of Westminster Abbey. She had a natural son, who married Lady Mary Walpole, a natural daughter of Sir Robert Walpole, the Prime Minister.

a short cloak, and have been glad to see one-half of mankind cut the other to pieces for the glory of God and the *Propaganda Fide*, took it into his head to write a most wretched satire against some pretty good comedies, which were exhibited very innocently every night before their majesties. He quoted the authority of the Rabbis, and some passages from St. Bonaventura, to prove that the "Œdipus" of Sophocles was the work of the evil spirit; that Terence was excommunicated *ipso facto;* and added that doubtless Brutus, who was a very severe Jansenist, assassinated Julius Cæsar for no other reason but because he, who was Pontifex Maximus, presumed to write a tragedy the subject of which was "Œpidus." Lastly, he declared that all who frequented the theater were excommunicated, as they thereby renounced their baptism. This was casting the highest insult on the king and all the royal family; and as the English loved their prince at that time, they could not bear to hear a writer talk of excommunicating him, tho they themselves afterward cut his head off. Prynne was summoned to appear before the Star Chamber; his wonderful book, from which Father Lebrun stole his, was sentenced to be burned by the common hangman, and himself to lose his ears.[6] His trial is now extant.

The Italians are far from attempting to cast a

---

[6] William Prynne, lawyer, pamphleteer, and statesman, was born in 1600, and died in 1669. Prynne in 1648 was released from imprisonment by the Long Parliament and obtained a seat in the House of Commons where he took up the cause of the king. Later, in the Cromwellian period, he was arrested and again imprisoned, but was released in 1652, and, after the accession of Charles II, was made keeper of the records in the Tower.

blemish on the opera, or to excommunicate Signor Senesino or Signora Cuzzoni. With regard to myself, I could presume to wish that the magistrates would suppress I know not what contemptible pieces written against the stage. For when the English and Italians hear that we brand with the greatest mark of infamy an art in which we excel; that we excommunicate persons who receive salaries from the king; that we condemn as impious a spectacle exhibited in convents and monasteries; that we dishonor sports in which Louis XIV and Louis XV performed as actors; that we give the title of the devil's works to pieces which are received by magistrates of the most severe character, and represented before a virtuous queen; when, I say, foreigners are told of this insolent conduct, this contempt for the royal authority, and this Gothic rusticity which some presume to call Christian severity, what idea must they entertain of our nation? And how will it be possible for them to conceive, either that our laws give a sanction to an art which is declared infamous, or that some persons dare to stamp with infamy an art which receives a sanction from the laws, is rewarded by kings, cultivated and encouraged by the greatest men, and admired by whole nations? And that Father Lebrun's impertinent libel against the stage is seen in a bookseller's shop, standing the very next to the immortal labors of Racine, of Corneille, of Molière, etc.?

JEAN JACQUES ROUSSEAU

Born in Geneva in 1712, died near Paris in 1778; his father
a mender of watches and teacher of dancing; lived from
hand to mouth until he was thirty-eight; achieved his first
literary reputation from a prize competition in 1749; published "Le Devin du Village" in 1752, "La Nouvelle Héloise"
in 1761, "Le Contrat Social" in 1762, "Emile" in 1762; the
latter work led to his exile from France for five years, during
which he lived in Switzerland and England; his "Confessions" published after his death in 1782; was the father of
five illegitimate children, each of whom he sent to a foundling
asylum.

I

OF CHRIST AND SOCRATES

I WILL confess that the majesty of the Scriptures strikes me with admiration, as the purity of
the Gospel hath its influence on my heart. Peruse
the works of our philosophers with all their pomp
of diction; how mean, how contemptible are they
compared with the Scriptures! Is it possible that
a book, at once so simple and sublime, should be
merely the work of man? Is it possible that the
sacred personage, whose history it contains,
should be himself a mere man? Do we find that
He assumed the tone of an enthusiast or ambitious sectary? What sweetness, what purity in
His manner! What an affecting gracefulness
in His delivery! What sublimity in His maxims!
what profound wisdom in His discourses? What
presence of mind, what subtlety, what truth in

170

His replies! How great the command over His passions! Where is the man, where the philosopher, who could so live, and so die, without weakness, and without ostentation? When Plato described his imaginary good man loaded with all the shame of guilt, yet meriting the highest rewards of virtue, he describes exactly the character of Jesus Christ: the resemblance was so striking that all the Fathers perceived it.

What prepossession, what blindness must it be to compare the son of Sophronicus to the son of Mary! What an infinite disproportion there is between them! Socrates dying without pain or ignominy, easily supported his character to the last; and if his death, however easy, had not crowned his life, it might have been doubted whether Socrates, with all his wisdom, was anything more than a vain sophist. He invented, it is said, the theory of morals. Others, however, had before put them in practise; he had only to say, therefore, what they had done, and to reduce their examples to precepts. Aristides had been just before Socrates defined justice; Leonidas had given up his life for his country before Socrates declared patriotism to be a duty; the Spartans were a sober people before Socrates recommended sobriety; before he had even defined virtue Greece abounded in virtuous men.

But where could Jesus learn, among His competitors, that pure and sublime morality, of which He only hath given us both precept and example? The greatest wisdom was made known amongst the most bigoted fanaticism, and the simplicity of the most heroic virtues did honor to the vilest people on earth. The death of Socrates, peaceably philosophizing with his friends, appears the most agreeable that could be wished for; that of Jesus, expiring in the midst of agonizing pains, abused, insulted, and accused by a whole nation, is the most horrible that could be feared. Socrates, in receiving the cup of poison, blest, indeed, the weeping executioner who administered it; but Jesus, in the midst of excruciating torments, prayed for His merciless tormentors. Yes, if the life and death of Socrates were those of a sage, the life and death of Jesus are those of a God. Shall we suppose the evangelic history a mere fiction? Indeed, my friend, it bears not the marks of fiction; on the contrary, the history of Socrates, which nobody presumes to doubt, is not so well attested as that of Jesus Christ. Such a supposition, in fact, only shifts the difficulty without obviating it: it is more inconceivable that a number of persons should agree to write such a history, than that one only should furnish the subject of it. The Jewish authors were incapable of the diction, and strangers to the morality contained in the Gospel, the marks of whose truth are so striking and inimitable that the inventor would be a more astonishing character than the hero.

II

OF THE MANAGEMENT OF CHILDREN [1]

I HAVE thought that the most essential part in the education of children, and which is seldom regarded in the best families, is to make them sensible of their inability, weakness, and dependence, and, as my husband called it, the heavy yoke of that necessity which nature has imposed upon our species; and that, not only in order to show them how much is done to alleviate the burden of that yoke, but especially to instruct them betimes in what rank Providence has placed them, that they may not presume too far above themselves, or be ignorant of the reciprocal duties of humanity.

Young people who from their cradle have been brought up in ease and effeminacy, who have been caressed by every one, indulged in all their caprices, and have been used to obtain easily everything they desired, enter upon the world with many impertinent prejudices; of which they are generally cured by frequent mortifications, affronts, and chagrin. Now, I would willingly spare my children this kind of education by giving them, at first, a just notion of things. I had indeed once resolved to indulge my eldest son in everything he wanted, from a persuasion that the first impulses of nature must be good

---

[1] From the "New Héloïse." The passage here given is from a letter supposed to have been written by a person who was visiting Héloïse. One of the earliest English versions of the "New Héloïse" appeared in 1784.

and salutary; but I was not long in discovering that children, conceiving from such treatment that they have a right to be obeyed, depart from a state of nature almost as soon as born—contracting our vices from our example, and theirs by our indiscretion. I saw that if I indulged him in all his humors they would only increase by such indulgence; that it was necessary to stop at some point, and that contradiction would be but the more mortifying as he should be less accustomed to it; but, that it might be less painful to him, I began to use it upon him by degrees, and in order to prevent his tears and lamentations I made every denial irrevocable.

It is true, I contradict him as little as possible, and never without due consideration. Whatever is given or permitted him is done unconditionally and at the first instance; and in this we are indulgent enough; but he never gets anything by importunity, neither his tears nor entreaties being of any effect. Of this he is now so well convinced that he makes no use of them; he goes his way on the first word, and frets himself no more at seeing a box of sweetmeats taken away from him than at seeing a bird fly away which he would be glad to catch, there appearing to him the same impossibility of having the one as the other; and, so far from beating the chairs and tables, he dares not lift his hand against those who oppose him. In everything that displeases him he feels the weight of necessity, the effect of his own weakness.

The great cause of the ill humor of children is the care which is taken either to quiet or to aggravate them. They will sometimes cry for an hour for no other reason in the world than because they perceive we would not have them. So long as we take notice of their crying, so long have they a reason for continuing to cry; but they will soon give over of themselves when they see no notice is taken of them; for, old or young, nobody loves to throw away his trouble. This is exactly the case with my eldest boy, who was once the most peevish little bawler, stunning the whole house with his cries; whereas now you can hardly hear there is a child in the house. He cries, indeed, when he is in pain; but then it is the voice of nature, which should never be restrained; and he is again hushed as soon as ever the pain is over. For this reason I pay great attention to his tears, as I am certain he never sheds them for nothing; and hence I have gained the advantage of being certain when he is in pain and when not; when he is well and when sick; an advantage which is lost with those who cry out of mere humor and only in order to be appeased. I must confess, however, that this management is not to be expected from nurses and governesses; for as nothing is more tiresome than to hear a child cry, and as these good women think of nothing but the time present, they do not foresee that by quieting it to-day it will cry the more to-morrow. But, what is still worse, this indulgence produces an obstinacy which is of more consequence as the child grows up. The very cause that makes it a squaller at three years of age will make it stubborn and refractory at twelve, quarrelsome at twenty, imperious and insolent at thirty, and insupportable all its life.

In every indulgence granted to children they can easily see our desire to please them, and therefore they should be taught to suppose we have reason for refusing or complying with their requests. This is another advantage gained by making use of authority, rather than persuasion, on every necessary occasion. For, as it is impossible they can be always blind to our motives, it is natural for them to imagine that we have some reason for contradicting them, of which they are ignorant. On the contrary, when we have once submitted to their judgment, they will pretend to judge of everything, and thus become cunning, deceitful, fruitful in shifts and chicanery, endeavoring to silence those who are weak enough to argue with them; for when one is obliged to give them an account of things above their comprehension, they attribute the most prudent conduct to caprice, because they are incapable of understanding it. In a word, the only way to render children docile and capable of reasoning is not to reason with them at all, but to convince them that it is above their childish capacities; for they will always suppose the argument in their favor unless you can give them good cause to think otherwise. They know very well that we are unwilling to displease them, when they are certain of our affection; and children are seldom mistaken in this particular; therefore, if I deny anything to my children I never reason with them, I never tell them why I do so and so; but I endeavor, as much as possible, that they should find it out, and that even after the affair is over. By these means they are accustomed to think that I never deny

A BURIAL IN PORTUGAL

By Noah Webster

A BURIAL IN PORTUGAL
A KILLING IN MALTA
FLICKERING DEATH

A BURIAL
IN PORTUGAL

NOAH WEBSTER

PUBLISHED FOR THE CRIME CLUB BY
DOUBLEDAY & COMPANY, INC.
GARDEN CITY, NEW YORK
1974

All of the characters in this book are fictitious, and any resemblance to actual persons, living or dead, is purely coincidental.

ISBN: 0-385-00968-2
Library of Congress Catalog Card Number 73–10865
Copyright © 1973 by Bill Knox
All Rights Reserved
Printed in the United States of America
First Edition in the United States of America

For Grace & Ross

QUEEN'S AND LORD TREASURER'S REMEMBRANCER.
H.M. Exchequer Office.

"Para. 35. With regard to Treasure Trove, articles of antiquarian or archaeological interest are claimed on behalf of the Crown and rewards are made to the finders after consultation with the Keeper of the National Museum of Antiquities of Scotland."

CHAPTER ONE

Early spring had returned colour again to Edinburgh after
the long Scottish winter. It burst triumphantly from the thou-
sands of daffodils and crocus in Princes Street Gardens,
danced and rippled on the dresses of girls freed after months
in fur boots and sheepskin jackets—even showed in the way
warm sunlight caught and played with the drab stone-work
of the Sir Walter Scott Monument, that high, ridiculous neo-
Gothic tracery on the Scottish capital's skyline.

But it would be raining again by lunch, decided Henry
Falconer. A big, heavy-faced man, senior administrative assistant to the Queen's and Lord Treasurer's Remembrancer,
he flopped down on one of the wooden benches spaced along
the gardens and ignored the flowers around. The sun was
hurting his eyes, his head wouldn't stop throbbing, and he
damned those extra drinks he'd had at the previous night's
Civil Service Golf Club dinner.

"You said you wanted to walk, Henry," murmured Jonathan Gaunt, fighting down a grin and stopping beside him.
"Feeling tired?"

"No." Falconer scowled around at the rest of the world, at
that moment mainly a mini-skirted blonde walking a large,
bored Labrador dog on a lead. Escaping from his office in the
Exchequer Building had seemed a good idea at the time, but
now he wasn't sure. "Sit down, man. I also said we'd talk."

Gaunt obeyed, watching the girl and the dog as they came
nearer. The girl had the kind of legs he liked, long, slim, and
firmly muscled all the way up to the thigh.

"Would it be too much trouble to ask you to listen?" asked Falconer acidly, his annoyance plain.

"Sorry." Gaunt reluctantly switched his attention. "What's the problem?"

"Yours—and you'll need a black tie," said Falconer with grim satisfaction. "You're going to a funeral tomorrow."

"I am?" Gaunt raised a mildly surprised eyebrow. "Anyone I know?"

"No, but someone we've been interested in." Falconer paused and shrugged. "This is the Remembrancer's idea, not mine and it happens no one else is free to go. You'll need—"

Gaunt held up a hand to stop him and let the grin slide openly across his wide mouth. "A black tie—you told me, Henry. That must have been one hell of a party last night."

"It was." Falconer winced at the reminder but went on doggedly. "But I intended to say you'll need your passport. The funeral is in Portugal."

"Portugal?" Gaunt stared at him.

It brought Falconer a little glow of pleasure. From his viewpoint, catching the younger man off guard was something which didn't happen often enough.

"Portugal," he agreed. "That's on the left-hand side of Spain, as I recall."

"Thanks, Henry," said Gaunt wryly, recovering. "All right, what makes it matter so much we can't just wire a wreath?"

Falconer looked at him, feeling a familiar irritation gathering. From outlook onward, Jonathan Gaunt just didn't blend with the accepted qualities of an external auditor in the Remembrancer's Office.

Gaunt was in his early thirties, tall and with a compact build. A raw-boned face, faintly freckled, went with moody grey-green eyes and fair hair which always seemed untidy and too long. Even his clothes were annoyingly wrong for the job, decided Falconer. A lightweight tweed sports suit worn with a blue shirt and a knitted tie in a darker blue, plus moccasin style shoes, didn't add up to Government service wear.

"You do have a black tie, I presume?" asked Falconer wearily.

"Somewhere." The girl with the dog went past. Gaunt made a clicking noise at the dog, who ignored him, and smiled at the girl, who appeared more interested. He waited till they'd gone a few yards then turned to Falconer again. "Well? What's it all about?"

Falconer shrugged. "The—ah—deceased is a man named Francis Preston." He saw the name didn't register, grimaced slightly and went on. "Preston mattered to us because he found something. Found it, then walked away and left it there."

Puzzled, Gaunt stared at him. "If you're trying out some new kind of riddle—" he began threateningly.

"I'm not." Falconer sounded bitter, looked down with a sigh, and scraped a foot along the ground. "Preston had us over the proverbial barrel. Now he's dead, the Remembrancer wants you to negotiate a reward of up to £50,000 to anyone who can tell us what he wouldn't."

"Fifty thousand!" Gaunt sat bolt upright on the bench, his lips shaping a startled whistle. "For what?"

"Treasure Trove. The file is on my desk." Falconer looked around at the flowers and shook his head uneasily, a man who needed more familiar surroundings when it came to business. "Maybe we should go back there."

"We'd better," agreed Gaunt fervently.

On the way, they stopped in a Princes Street shop while Gaunt bought a new black tie. Francis Preston already sounded as if he deserved it.

The Queen's and Lord Treasurer's Remembrancer occupies part of the Exchequer Building in Edinburgh's George Street. Henry Falconer's office was on the second floor and he settled into his chair with considerable relief.

"What do you know about Treasure Trove?" he demanded with a new assurance.

"From a legal viewpoint?" Jonathan Gaunt scrubbed a hand along his chin. "The usual definition is anything of value found hidden for which no owner can be discovered. *Ultimus Haeres* section usually handle it."

Falconer nodded. "Any man-made items are presumed to have once had an owner. But in his absence they belong directly to the Crown, not to the finder. The law is fairly similar in most countries—the only difference is whether the finder gets a specific share of the value or whether he simply gets a reward."

He stopped as there was a knock on the door. His secretary, a well-built brunette with a distant air, brought in two mugs of coffee. The one she placed before Falconer was black, and she gave him a cold glance of disapproval then left without a word.

"Damn the woman," muttered Falconer, using a government issue pencil to stir his brew. "What she needs—" he stopped and sighed.

"The word is anyone who tries that with her gets frostbite." Gaunt sipped his mug then set it down. "She's your problem, Henry. What about mine? I thought we had a clear routine for Treasure Trove claims?"

"We have—for the regular variety." Falconer took a long, thankful gulp of his coffee and dabbed his lips with a handkerchief. "Maybe a bulldozer digs up a chest of old coins, or a child playing in some ruin comes out clutching a bag of gold. We once had a farmer who had a cow fall down a hole— when he got it out, he discovered a Bronze Age hoard of vital archaeological importance."

"I could use a cow like that," mused Gaunt.

Falconer ignored him. "Large or small, all finds of value must be surrendered. Then the Remembrancer puts a committee of experts to work. They decide the probable open market value and pay a reward to the finder."

"Who goes away happily?"

"Not always," admitted Falconer. "But the law is specific. Find something and keep it and you commit a criminal offence. The penalties are severe." He stopped and swirled his coffee, frowning. "But find something, cover it up again, walk away and refuse to talk about it—that's not an offence."

Suddenly, Gaunt began to understand. "Francis Preston?"

"Preston," agreed Falconer grimly. "He was a fairly well-known amateur archaeologist, among other things. About a year ago he contacted the Remembrancer direct and said he'd made an important find somewhere on the north-west coast. From the description he gave, it amounted to a major find of early Christian church plate—probably hidden just before a Viking raid, with the people who concealed it massacred soon afterwards."

"Uncomplicated people, the Vikings," murmured Gaunt. "But Preston found the stuff—then tried to do a deal?"

Falconer nodded. "Money didn't particularly interest him. But he wanted the final say on what happened to the church plate. His main demand was that most of it should be gifted to some Scottish university for all time as the Preston Collection."

"Reasonable enough, Henry—he found the stuff."

"But the system doesn't work that way," snapped Falconer and scowled. "It was explained to him, but—"

"But he told the Remembrancer to get stuffed?"

Falconer nodded. "Then walked out. He hadn't removed the plate from where he found it so we couldn't touch him. And though we had certain people try, we couldn't find a single lead to where he might have been." Still scowling, Falconer stopped, shoved a thick manila file across the desk towards Gaunt, and glanced at a slip of paper. "So you're booked on a flight which gets you to Lisbon early tomorrow afternoon. The funeral is at four P.M., and afterwards—"

"Use tact, discretion, and wave all that money around,"

nodded Gaunt. "Henry, suppose I tell you I'd have been on Preston's side?"

"I'm not interested in any parade of your morality or conscience," said Falconer wearily. "Just find where that damned stuff is. It may take you a few days, but we'll switch any work you've got at the moment onto someone else."

Gaunt grimaced. "That leaves a few personal problems—"

"We all have those," said Falconer bleakly, uninterested. "You'll see from the file that Preston died rather oddly. He was on some archaeological project on the Portuguese coast when a trench collapsed on him. He was dead when they dug him out."

"When?"

"Two days ago. Word only got to us this morning. We have to gamble that those people closest to him, people who might know, will be there at the funeral. What matters is we're offering £50,000—if the plate is what he claimed."

Gaunt picked up the file and rose.

"Thanks," he said sardonically. "Anything else?"

"A small warning." Falconer nursed his coffee mug between both hands. "As I recall it, there's a casino in Estoril, just along the coast. Just remember your expenses only cover legitimate claims."

"And if I win?"

"In that unlikely event"—Falconer's face thawed into the makings of a hopeful smile—"you might remember less fortunate colleagues who are tied to their desks by responsibility. The wine of the country—"

"I'll remember," promised Gaunt.

"Good. And—ah—you can charge that black tie to the Department, of course," said Falconer expansively.

"I'll try to remember that too," said Gaunt, keeping a straight face as he went out.

Once the door had closed Henry Falconer sighed, fumbled a couple of aspirins from his waistcoat pocket, and swallowed them down with the rest of his coffee. He looked at the other piled papers spread over his desk, rubbed a hand across his forehead, and once again damned that golf club dinner.

Treasure Trove . . . it came well down the list of responsibilities in the web of the Queen's and Lord Treasurer's Remembrancer's function. The antiquated title covered an organisation which, throughout all its long history, had always possessed power in a way few people dreamed existed.

Even at the beginning, when the first, medieval Remembrancer had been a body-servant of the early Scottish kings and queens—going around with them everywhere, charged with quite literally remembering things for them.

Or occasionally forgetting, if that was more important.

A blend of walking notebook and royal conscience in the beginning, the office of Remembrancer had gradually altered in emphasis and grown.

The 1970s brand of Remembrancer was a senior-grade professional civil servant who became involved in most things that mattered in Scotland. From being paymaster for every government department north of the border to constituting his own court of law in many a revenue case. From being responsible for the processing of what was vaguely termed "state intelligence" to looking after the security of the Scottish Crown Jewels.

Regulation of company registrations, auditing the Scottish law courts, making sure fines in those courts were collected and paid over to the crown . . .

The list went on and on, even to making sure tax inspectors paid the right amount of income tax on their salaries.

A sudden thought came to Falconer and he glanced at his desk calendar. The fifteenth of the month—he brightened.

It was his day to sign cheques. Maybe twenty million pounds worth, being paid out for everything from new motorways to the bill for the little man who went up and cleaned the Crown Jewels at Edinburgh Castle.

Twenty million in a day wasn't bad going for anyone.
Even with a hangover.

Two hours flying time from London to Lisbon aboard a
Transportes Aeros Portugueses jet gave Jonathan Gaunt ample
opportunity to study the Department file on Francis Preston.
The Boeing left London shortly after noon and by the time
the "Fasten Seatbelts" sign winked on and they began de-
scending through heavy cloud he reckoned he'd memorised
most of the essentials.

Stubbing his cigarette and stowing the file in his brief
case, Gaunt sat back and considered what mattered. At forty,
Preston had been an engineer who sold out a patent on a
minor steel-making process for enough money to mean he
didn't have to worry too much about working. A bachelor,
he'd changed what had been a hobby into a full-time interest in
archaeology.

The file listed some of the ventures that had resulted in a
handful of years. They ranged from locating a Greek temple
site in Cyprus and a Bronze Age fort in Germany to a nibbling
attempt at salvaging a sunken Spanish *guarda costa* frigate in
the Caribbean.

Nibbling was a good word, decided Gaunt. He looked out
of his window as the Boeing broke cloud for a moment, showing the broad, muddy estuary of the Tagus River far below
and busy with shipping. The slim thread of a four-lane sus-
pension bridge across its neck, more than a mile in length,
was new since the only other time he'd been in Portugal.

He winced at the reminder. It had been a honeymoon trip.

"Quite a sight, eh?" nudged the large, hearty Englishman
who occupied the next seat and who had been trying to make
conversation ever since London. He leaned across to get a
better view. "That's the Salazar bridge. Any notion what that
cost them?"

Gaunt shook his head, knowing it was coming anyway.

"Thirty million pounds, seventy-five million if you think in dollars." The man, who had the smooth-shaved look of a sales rep. hunting some business deal, gave a grunt of satisfied amusement. "These people may have the lowest per capita income in Europe, but they are spending money, wherever it comes from."

The jet's hydraulics began a new gobbling noise for flaps and undercarriage and another cloud wiped out the bridge and the sprawling city beyond it. Shrugging, the man settled back in his seat, while Gaunt wondered how you rated assets like pride and tradition.

He switched his thoughts back to Francis Preston.

Nibbling . . . Preston hadn't specialised and hadn't gone in for the really big-time expeditions. He either operated alone or gathered a few people for a particular purpose, and on that basis his success to failure ratio had been surprisingly good. Good enough to lend a lot of credence to the claims he'd made for his Scottish find.

But the file told little about the rest of the man. His nearest known relative was a sister somewhere, he had no close friends, no particular attachments.

Francis Preston emerged as a solitary, perhaps even lonely man whose life had held only one passion. A passion that had killed him near a little village named Claras where the file said he'd been exploring round the site of an old Moorish fortress called Castelo de Rosa.

For a man like Preston, that might have been as good a way to go as any.

It was raining when the TAP Boeing landed at Lisbon International Airport, its passengers emerging from customs and immigration into a main concourse which was a damp noisy chaos. A couple of charter holiday flights, delayed on the ground, were the main trouble and the way out was through an obstacle course of scattered luggage, arguing passengers and harassed officials.

It had been that way the last time too, remembered Gaunt

as he elbowed his way through to the main exit and found the airport cab rank. The lead cab was a green and black Mercedes of uncertain vintage, the driver a moon-faced character in a leather jerkin who shoved away a girlie magazine before he leaned across to open the passenger door.

"Por favor . . . I have to get to a village called Claras," said Gaunt, heaving his suit case aboard and getting into the back seat. "You know it?"

"Sim, senhor." Sharp eyes quickly assessed Gaunt's luggage and brief case and were satisfied. "It is a long way, of course. Also, there is a toll on the *auto-estrada—*"

"Just get me there," said Gaunt, cutting the recital short. "I'll pay."

"Okay." The driver nodded cheerfully and started the cab. "You go to a funeral maybe, *senhor?"*

"That's right." Gaunt raised a surprised eyebrow, the black tie still in his brief case. "Does it show?"

"My brother also drives an airport cab. Today he took two people from here to Claras—for a funeral, they said." Sending the Mercedes weaving out into the traffic, its tyres hissing on the wet roadway, the man bounced a grin back through the rear-view mirror. "Not many people go to Claras this time of year."

"What else did your brother tell you?" asked Gaunt, suddenly interested.

"They were a man and woman, both young and English." The driver took a moment to horn-blast past a lumbering truck then glanced back again. "It is a long way for people to come to say *adeus.* Someone important must have died, eh?"

"Some people must think so," answered Gaunt vaguely, lighting a cigarette. He settled back, relieved to know he was guaranteed some company at Preston's graveside. "What size of a place is Claras?"

"Small, *senhor* . . . very small. Tourists in the summer maybe, but in the winter there is nothing." His driver took one hand from the wheel and waved expansively, ignoring the bustling traffic. The cab had a posy of plastic flowers in a tiny holder and a small crucifix had been glued above the ignition switch. "They say there are big plans for Claras, but in Portugal we always have plans—more plans than money."

Gaunt nodded and fell silent, stifling a grimace as a familiar dull ache stabbed again in his back, the way it had been doing on and off for the past half hour.

Travel ache, the specialists called it. One of the things to expect after a broken back.

Two years had passed since a partial 'chute failure in a training jump had nearly killed Lieutenant J. Gaunt of the Parachute Regiment. After six months recovering in a military hospital he'd been discharged—to a disability pension and a wife who wanted a divorce.

Patti, who was someone else's wife now—though he couldn't get used to that part.

The cab took a roundabout without slowing, the traffic thicker than ever. On a little platform in the middle of the roundabout, a points policeman wore a plastic raincoat with his white sun helmet.

Gaunt smiled absently, realising the rain was still drizzling down. He still couldn't blame Patti. She'd been young, she'd married a pair of paratroop wings, she hadn't hinted things were wrong till after he was out of hospital.

They'd even managed to finish almost amicably, with no family to add extra strain . . .

He pushed that part out of his mind, the ache stabbing again. The last medical board had cut his army pension, reckoning his back was improving. The painkiller pills he had to carry were incidental, as incidental as the occasional nightmares that still came. Nightmares when he was falling again, always waking just before he hit the ground.

The worst time for them had been after the divorce. He'd been drifting, his only nebulous asset a few University terms spent studying law and accountancy before he'd gone into the army.

Then somebody, somewhere had a contact, the Queen's and Lord Treasurer's Remembrancer had called him for an interview . . . and he'd gone on the payroll.

Things could have worked out worse. Jonathan Gaunt, thirty-four years of age, unattached, and living again, was enjoying most of it. Gathering some fresh interests, like the potent little Mini-Cooper he ran on a shoe-string. Or playing the stock market for a new brand of small-time excitement, usually on an overdraft.

Like now—the last thing he'd done before he left home. There was a hint of a reverse takeover involving a couple of English breweries. He'd sold a bundle of low-cost African tin shares, caught in the aftermath of a presidential coup, switching the money to take an option on a thousand brewery shares.

By the time he returned they'd either be ripe for a profit or he'd have to live on beans for a couple of months.

But what the hell? He was living, and that was what mattered.

Skirting Lisbon, the route to Claras started as a long concrete slash of busy *auto-estrada* with heavy traffic pouring in both directions. That ended near Estoril, where the rain had stopped and the sun was steaming the roads dry. The cab purred through the resort's clustered hotels, the highway running along the edge of the shore where sandy beaches were backed by unbroken blue Atlantic.

Then they swung inland again, small villages and fields punctuated by white, wide-sailed windmills rapidly giving way to rising, wooded country. At last, leaving the main highway at a sign for Claras, the cab followed a narrow, winding road down towards a little township of red roofs and white walls. It had a tall church spire near the middle and several large villas were scattered around its tree-fringed outskirts.

Gaunt glanced at his watch. Little more than an hour had passed since they'd left Lisbon, which was better than he'd hoped. Leaning forward, he tapped the moon-faced driver's shoulder.

"Find the cemetery first, then a hotel."

"*Sim, senhor.*" The man grinned and nodded. "No problem. There is only one of each in this place."

For Claras's size that seemed enough. The cemetery was on the way in, a small neat patch of ground with two broad-leafed palm trees at its entrance. From there a couple of minutes brought them to the village square and the cab pulled in at the Hotel Da Gama, a three-story building with balconied windows and an ornately tiled doorway.

Gaunt got out, collected his suit case, and stonily paid a fare which was probably twice what he should have been charged. Then, as the green and black Mercedes accelerated away in a scatter of dust, he looked around.

Claras seemed deserted. A few cars, an old truck and a couple of donkey carts were parked beside a small fountain in the middle of the cobbled square. But the only people were two women in black gossiping outside a bakery shop and a man in a sports shirt and sunglasses lounging at a pavement cafe table.

Picking up the suit case, Gaunt went into the Da Gama's cool, dark lobby. He had to ring a bell before the reception clerk, who was thin and balding, emerged from somewhere at the rear still pulling on his jacket.

"*Senhor?*" The man had bad teeth but the smile was friendly enough.

"I need a room, probably for a couple of nights," Gaunt told him.

"*Por favor . . .*" the desk clerk frowned, looked around and shouted. "Jaime!"

The boy who answered was still in his early teens. Brown skinned, lanky, and with a mop of jet black hair, he wore slacks, a torn white sweatshirt and leather sandals. After listening to the desk clerk's mutter he grinned, turning to Gaunt.

"You wish a room, *senhor?* I speak English."

"Yes, for tonight or maybe longer," nodded Gaunt.

The hotel register was pushed towards him. He took his time signing, noting the two names immediately above his own. A Mr and Mrs John Marsh had booked in, taking a double room with bath and giving the curt address, "Liverpool, England."

When he turned, the boy had his suit case and a room key. Gaunt followed him, the youngster whistling cheerfully as he led the way up a carpeted stairway to the top floor. The room was near the end of the corridor, the window shutters closed. But as they were swung open sunlight flooded in on a bed that looked clean and comfortable and furnishings which were plain but sturdy.

"You look out on the square," volunteered the boy. "Okay?"

"Fine," agreed Gaunt. "You're Jaime?"

"Yes, *senhor.*" The boy opened the last shutter and faced him, smiling.

"Maybe you can help me then, Jaime. I've come to Claras for a funeral—the funeral of an Englishman named Preston. Did you know him?"

The smile vanished and Jaime nodded.

"He was a good man," he answered seriously. "I liked him— he and his friends came here often in the evening." A grimace crossed his face. "*Senhor* Preston would laugh and joke, but his friends were not always so happy—or so liked."

"I never met him," admitted Gaunt. "But I'll take your word for it. How many other guests in the hotel are here for the funeral?"

"None, *senhor.*" The youngster shrugged a little. "Two did arrive this morning, but then Doctor Sollas came to see them and they went off with him instead."

"Who's this man, Sollas?"

"A *medico* . . . a doctor. He came with *Senhor* Preston

to be his partner in the digging at the Castelo," explained Jaime patiently. "The digging people rent a villa outside Claras —I think maybe he took those two to stay with him there."

"I'll need to meet Doctor Sollas," mused Gaunt. "What does he look like?"

"A big man, big like a bull," said the youngster almost grimly. "He has a scar, like this"—he traced a finger across the bridge of his nose—"and a loud voice. He is easy to recognise."

"Good." Going over to the window, Gaunt went out on the little balcony beyond the glass and looked down at the cobbled square. There were now three women gossiping outside the shop, but the man in sunglasses had vanished. "Jaime, how far away is this Castelo de Rosa?"

"A few kilometres—you can almost see it from here. There is a hill to your left, okay? The Castelo is there, an old watch-tower place halfway up, among the trees." The boy hesitated. "You know the funeral is at four o'clock, *senhor?*"

"Yes." Gaunt nodded, his eyes on the wooded, hog-backed hill and the higher peaks which lay beyond it. "Thanks."

"Obrigado, senhor." The boy went out quietly, clicking the room door shut.

Gaunt stayed on the balcony. The man in sunglasses had appeared again, coming from immediately below him as if leaving the hotel. Walking briskly, the figure headed across the square then his bright sports shirt vanished up a side-street.

Shrugging, Gaunt returned to the room, opened his suit case, and unpacked a little. Then, the ache in his back still a low-key throb, he sprawled out on the bed and smoked a cigarette.

At last, as the hands of his watch came round towards four, he got up again. A wash left him feeling fresher as he put on the black tie and checked its knot in the mirror. Grimacing at his reflection, he checked that his cigarettes were back in his pocket and set off.

Downstairs, the hotel lobby was deserted. But a few more people were moving around in the square as he went out and started in the direction of the cemetery.

It was a pleasant walk. Claras liked colour. It was there in the brightly painted woodwork of its little houses with their clean stucco walls and ornate roofs, in the gay flower boxes outside every window, but above all in the glazed *azulejo* picture tiles which framed most doorways.

Some were built in elaborate mural panels, often with a religious theme, others formed pure geometric patterns of clean, cool blue and white. That other time he'd been in Portugal he and Patti had seen *azulejo* tiles in plenty. But never so many, never so varied. In Claras, they were an art form.

Strolling on, the sun warm between his shoulders, Gaunt had the cemetery in sight ahead when the sound of cars approaching made him look round. A small convoy of vehicles was coming towards him.

In another moment the lead vehicle went past. An elderly motor hearse with black paintwork and tarnished chrome, it carried a polished oak coffin topped by several wreaths.

Behind it came two large limousines filled by an assortment of dark-garbed mourners then, like a rear-guard, four men in a battered green jeep. They were a quartet with solemn, sun-tanned peasant faces and wore clean work clothes with black arm-bands.

The funeral cortege reached the entrance gates and turned in. Quickening his pace, Gaunt was almost there too when another car swept up, travelling fast in a way which made him side-step quickly towards the hedge of prickly pear which lined the opposite side of the road.

He had a brief glimpse of a small red Lancia coupe with a woman behind the wheel. She was young and good-looking, with long, raven-black hair caught back by a silver clasp, but before more could register the car had gone, a brisk gear-change being followed by a spurt of gravel and dust from its tyres as it followed the others into the cemetery driveway.

Plodding on, Gaunt entered the gates. Ahead, the red Lancia had pulled up behind the other vehicles at the far side of the cemetery where a clump of almond trees were in dazzling white blossom. Already grouped beside a new mound of chalk-streaked earth, the mourners were waiting while the coffin, brass handles glinting in the sunlight, was carried over from the hearse.

Reaching the Lancia, which had a tiger-cat transfer snarling from its trunk lid, Gaunt stopped and watched as the service got under way.

It was in English, with a priest officiating who wore Church of England robes. But the words reached him as little more than a murmur and he ignored them, considering the mourners instead. The girl from the Lancia, a black lace shawl now over her hair, stood a little apart from the others. Slim and tall, wearing a coffee-coloured dress, she glanced round twice towards the car and each time gave a slightly puzzled frown in his direction before she turned away.

A second girl, fair-haired and younger, was among the small group closest to the graveside. In a cream suit with a black, wide-brimmed hat, she gave an impression of only detached interest in the whole proceedings but looked away for a moment as the coffin was lowered.

The clergyman's voice sounded again, his hand rose in a symbolic sprinkling of earth, then the mourners fell back and the grave-diggers picked up their shovels.

The thud of soil on hollow wood was already under way as the little group began to drift back towards the cars. Two of the men stopped to speak to the girl from the Lancia but though she smiled at them, she shook her head at what they said.

One figure was moving more purposefully. A big man in a dark suit, with thinning, mousy hair, he strode towards Gaunt with an expression of wary curiosity on his heavy features.

And he had a scar across his nose. Gaunt went to meet him.

"Doctor Sollas?" he asked.

"That's right." The voice was a booming rumble and Sollas's blue eyes were cool in their appraisal. "I saw you standing back here. Were you a friend of Preston's?"

"No." Gaunt shook his head.

"Then . . . ?" Arthur Sollas's manner chilled several degrees.

"I was sent." Gaunt shrugged apologetically and brought out his Remembrancer's Office identification card. "The timing wasn't my idea—but it may save complications."

"I see." The big man's scowl made it plain he didn't as he examined the card. "All right, Mr Gaunt, what's it all about? If you're some kind of tax vulture—"

"No." Gaunt stopped him with a quick, fractional smile. "You could say it's more the other way round. My job is to talk to Preston's colleagues and friends—and any relatives I can find. Somebody could be feeling very happy by the time I'm finished."

The scowl faded but Arthur Sollas still treated him with a chilly caution.

"I'd like to know why," he said bluntly, with a glance back over his shoulder. "Most people would at least wait till a man's grave was filled in."

"I'm not exactly stopping that," said Gaunt patiently. "But I want to make sure people know I'm here—let them know before they scatter again." He shrugged mildly. "No harm in that, is there?"

"Depends what you want, doesn't it?" countered Sollas grimly.

"Information," Gaunt told him. "If we get the kind we want then it could mean someone collecting a sizeable amount of money."

"From the British Government?" Arthur Sollas gave a humorless grin of disbelief.

"Taxpayers' money," nodded Gaunt. "We draw the line at using our own." He paused, meeting Sollas's gaze cheerfully.

"Would it help if I said we were specifically interested in Treasure Trove—and what Francis Preston was doing in Scotland last year?"

"It—yes, it might." Arthur Sollas rubbed a slow, thoughtful finger along his scarred nose, his manner thawing. Then he gave a grunt of near amusement. "Yes, I'd say it makes things a lot clearer. Give me a moment." He turned and raised his voice. "Carlos—"

A thin, pock-faced individual, one of the workmen who'd arrived aboard the jeep, trotted over.

"Take the men back to camp. *Immediatamente* . . . I don't want them diving into a bar somewhere. And Carlos, I'll want to see you later." As the man nodded his understanding and turned away, Sollas switched his attention back to Gaunt. "They're from our digging team—though right now I've stopped all work. In fact, we've still to decide whether we go on or just pack it all in. You know Preston was killed at the site?"

Gaunt nodded. "That's all we heard. What happened?"

Sollas shook his head bleakly. "The one damned fool thing Preston kept warning everybody else not to do. He went wandering around the site on his own late at night, after dark. Either he fell into part of the main trench or it caved in while he was down in it—but we found him in the morning, under about ten feet of muck."

Behind them, the Lancia's engine suddenly rasped to life. Gaunt swung at the sound and saw the raven-haired girl was back behind the wheel. Dark, strangely questioning eyes in a face which was beautiful yet somehow strained met his own for an instant. Then her lips tightened and the car began moving.

"Well, I've things to do right now." Sollas spoke again as the Lancia drew away. "Where are you staying, Gaunt?"

"In Claras—I've a room at the Hotel Da Gama."

"That's handy enough." Sollas gave a casual flick at a fly which came buzzing near his face. "Suppose you come out to our place tonight, about nine—the villa, not the camp? Anyone will show you where it is, and we can talk then."

The jeep, its crew aboard, was also growling off and the Lancia had just disappeared through the cemetery gates. Pointedly, Gaunt considered the handful of mourners who remained.

"Will everybody be there?"

"Everybody you're likely to want to meet," said Sollas shortly.

"Doctor"—Gaunt took the chance while he had it—"how much do you know about that Scottish trip?"

"That can wait." The man grinned a little and shook his head. "As for tonight, I'll be there with the two men who were helping us organise this dig, plus a couple of relatives who flew in for today." He gestured caustically towards a young man with long, mousy hair and a dark suit who was standing beside the blonde girl. "That's Preston's nephew, John Marsh—the girl is his wife. Five minutes with them and you find it easy enough to guess what brought them galloping over. But—anyway, is that enough for you?"

"It makes a start," declared Gaunt hopefully.

"Good." Arthur Sollas drew a deep breath, as if relieved that part was over. "The villa tonight, then—right now I've got to get that damned clergyman started for home. We had to fetch him out from one of the English churches in Lisbon and he's itching to get back."

Turning on one heel, the bulky figure strode away.

Left on his own, Gaunt lit a cigarette and stayed where he was for a moment. Then, feeling he'd made a reasonable start, he set off along the gravelled driveway towards the road.

He had reached the gates when the two limousines and their returning mourners overtook him again. As the first car purred out, turning onto the roadway, Arthur Sollas raised a hand in greeting from the front passenger seat.

The second limousine followed. But as they began to pull

away two figures sprang into sight behind the hedge of prickly pear on the opposite side of the road.

A shout rang out, two large stones flew through the air—and there was a crash of glass as one of the stones shattered the first limousine's windscreen.

It skidded to a halt. There was another bang as the second limousine, brakes squealing slammed into its rear—while the two stone-throwers, youngsters in their teens, were already running from the hedge to the start of a patch of thick woodland.

Gaunt began running too. He reached the scene as Arthur Sollas tumbled out of the first limousine with livid fury on his face and a small cut trickling blood down one cheek.

"Damn them!" Sollas shook an impotent fist in the direction of the two figures, already vanishing among the trees. Then, as more of the shaken passengers appeared he grimly dismissed the matter. "Let them go. We wouldn't have a chance of catching them in there."

"You mean we just let them get away with it?" protested a voice indignantly. A bald man with peeling sunburn pushed forward. "Look, Doc, suppose we try—"

"I said forget it," snarled Sollas. "Is anyone hurt?"

The group looked at each other then shook their heads. Sollas turned, took another glance at the two limousines, and was satisfied.

"They can still be driven. We'll move on." He came over to Gaunt. "You saw those damned hooligans?"

Gaunt nodded. "But not well enough to pick them out, if that's what you mean."

"It's always that way," said Sollas bleakly, dabbing at his cut with a handkerchief.

"Meaning this has happened before?" asked Gaunt with some surprise.

"Other things have." Sollas pursed his lips. "Not everyone around here likes us."

"Why?"

"Ask them," grated Sollas. He looked at the blood on his handkerchief and cursed. "Some of them just don't like strangers. Others go around with a crazy story that we're waking ghosts—but I'll tell you this. The first of those characters we catch will wish he'd never been born."

"But they've been trying to frighten you off?"

Sollas bristled. "Nobody scares me off, Gaunt. I leave when I'm ready, not before."

The last of his companions had gone back aboard the limousines. Sollas strode over and climbed into his seat beside the driver of the lead vehicle, who still looked shaken. More glass showered out as he cleared loose fragments from the windscreen then the engine fired and it grated into gear.

It moved away, the second limousine following and neither driver wasting time.

Left alone again, Gaunt looked at the glass scattered across the roadway and shrugged.

He'd meant it when he told Sollas he couldn't have identified the stone-throwers again. But one had been lanky, with a mop of black hair and a white sweatshirt. It might have been Jaime, the young porter from the Da Gama—or someone near enough his double.

But possibility held its own dangers in Sollas's present mood, quite apart from his own instinctive curiosity to find out more about the reason behind what had happened.

A fat, black-backed scavenging beetle suddenly appeared beside his feet, weaving an excited path through the glinting fragments in search of food. Mandibles quivering, it stopped where a tiny splash of blood from Sollas's cut cheek had landed on the tarmac.

Gaunt raised his foot in disgust, ready to crush it. Then he stopped and turned away with a grimace, remembering his own reason for being involved.

Though that could wait till evening now. For the moment he was more conscious of the afternoon's heat, the way his sweat-soaked shirt was sticking to his back and the dry, dusty taste gathering in his throat.

Taking a last glance towards the trees he started back down the sun-baked road towards the village.

CHAPTER TWO

Children were playing barefoot round the edge of Claras's fountain when Jonathan Gaunt got back to the cobbled square. He watched their laughing antics for a moment, envying the way they splashed in and out of the bubbling water, then made his way thankfully into the cool shadow of the Hotel Da Gama's lobby.

As usual, it was empty. But the bar was on the left and he pushed his way through a beaded curtain into a long, narrow room with a few old tables and chairs and a counter which was faced in faded red leather with a black marble top.

"Boa tarde, Senhor Gaunt." Dark hair slicked back, a clean white jacket buttoned up to his young neck, Jaime grinned from the other side of the counter. "It is a hot day outside, eh?"

"If you've been walking—or running." Gaunt met the grin neutrally. "What did you do, Jaime?"

"Me?" The teen-ager stayed unconcerned. "There was work to do in the cellar, *senhor.*"

"Anybody helping you?" asked Gaunt.

"In the cellar?" Jaime's dark eyes showed an almost childish innocence, and he shook his head sadly, "No, I was alone. But at least it is cool down there."

"It pays to stay cool," agreed Gaunt grimly. "I'll have a beer."

"A beer—and another brandy," said a lazy, new voice behind him. "You will join me, *Senhor* Gaunt?"

He turned. It was the man with sunglasses and sports shirt he'd noticed earlier in the square, and the words came with a gold-toothed smile. Gaunt considered the stranger's thin, hawk-like face while the smile lingered, then nodded.

"*Obrigado*. As long as you're not selling anything."

"Me?" The man shook his head with a chuckle then snapped finger and thumb together. "Move, Jaime. A man could die of thirst while you stand staring." He turned to Gaunt again as the youngster jerked to life. "My name is Costa—Manuel Costa."

"*Policia*," muttered Jaime, busy with a bottle.

"Sergeant of detectives in this district," confirmed Costa, unperturbed. He waited until their drinks were on the counter then spun a coin towards Jaime. "Suppose we go over to a table, *Senhor* Gaunt?"

Gaunt nodded, but took a long swallow from his beer before he followed Costa across towards a table in a shaded corner. Sitting down, nursing the cool, moist glass between his hands, he raised a quizzical eyebrow.

"Local hospitality, Sergeant?"

"In a way." Costa, a man in his mid-thirties with a wiry build, had a sallow complexion and long sideburns. He sipped his drink then sucked his lips happily. "*Ginjinha* . . . our local brandy. Smooth yet fiery. I can recommend it."

"Right now I'll stick to beer." Gaunt washed more of the thirst from his throat and sat back with a sigh. "Well, Sergeant, what do you want?"

"Just a friendly talk." Costa waved a vague hand, in no hurry. "I heard, of course, that you came to Claras for *Senhor* Preston's funeral. An unhappy reason." He paused, leaning forward on the table. "Yet a strange one—when you did not know him."

"Any prize for guessing who told you?" asked Gaunt. He glanced over to the bar counter, where Jaime was making a lack-lustre job of polishing glasses, and shrugged. "Do you check on every visitor, Sergeant?"

"Only the interesting ones, believe me." Costa grinned,

produced a battered pack of cigarettes, and lit one using a book of matches. "I find you interesting—and unusual."

"I've been called worse." Gaunt waited calmly.

"*Senhor* Gaunt, I will be honest with you," said Costa patiently. "First, I find myself with a certain problem. Then you arrive—and what I hear makes me wonder if your interests might be like my own."

"You think they could be?" fenced Gaunt, wondering what was coming.

"Perhaps." Costa nodded hopefully. "For instance, I would say you are not a lawyer. A lawyer would not walk to a client's funeral. He would hire a car, then add the expense to his bill."

"The expense plus ten per cent," grinned Gaunt. "They're the same breed everywhere. Why didn't you do this the easy way, Sergeant—borrow a pass-key from Jaime and check my room."

"I did." The policeman removed his sunglasses, revealing lazy brown eyes which held a faint twinkle. "You have an excellent lock on your brief case. I would not want to damage such an item."

"Thanks," said Gaunt dryly. "All right, let's save time. Are we talking about Francis Preston?"

Costa nodded.

"Then I'll put you straight, Sergeant. I'm a plain, ordinary British civil servant sent out because Preston's death has left us with a headache. My department simply wants me to try and pick up any pieces he left behind."

"But the matter must be important?" persisted Costa.

"There's money involved—that's why I'm meeting his partners tonight. But it only concerns something that happened back in Scotland." Gaunt paused as two men in work clothes entered the bar. They ordered drinks at the counter and stayed there, gossiping with Jaime. "What's your interest, Sergeant?"

"How the man died," said Costa gloomily.

"Preston?" Gaunt fought down a whistle of surprise.

"It may be foolishness, a waste of time, I know." Costa nodded wryly. "But it is my job to be sure."

"Do they know about this at the digging camp?"

"No." Almost sheepishly, Costa shook his head. "But then, nearly all I have is what you would call a hunch."

"A hunch?" Gaunt stared at him.

"*Por favor* . . . let me explain, eh?" Costa's lazy voice took on a weary edge. "That day, *Senhor* Preston was at the Castelo site till afternoon. Then we know he drove into Lisbon alone and saw a few people—museum officials, a doctor, all eminently respectable. It was late evening before he left to drive back to Claras."

"And then?"

"Nothing till next morning." Costa scowled at the table. "Then he was found dead at the Castelo site, buried at the bottom of a trench which had fallen in." He stopped and looked up grimly. "It could have been an accident, as people say—there had been heavy rain before and the sides might just have collapsed. Even the *medico* who did the autopsy confirmed suffocation there as the cause of death.

"But there was another injury, *Senhor* Gaunt. A severe bruising on the head caused by a blow—"

"Maybe a chunk of stone hit him during the cave-in," countered Gaunt sceptically.

"Many reasons are possible." Costa swallowed what remained of his brandy, laid down the empty glass, and considered it sadly. "But we have had trouble between the village people and Preston's men, who are outsiders—and there are stories of quarrels inside the digging camp."

"I'd heard," murmured Gaunt. "About the first part, anyway."

It was Costa's turn to be surprised. Muttering under his breath, he glanced towards the bar.

"Jaime didn't tell me," said Gaunt with a mild amusement. "He's your contact, not mine."

"Jaime is anyone's contact for a few *escudoes,*" answered the sergeant with a wry disgust. "Behind that angel face lies all the natural charm of a new-born rattlesnake—a useful rattlesnake." He rubbed his chin, puzzled. "But if it wasn't Jaime—"

"I heard from Doctor Sollas. It was after the funeral and he'd just had a brick thrown through a limousine windscreen."

Costa winced at the news. "You saw this happen?"

"Uh-huh. There were two of them, young, and they got away." Gaunt left it at that. "He also told me about some crazy notion that the digging at the Castelo is annoying the local ghosts."

"Lights and noises—children's tales." Costa sighed and shook his head. "There are stories, and as always there are fools who will believe them. But the rest is real enough. All the ground around the Moorish fort has been fenced off, local people are turned away—and some who protested too much have been roughly handled."

"Have you done anything about it?"

"The project has full government backing with some powerful people interested," said Costa, shrugging. "There are times when a humble sergeant of detectives must use discretion."

Gaunt chuckled his sympathy. "So this hunch you've got about Preston's death won't be particularly popular?"

"Shall we say that my superiors are dismayed?" countered Costa with a bitter cynicism. "I have been reminded that, among other things, there is the tourist trade to consider. All the guidebooks emphasise that foreigners can come to no harm in Portugal."

"I'll remember that. But I still can't help." Gaunt pushed back his chair, ready to leave. "Sergeant, do you know a dark-haired girl, good-looking—a girl who drives a red Lancia? She was at the funeral."

"Maria-Inez," answered Costa without hesitation and brightening. "She is a *fadista,* a folk singer. Our local celebrity."

"Was she a friend of Preston's?"

Costa gave him an old-fashioned look. "Not that way, whatever you may hear. But they knew each other." He paused and his voice warmed. "Maria-Inez has a voice of gold. At the Casino in Estoril they say even the roulette wheels stop when her act begins—and of course, she makes more money in a week than . . . than . . ."

"Than a humble sergeant of detectives collects in a year?" Gaunt rose and grinned down at him. "Where's the best place to hire a car around here?"

"Self-drive?" Costa frowned and shook his head sadly. "That could be difficult. Except"—an idea seemed to strike him— "yes, there might be a way. When would you need it?"

"From tonight, maybe for a few days."

Sucking his teeth, Costa nodded. "Then maybe I can fix something. When you are ready, look over at the police station. Okay?"

Gaunt thanked him and left. But on the way out of the bar he stopped by the counter, beckoning Jaime.

"*Senhor?*" The youngster approached with a touch of caution.

"Just a warning," said Gaunt softly. "Never try throwing a brick at me, Jaime. Because I'll heave it straight back at you . . . and I don't miss."

Leaving the youngster open-mouthed, he walked out.

The restaurant at the Hotel Da Gama had faded velvet curtains, dark oak woodwork, and an evening menu which concentrated on seafood soaked in olive oil. Gaunt ate alone at a small table and took his time, the only other customers being a couple of salesmen more interested in wine than food and a family group celebrating a birthday.

He finished with the *Ginjinha* brandy Costa had suggested. But one fiery glass was enough as an introduction. His palate still feeling blistered, Gaunt went back up to his room and smoked a cigarette while he once again read through the Preston file.

When he reached the last page he had to admit that what he'd hoped for just wasn't there. Everything pointed to Francis Preston having been a man who combined a belief in the direct approach with little patience for diplomacy. Yet there was no hint of major trouble on any of his previous recorded projects, no suggestion that antagonism had ever stoked up against him to any kind of flash-point—and even antagonism fell a long way short of murder.

Which left only Costa's uneasy hunch and that bruise the Portuguese sergeant declared had been found on Preston's head. Grimacing, Gaunt put the file back in his brief case and locked it, ready to take along to the meeting at the villa. A brief case usually made a good calling-card, a vague hint at authority—the kind he had a feeling he might need.

He left the hotel at eight-thirty. Outside, dusk had already transformed the cobbled square to a bustling life. Brightly lit open-air cafes fringed its outline, cars and trucks were parked in rows around the fountain, now a flood-lit glow, and most of Claras's inhabitants seemed to have decided that the cool, dry evening was ideal for a stroll and gossip.

Heading across the square, dodging traffic still coming in, Gaunt made his way through the strolling groups and located the police station tucked neatly round the corner of a side-street. A shoe-box architected concrete building with iron bars on the windows and a "Policia" sign nailed above the door, it looked strong enough to withstand a siege. But what really drew his attention was the sight of a red Lancia coupe parked empty at the kerb beside the door.

The black tiger-cat sticker on the car's trunk brought a grin to his lips as he shoved open the police station door and went in. But the only figure in the front office was a sleepy-looking policeman dozing in a chair beside a wood stove.

"*Senhor?*" The man came awake and murmured a greeting.

"Sergeant Costa, *por favor?*" smiled Gaunt.

Nodding, the man rose and wandered over to another door at the rear. Knocking, he opened it and went in, leaving the door open. Gaunt heard a woman's voice for a moment, another which sounded like Manuel Costa answering her, then the conversation ended as the other officer murmured an explanation.

Manuel Costa emerged within seconds, escorting the girl from the Lancia and beamed a greeting.

"I came over about the car," said Gaunt, then switched his attention to the girl, suddenly in no hurry.

She looked more at ease than the last time he'd seen her. Maybe the different outfit helped—she'd changed into white trousers and a red shirt-blouse which emphasised a slim, firm-breasted figure. Her feet were in white sandals and her long black hair, gleaming under the lights, was caught back by a simple, white ribbon. A heavy gold charm bracelet was her only jewellery.

But it was her face which mattered most. Fine-boned, lightly tanned, lips already framing a calm amusement at his inspection, it held a compelling beauty. Yet there was something else, something still trapped in those clear hazel eyes . . . something he couldn't quite name.

"The car, *Senhor* Gaunt?" Manuel Costa took a moment to descend to such practicalities. "Yes, it is arranged."

"Good." Gaunt kept his eyes on the girl and smiled at her. "Well, at least I get a chance to say hello this time."

She nodded. "I saw you at the funeral—Manuel has told me who you are, Mr. Gaunt. I am Inez Torres."

"He said Maria-Inez when I asked him," mused Gaunt.

Inez Torres laughed, a light, husky sound. "Most *fado* singers add Maria to their names—it is an old custom."

"But she was just Inez when we were children together," added Costa proudly. "Her brother and I—" he stopped awkwardly then switched quickly to a mock formality. "My apologies. *Menina*, Maria-Inez, may I present *Senhor* Jonathan Gaunt, of the English government."

"One of their hired hands," qualified Gaunt sadly. "And I'm from Scotland. There's a difference."

"I'd heard." The smile widened. "You wear kilts and blow bagpipes."

"And drink too much whisky," he completed with a grin.

"Like the Irish? I had an Irish grandfather—a sailor who ran away from his ship." Inez Torres turned away almost reluctantly to face Costa. "Manuel, I'm sorry. But I must get back—I promised."

"Then remember what I said." Costa frowned a little. "There is no reason to worry—if there was, I would know."

She kissed him lightly and unexpectedly on the cheek then held out her hand to Gaunt, the grip light and friendly. *"Adeus, Senhor* Gaunt. Maybe I will see you again."

She left them quickly. As the main door closed behind her, Costa muttered to himself then glanced at Gaunt.

"If I had known she would grow up to be like that—"

"Never ignore the girl next door—old Chinese proverb." Gaunt made a sympathetic noise then checked his watch. "Where do I collect this car?"

"Right here." Costa thumbed towards the rear of the police station. "One hundred *escudoes* a day and you pay for the gasoline. It belongs to my brother-in-law."

They went through the building and out into the yard at the rear. A small, battered Fiat, the paintwork green but rust-flecked, was parked beside a couple of patrol wagons. Climbing aboard, Gaunt tried the engine. It fired first time and sounded reasonably healthy.

"Fine." He eased back on the accelerator. "Tell your brother-in-law that he's got a deal. Now how do I get to Sollas's villa?"

"It's four, maybe five kilometres, no more." Costa gave the directions in painstaking style, then his thin face showed an unusual touch of worry. "When you are there, you will say nothing of what we talked about?"

Gaunt shook his head. "That's not my business, Sergeant."

"Good." Costa relaxed. "Though at the same time—"

"You want it both ways," paraphrased Gaunt, sighing. "*Adeus,* Sergeant. I said it wasn't my business."

He flicked the Fiat into gear and set it moving, out of the yard towards the street. Behind him, Costa gave a satisfied grin, lit a cigarette, then made a leisurely return to his office.

Sergeant Manuel Costa always felt happier when he knew someone else was doing his legwork.

Gaunt's destination was north-east of Claras, out along a narrow, winding strip of mainly dirt road fringed by pine trees and scrub vegetation. Dusk had blended into night quickly enough for him to need the Fiat's lights, but the moon was out and over to his left he could see he was travelling almost parallel with the black, hump-shaped hill where the Moorish fort was located.

He tried to remember his history. It was sometime about the start of the eighth century that the Moors had come storming across from North Africa into Portugal, over-running the entire country for a spell then stubbornly fighting off generation after generation of Crusader armies bent on freeing it from Moslem rule.

Stubborn was the word. The Moors had retained a substantial foothold right up into the thirteenth century—and five hundred years was long enough for any invasion to leave a long-term imprint on a nation's character. Long enough, too, to lay down a rich fascination of artifacts for any latter-day archaeologist with a digging urge.

A roe deer flickered across the road ahead, a brief vision in the Fiat's headlamps. Portugal was supposed to have wolves up in its north, he remembered. But this was gentler country.

Unless Costa's hunch was right and a killer on two legs was on the loose around Claras.

Gaunt grimaced at the thought, reached for a cigarette, then decided against it as lights appeared through the trees ahead. Another couple of minutes and he was turning off into a short driveway.

The house at its end was a large, white, two-story villa with a pillared main entrance and a long balcony. Three large, smartly expensive cars were parked outside and the Fiat rolled into place beside them like a poor relation in search of a handout.

Leaving it, Gaunt walked towards the flight of steps which led to the villa's doorway. The night was warm, he could hear crickets sawing in the grass around, and music was coming from a radio in one of the rooms above. The steps creaked as he climbed them and the door had an old-fashioned brass knocker in place of a bell. Rapping on it, he waited then heard men's voices on the other side of the wood. Another moment and the door swung open.

"You're punctual," boomed Arthur Sollas, looking larger than ever in the frame of light. A white strip of adhesive dressing covered the cut on his cheek and another man was standing beside him. "Come on in, Gaunt. Oh—and meet our landlord, Georges Salvador."

"Who is just leaving." Salvador was medium height and plump, sallow-faced, and had dark hair and a small moustache. He wore a blue lightweight suit with a polo-necked grey silk shirt. "*Senhor* Gaunt, I hope you enjoy your stay—despite the circumstances."

"Before you go, Georges, have we left any loose ends?" demanded Sollas. He added for Gaunt's benefit, "Georges has been transferring the lease over from Preston's name to mine —I like to be sure of things."

"Everything we need is done," assured Salvador then, glancing at his watch, made an apologetic murmur. "I should have left earlier. I have friends waiting in Estoril—visitors with money burning a hole in their pockets and the Casino tables waiting to solve the problem."

"They'll be lucky to get out with their shirts," grunted Sollas.

"Probably." Salvador chuckled at the thought. "Doctor, I'll bring any papers that need to be signed later. But the matter is agreed. Good night."

He left them, went down the steps and over to a blue Jaguar saloon, and waved before he climbed aboard. The car's lights blinked on, then as its engine fired and it purred away, Sollas gave a grunt of relief.

"One problem less. He could have tossed us out on our ears—Preston signed the lease agreement on his own, which might have been awkward."

"He chose a nice place." Gaunt looked appreciatively along an oak-panelled hallway with a polished parquet floor and animal-skin rugs. An open-plan stairway curved from halfway along towards the upper floor. "Does Salvador usually live here?"

"No, but he will once we leave." As the Jaguar's tail lights disappeared from the driveway Sollas closed the house door. "The last owners left a few months back, but Salvador doesn't want to move in till summer. That's how we got the villa." The big man came closer and lowered his voice to a confidential rumble. "I've told the others who you are, Gaunt—but not much more. They're all in the main lounge."

"Fine." Gaunt nodded cheerfully and hefted his brief case. "Let's hope I strike lucky."

"They probably feel the same," grunted Sollas. A look of puzzled distaste crossed his broad face. "I still think this could have waited, but now you're here, let's get it over."

Leading the way down the hall, he opened a glass-panelled door and waved Gaunt through. On the other side was a large room with a high, frescoed ceiling and broad windows which were flanked by floor-length curtains of dark red velvet.

The five people already in the room stopped anything they were doing as he entered and swung their attention his way. One was the blonde girl he'd seen at the cemetery, the four men with her had all been with the funeral party, and all except the bald man with sunburn, who was over at a cocktail cabinet, were seated in leather armchairs which had been arranged with precision in a semi-circle facing a small table with a waiting, empty chair behind it.

The mood in the room was relaxed and underlined by the group's casual clothes and the drinks in their hands. But Gaunt still felt himself under close inspection as Arthur Sollas nudged him forward.

"Better start with introductions," said Sollas gruffly.

"We know who he is, so why not give him a drink first?" suggested a cheerfully sardonic voice from one of the chairs. The man who had spoken was young but almost white-haired, a lanky figure with reddened skin stretched tight across high cheekbones. He grinned at Gaunt. "I'd call that a reasonable priority."

"I wouldn't complain about it," confirmed Gaunt easily.

"Sorry." Sollas gave an irritated grunt. "Whisky, Gaunt? I don't guarantee the blend."

"Sounds fine," agreed Gaunt, looking around.

"I'll get it," volunteered the bald man at the cocktail cabinet. "On its own, Scottish style?"

"With water—I'm a renegade." Gaunt kept the smile on his lips.

"Introductions," said Sollas doggedly as the bald man began pouring. "Starting from your left, Bernard Ryan, our photographer and supply officer—"

"Known as Bernie." The white-haired younger man raised a hand in greeting. "But this happens to be my first digging caper so whatever you want, friend, pass on."

Pursing his lips, Sollas gestured again. "Then our site foreman, Carlos Pereira. He's here because of another matter we've been discussing."

"*Senhor* Gaunt . . ." Pereira, his pock-marked face woodenly devoid of expression, nodded politely. The sleeves of his coarse plaid wool shirt were rolled up, showing hairy, muscular forearms tanned dark by the sun except for a pale strip across one wrist where he might normally wear a wristwatch. "Ah . . . maybe I should go now, Doctor?"

"Finish your drink first." Sollas drew a deep breath as the bald man took that as a cue to bring over Gaunt's glass. "Next, this is Martin Lawson—a professional in the archaeology game. In fact, the only professional among us."

"But still a paid hand like Ryan and Carlos." Lawson smiled mildly as he handed over the glass. "Preston and Doctor Sollas organised this dig—I was just happy to come along. We wouldn't be here but for them."

"I'm trying to forget that," said Sollas wearily. He paused as Gaunt sipped the whisky then forced a brighter note. "Last, but maybe the people who'll interest you most, Preston's relatives."

"His only relatives," emphasised the slender young man with the long mousy hair. Rising from his chair he held out a hand. The grip, Gaunt found, was moist with sweat while the faint smile on his face had a nervous quiver at the edges. "I'm John Marsh—Uncle Frank was my mother's brother, and my mother died a few months ago. So I'm all the family he had left. Ah—this is my wife, Sarah."

The blonde stayed where she was but murmured a greeting. Seen in close-up, she was still pretty in a china-doll way, but her eyes were small and greedy and her full figure, several pounds overweight, wasn't helped by a loose sweater and tight black ski-pants.

"I didn't know your uncle," said Gaunt, facing Marsh again. "But from what I've heard he was the kind of man people will certainly miss."

"We didn't see much of him," said Marsh almost indifferently. "To be honest, we didn't even know he was out here— not till we heard he'd died on the job."

Behind them, the blonde stifled a sudden giggle then looked away and reached for her drink.

"Doctor Sollas made a bit of a mystery about you, Gaunt,"

declared Marsh quickly. "But you want to do some kind of deal, right?"

"You could put it that way." Gaunt glanced at Sollas. "I can start anytime, Doctor."

"We're ready." Sollas waved towards the table in the centre. "If you've any papers to spread around—"

"That might come later." Gaunt went over and drew out the chair while Sollas nodded at Pereira and thumbed towards the door.

"*Obrigado,* Carlos. You know what we're doing. Tell the men they'll be at work again tomorrow and that they'll get full pay as usual for this week. That should keep them happy."

Grinning, the foreman rose and went out. Sollas slumped his heavy figure down into the vacated armchair.

"You're going to continue?" asked Gaunt.

"Yes." Sollas made it a rumble and rubbed a finger across his scarred nose. "Why throw away nearly three months slogging when we're nearly finished? There would be no damned sense in it."

"Not after all the trouble you and Preston went through to get those government permits," murmured Martin Lawson in dutiful support. "The Portuguese have their charm, Gaunt— but they operate like the mills of God. When it comes to action they grind exceeding slow."

"We think you're great too, Martin," drawled Bernie Ryan. "Now shut up, will you?"

Lawson flushed, the colour going up to match the red of his bald, peeling head. But he stayed silent, leaving Ryan to grin a little and light a cigarette.

"This was basically Frank Preston's project," said Sollas, frowning down at the floor and ignoring the exchange. "We'll miss him—but the work that is left shouldn't pose problems."

"Any chance of another member of the family stepping in?" Gaunt posed the question casually to John Marsh.

"Me?" The dead man's nephew gave a yelp of protest. "No.

I'm a salesman—groceries, on the wholesale side. Every minute I'm here is costing me money as it is. Right, Sarah?"

"We've done our duty coming to the funeral," declared the blonde with equal indignation. "We know John's the only heir. But a London lawyer is handling that side, so why should we wait?" She stopped and switched to a forced smile. "Unless we can help you, of course, Mr Gaunt."

"Let's find out," said Gaunt dryly, his dislike for the couple growing rapidly. "Your uncle was in Scotland at the start of last year. What do you know about his trip?"

"Not much." Marsh looked puzzled. "He sent us a postcard, that's all."

"Where was he when he sent it?"

"Can't remember." Marsh exchanged an uneasy glance with his wife. "It was just one of those Highland sunset things. We—Sarah threw it in the bucket. We didn't bother to read it."

"Uncle Frank was always sending postcards," said Sarah Marsh defensively. "They didn't matter much."

"This one might have mattered a lot," said Gaunt, wooden-faced but almost liking the situation. "It could have been worth a lot of money."

The blonde went pale and stared at him. "How much?"

"Depending on what it said, up to fifty thousand pounds."

Sarah Marsh gave a low moan and seemed to shrink in her chair. Struck dumb, her husband could only stare. Even Bernie Ryan was jolted out of his cynical disinterest. The white-haired photographer laid down his cigarette and gave a soft whistle of surprise.

"The old devil—he must have meant it! Martin"—he swung towards Lawson, gesturing an appeal—"remember all that malarkey he spouted one night when we'd killed a few bottles? That crazy story about walking away from a cave-load of treasure?"

"Church plate—I remember." Licking his lips, Lawson

nodded. "My God, I thought he'd just had a few too many, that it was the booze talking . . ." he stopped, awestruck.

"Doctor Sollas?" queried Gaunt quietly.

"I heard him." Arthur Sollas nodded calmly, unperturbed. "But drunk or sober, he didn't give any hint where this case was supposed to be—only that it was in Scotland."

"That's right. And I laughed at him." Ryan shook his head despairingly. "Bernie Ryan, champion idiot—damn my luck. Martin, what about you?"

"The same." The older man shrugged with an equal gloom. "Where it was didn't matter much—I didn't believe him."

"None of us did, not for a moment." Sollas shifted his bulk in his chair to a squeak of springs. "Have your people any reason that makes them feel differently, Gaunt?"

"All I know is he convinced them." Gaunt drank more of his whisky with mixed emotions. "But if it does exist then that hoard rates as Treasure Trove. We'll pay out to the first person who can take us to it."

"The first?" Sarah Marsh seized on the point with a gasp of indignation. "But if John's uncle found this treasure, then surely John—"

"No." Gaunt stopped her firmly. "Preston had no rights to the plate and knew it. That doesn't change—the stuff belongs to the Crown and we're simply offering a reward for help."

"Damn the Crown." She had a new idea. "Suppose John's uncle left a map somewhere, a diary—anything like that?"

"Yes." Her husband brightened at the thought. "That would be different, wouldn't it?"

"You'd have a claim on the reward—if you had legal ownership of the details."

"Right!" John Marsh's pasty face showed triumph. "Doctor—my Uncle Frank's gear is still upstairs, isn't it?"

"Packed ready to move," confirmed Sollas dryly. "But I didn't notice any map with an 'X' on it."

"Mind if we have a look?" asked Marsh eagerly.

Shrugging, Sollas reached into his pocket and brought out a

key-ring. He looked at it for a moment then tossed it on the table with something close to scorn.

"Go ahead," he invited.

"Thanks." Marsh rose quickly and scooped up the key-ring. Then, as his wife joined him, he hesitated, glancing at the others. "I mean—well, we want to find out, don't we?"

"Straight away," said Bernie Ryan acidly. "Don't trip on the stairs, friend."

Grinning weakly, Marsh turned to his wife and nodded. They went out quickly, the door banging shut behind them.

"Half a chance, and they'd have Preston out of that grave to go through his pockets." Ryan swore softly but pungently then sighed and rose lazily. "To hell with them. I've still got work to do."

"Those equipment lists." Sollas nodded absently. "Help him, Martin. Now we're starting again I don't want any hold-ups we can avoid."

Obediently, Lawson followed the photographer from the room. Left alone with Gaunt, Sollas grimaced his disgust.

"We all have relatives, I suppose," he said with a surprising mildness. "Still, they're wasting their time. I went through Preston's kit and didn't find anything." He saw Gaunt's raised eyebrow and twisted a smile in reply. "Just an old army habit—never leave shocks for the next-of-kin."

"You thought there might have been?" queried Gaunt.

"He had a friend in Claras—she was at the funeral."

"I noticed."

"I don't think it was that way with them, but I just made sure." Spreading his thick fingers, Sollas levered up from his chair. "Anyway, while you're here, come through to the office. I'll show you what brought him to Portugal."

He led the way out of the lounge and through to a small study near the back of the villa. It held two desks, one now conspicuously bare and the other covered in papers. Trestle tables had been set up round the walls and carried an accumulation of charts and reference books mixed with fragments of tile and pottery.

Crossing to the paper-littered desk, Arthur Sollas opened a drawer and brought out an unframed photograph.

"That's what he was like," he said shortly.

The photograph showed a stocky, middle-aged man with a bearded, handsome face and a piratical grin. He was sitting on a rock, wearing only shorts and sandals, a can of beer in one hand.

"How well did you know him?" asked Gaunt, studying the print.

"We'd met a few times." Sollas flicked the photograph back in the drawer. "I'm another hobby archaeologist—the practice of medicine pays my bills." He shrugged. "Preston wanted someone to split the cost on this dig and contacted me through Lawson—he already had Ryan lined up."

"Preston had a fair reputation for choosing a site," mused Gaunt, looking round the rest of the room. "How has it been here?"

The big man eyed him oddly then made the nose-stroking motion which always seemed to precede a decision.

"We didn't come to play around what's left of a second-rate Moorish watch-tower," he said slowly. "You'll find plenty the same all over this damned country."

"Then—"

"You'd have to know Preston to understand." Sollas went over to the nearest bench and unrolled one of the charts. "His genius was that he knew damn-all about conventional archaeology. Preston was an engineer and he thought like an engineer—local geography, materials, construction, all from a slightly different angle. One that usually paid off."

Gaunt frowned down at the opened chart. It showed two outlines, one small and firm, the other still with broken lines but considerably larger. Puzzled, he tried to understand.

"You're working on something better?"

Arthur Sollas nodded. "Preston saw photographs of this

watch-tower and had a hunch it was different, that the Moors might have built on an earlier site, using existing material." A stubby finger traced round the larger outline. "We've un- covered a second century B.C. Roman villa nobody dreamed was there. As far as Preston was concerned even that was a disappointment—he thought we'd find something bigger." His voice hardened a shade. "But the villa is important enough, and I don't want any outside leak about it till we're ready to start shouting."

"I'd like to see the place," murmured Gaunt. His attention switched to a large-scale map pinned on the wall. "Can I come visiting—or do I have to pass a loyalty test first?"

"Make it tomorrow, after breakfast, and I'll show you around." Sollas tapped the map. "We're here right now. Branch off the route you came at about two kilometres back, stick with the side-road till you come to a fork, then veer right—you'll find it's a fairly rough track. We're where it ends, or where it ends now at any rate. I told you we had to close a route."

"Something which didn't make you popular," mused Gaunt.

"We've enough problems without the locals clumping around the diggings." Sollas scowled at the notion. "Give those people half a chance and they'd loot anything they could carry—then sell it to tourists later. We've got to be careful, Gaunt. The Portuguese government made a tough deal—Preston had to promise we'd settle for glory and knowl- edge, with anything recovered belonging to the State. Any trouble, and they'd be down on our necks—particularly now."

It sounded familiar enough. Gaunt gave a sympathetic grin. "So you won't be too upset about those ghost stories scaring people away?"

"We didn't start them, if that's what you're hinting. But whoever had the notion did us a favour." Sollas glanced at his watch then yawned deliberately. "Ten-thirty already—

well, whatever that pair of married vultures are scavenging upstairs, I'm for bed. I need an early night."

"I feel the same." Gaunt let Sollas steer him out of the room then, as the door closed behind them, mused almost to himself, "Still, I'm curious about the way Preston died. I thought you'd have a night watchman at the site?"

"The digging squad take the job in turn." Sollas scowled at the thought as they started down the hallway. "Usually with a bottle of wine for company—the idiot on duty that night woke up about dawn, saw Preston's car parked at the gate, and went into a squealing panic when he found the main trench caved in."

"And nobody missed Preston till then?" asked Gaunt.

"Get something straight, Gaunt—" the big man came to an irritated halt. "This isn't a Boy Scout camp. We don't operate any kind of lights out bed-call. We knew Preston had gone into Lisbon on personal business and what he did afterwards was his affair." His lips pursed angrily. "Usually when he didn't show up it meant he'd gone off on a drinking kick—I didn't see the autopsy report, but I'll bet it showed he'd enough alcohol in him to pickle an elephant."

"I didn't know," soothed Gaunt.

"Why should you have?" Sollas strode on till he reached the front door of the villa, swung it open, then shook his head bitterly. "It was a damned waste of a life, Gaunt. Why shout about the details and make it worse?"

Saying good night, Gaunt left. Back aboard the Fiat, he started the engine and slipped the little car into gear. As it moved off, Arthur Sollas's bulky figure was still framed in the villa doorway.

Spring in Portugal can mean crisp, chill nights with a sky like moon-spun velvet then a milky fog around dawn. The velvet was overhead as Jonathan Gaunt steered the Fiat along the dirt road, the brief case he hadn't had to open beside him in the passenger seat. His thoughts drifted mutinously round what he might do if John and Sarah Marsh came up with a claim for the Remembrancer's reward money.

The more he heard about Francis Preston the more he found himself liking this man he'd never met. A man who, drunk or sober, had been driving on the same road only a few nights before, heading towards a hunch that had somehow gone wrong.

The Fiat lurched savagely over a pothole and he had to fight the wheel to avoid landing in the ditch. Gaunt grimaced as the car steadied, deciding Preston couldn't have been so drunk if he'd been able to handle a car in these conditions.

The dark bulk of the hog-back hill began growing on the right while he mulled over the thought, warier now, keeping to a slower pace and watching curiously for the turn-off he'd seen on Sollas's map. It showed in the headlamps in a couple of minutes, a black plunge into the trees. Humming softly, no particular reason in mind, Gaunt glanced beyond it, up towards the hill.

Then he swore and braked, knocking the Fiat's gear-change into neutral. Stopped there, the engine ticking gently, he wound down the Fiat's grimy side-window and looked again. Lights were moving up among the trees, three of them, working along one small section of hillside in a wavering but methodical pattern.

A moment later the harsh crack of a shot reached his ears. The flecks of light stopped, there was another shot, then they were wavering on again.

Sighing, he flicked the car back into gear and started it on the track towards the hill. The Moorish fort might have its ghosts, but he'd never known a spirit that used a high-velocity rifle when it went haunting.

CHAPTER THREE

Within a minute of leaving the main road the track through the trees took a sudden dip into a world which became pitch-black as the timber thickened and leafy branches closed overhead.

Bouncing and shuddering over a surface of broken stone and loose dirt, the Fiat struggled on while its headlamp beams sent rabbits scurrying and reflected back bright eyes glaring from the protection of the trees. The fork on the map came up and he turned right, past a warning signboard, while the new track began to climb again.

Fighting the jarring steering-wheel, he eased round a tight bend—and next moment the Fiat gave a lurch then canted mildly towards the near side. A thud shook its way through the metal body and the engine stalled.

Shoving open the driver's door, Jonathan Gaunt climbed out, looked, and cursed. The nearside front wheel was buried to the axle in a ditch. For a moment he stood there, tempted to give up, hearing only the soft spitting of the cooling car exhaust and the faint rustle of wind in the trees. Then, shrugging, he switched off the Fiat's lights, took the ignition key, and started off again on foot.

Stumbling through the darkness, the track still an upward climb, he'd been walking only a couple of minutes when the ground began to dip again. At the same time the trees started to thin, giving way to scattered clumps of thick, sweet-smelling scrub bush and patches of cactus. Surprisingly, the moon was still out—and the same lazy fireflies of light, now easily identifiable as hand-torch beams, were continuing their movement ahead.

The track showed as a narrow ribbon, wandering down the gentle reverse slope towards a gate in a high fence. Two tin-roofed huts were located behind the gate and beyond them an intricate pattern of long, low mounds of earth lay centred round the squat, roofless silhouette of a ruined tower.

The scent of woodsmoke reached his nostrils, probably from a stove in one of the huts. But Gaunt switched his attention back to the lights. They were outside the fence, over to his left, and methodically searching their way down another slope of scrub. As he watched, there was a shout, another voice answered—and immediately all three lights veered in a new direction.

Common sense urged him to stay clear but curiosity won out. Leaving the track, he began working along the edge of the trees, heading towards the lights but keeping on the saucer rim of the slope.

A shot slammed out, not the high velocity crack he'd heard before but the duller bark of a shotgun. He froze, while the men behind the lights exchanged shouts then formed into a new pattern.

Simultaneously the moonlight gave a fleeting glimpse of something being driven ahead of them. Man or animal, it was coming nearer, making for the shelter of the trees. Heading his way.

Easing into the cover of a bush, Gaunt waited. Twigs snapped below then, suddenly, a man staggered into the middle of a band of open ground. Thin, swaying on his feet and obviously close to collapse, the hunted figure glanced back over his shoulder then tried to stumble on. Two steps forward and he fell. When he tried to rise he could only get to his knees.

So he started to crawl.

But the little drama was only beginning. Another figure appeared in the moonlight, running from the edge of the trees to Gaunt's left and still hidden from the approaching pursuit.

It was a girl—and with that long, black hair, those white trousers showing under a dark, belted raincoat and that slim silhouette it could be only one girl.

Inez Torres reached the crawling figure, stooped, put an arm round the man's waist, and pulled him upright. Then, half-dragging and half-carrying him, she started back towards the trees.

The torch-beams were still flickering through the scrub some three hundred yards away, coming on steadily and methodically. Only luck would get Inez Torres and her companion back to the trees in time—and even then they weren't likely to get much further.

Sighing, Gaunt abandoned his cover and headed across the open ground at a fast lope. Struggling on, intent on her task, the girl didn't see him until he had almost arrived. Then she gasped and swung round, placing her body like a shield between Gaunt and her burden.

"I'll take him," said Gaunt simply. Then, seeing her startled recognition, he added a quick reassurance. "It's all right. But let's get to hell out of here."

She hesitated for a moment then nodded and released her grip. Taking over, Gaunt discovered the frail figure weighed little more than a child might—while a sunken, young-old face stared at him with eyes which held only confusion and fear. Shifting his grip, Gaunt lifted the stranger bodily, cradled him in his arms, and started off at the same fast lope back towards the trees with Inez Torres hurrying at his side.

At most, there was eighty yards of clearing to be crossed. That was still eighty yards of being a clear, moonlit target, eighty yards when every step might bring a shout or a shot if they were spotted.

But somehow nothing happened. They reached the trees again and Gaunt swung in behind the shelter of a tangle of tall, spikey cactus. Lowering the stranger to the ground, he crouched beside him and looked back the way they had come.

For a moment the clearing stayed empty. Crouching close to him, taking short, quick breaths, Inez Torres stared in the same direction then tensed and pointed.

The first of the torch-beams had reached the opposite edge of the clearing. A burly figure strode out then came to a puzzled halt, the light's powerful glare swinging in a purposeful arc. Gaunt pursed his lips in a silent whistle as the moonlight showed the man was carrying a shotgun at the ready, the torch taped to the underside of its barrel.

See and shoot. It wasn't particularly clever if you were stalking an armed opponent. But in this kind of hunt it could be grimly effective.

Suddenly stirring, the stranger at Gaunt's feet gave a soft moan and tried to rise. Quickly, he laid a warning hand on the man's mouth—and saw him shrink back in near terror at the touch, one arm going up instinctively to ward off a blow.

"*Nao* . . . no, Luis. It's all right." The girl bent low over him, her voice an anxious murmur. As the man relaxed again, she looked up at Gaunt. "He doesn't understand. He—"

"He's not the only one," Gaunt cut her short. All three men who'd been hunting the stranger were now in the clearing. The two newcomers, torches similarly mounted on their guns, stood as he had for a moment then came over to join him and talk. Grimacing his relief, Gaunt glanced down at the thin figure on the ground. "We've got an edge on them now. But they'll try up here soon enough, and if he's wounded—"

"He isn't." She shook her head. "Not the way you mean. It—he just isn't well."

"Is he a friend?" queried Gaunt dryly.

"My brother." She bit her lip. "He hasn't done anything wrong."

"They seem to have a different idea." Gaunt glanced down at the men again then eased round a little to face her in the tree-filtered moonlight. "Either way, we've got to get him out of here."

She nodded. "If I could get him back to my car—"

"Where is it?"

"Not far." She pointed in towards the black heart of the wood. "I left it hidden near the road fork and I know the way."

Gaunt remembered his own car and thought swiftly.

"Could you get him there on your own?" he asked.

Her eyes widened in surprise but she nodded.

"Then give me a couple of minutes then start moving. If things work out, wait for me on the main road just this side of Claras. All right?"

"Yes." She was puzzled. "What are you going to do?"

"Give them something else to think about. Just stay ready—and keep him quiet." He smiled at her, then started off at a low crouch, moving parallel with the edge of the trees and heading back in the direction of the track which led to the digging site.

When Gaunt judged he was halfway he rose and looked round. The men in the clearing had come to a decision. Fanned out again, they were starting up the slope towards the trees.

A couple of long strides took him out into the open. Waving an arm, he hailed them loudly.

"Hey, over there! *Por favor* . . . I need some help."

The torch-beams swung in startled fashion, catching him in their combined glare as he strode nearer. Keeping a grin on his face, putting one hand up to shield his eyes from the light, Gaunt kept on. As he reached the silent, waiting trio he heard a sudden grunt of recognition from one of them.

"*Senhor* Gaunt—" the man lowered his gun and stepped forward. It was Pereira, the digging team foreman, and his pock-marked face scowled in a mixture of anger and indecision. "Why are you here?"

"Car trouble." Gaunt grimaced and thumbed towards the

track. "I'm stuck in a ditch back there." He eyed the fore-man's rifle, a .30-calibre Remington, new and well oiled. "Out hunting, Carlos?"

"*Sim* . . . a deer," said Pereira curtly. He sucked his thin lips then glanced at his companions and nodded. As they lowered their guns he forced a smile. "Maybe you saw it, eh?"

"Sorry." Gaunt shook his head innocently. "Probably I frightened it off. A deer—I should have known." He paused and sighed realistically. "I saw lights moving up here and remembered those ghost stories I'd heard. So I thought I'd take a look—and landed in that ditch instead. A pity about your deer, though."

"Another time will do." Pereira shrugged unemotionally. "Where is this car, *senhor?*"

"Not far." Gaunt paused hopefully. "You know, if you and your friends could spare a couple of minutes I'd be grateful. You see, I've got a bad back—the *medicos* won't let me lift anything heavy."

The Pension Board members, he decided, would probably have docked another 20 per cent off that pension if they'd seen him five minutes back. The hopeful smile still on his face, he waited.

Slowly, reluctantly, Pereira hitched his rifle by the sling over one shoulder and gestured to his companions. They followed Gaunt in silence to the track and along to where the Fiat lay ditched then, scowling, set to work while he watched and made apologetic noises about his back.

A few minutes heaving and struggling, occasionally broken by a curse, and the little car was finally man-handled clear. Cheerfully, Gaunt slapped the foreman on the back and beamed around.

"*Obrigado, multo obrigado,*" he declared enthusiastically, reaching into his pocket. "Carlos, about that deer—"

"No matter." Pereira shook his head grimly. "But you might remember, *senhor,* that it is not wise to wander around these hills after dark." His lips tightened. "A man has been shot in mistake for a deer before now."

"It was damned stupid," agreed Gaunt, opening the car door. "I'll remember, believe me."

"Good." A wintery smile touched Pereira's mouth. *"Boa noite, Senhor* Gaunt. There is a place where you can turn just a little way up."

Nodding, Gaunt climbed aboard, closed the door, and started the engine. As he set the Fiat moving, he gave the grim-faced trio a final wave.

The track widened enough to make a turn about fifty yards up. He brought the Fiat round then stopped for a moment, glancing at his watch.

He'd given Inez Torres almost fifteen minutes—and in the process got himself mobile again. Which was a reasonable enough success. Lighting a cigarette, well aware he was still being watched from the timber, he took a long draw on the tobacco and shivered, remembering the Remington.

A .30-calibre rifle had a muzzle velocity of 2,200 feet per second, a muzzle energy of close on 2,000 foot pounds. Which meant it punched a hole and kept on going. Or, as his old Parachute Regiment sergeant-instructor had loved to put it to the squad, "just stand in line an' one shot will take care o' the damn lot of you."

Inez Torres and her brother had been lucky. He'd been equally lucky.

Now, he reckoned, it was time he found out exactly what he'd got into. Sergeant Manuel Costa's apparently wild-cat hunch about how Francis Preston had died suddenly seemed much less of a wisping whimsy than it had before—and that might be only a start.

Though that august and very practical civil servant, the Queen's and Lord Treasurer's Remembrancer, secure behind his desk in Edinburgh, might have taken the view that it was none of his department's damned business.

Gaunt shrugged. Edinburgh was a long way away. And if

someone had murdered Preston, then maybe the Remembrancer's external auditor should get involved—even if just to express annoyance.

The cigarette glowing between his lips, he set the Fiat trundling down the track again. When he passed the spot where the car had ditched the three men had gone.

But he'd a feeling they'd probably given up hunting that deer.

Stopped at the roadside with side-lights on and exhaust burbling, the red Lancia was waiting about a kilometre's distance outside Claras. Slowing the Fiat as he approached, seeing two shadowy figures aboard the coupe, Gaunt flicked his headlamps.

Inez Torres didn't waste time. Immediately he'd signalled the Lancia's main beams were switched on and it pulled away, leaving him to follow.

They turned right at the first junction and went roughly half a kilometre, then the Lancia signalled another turn and swung right again, this time into a narrow, tarmac road and from there into a short, gravelled drive lined with young, carefully spaced rose bushes. It led to a modest, hacienda-style bungalow and they stopped outside.

Switching off lights and engine, Jonathan Gaunt climbed out. The bungalow stood high above the twinkling lights of Claras, completely on its own, the only sound the faint rustle of the wind in the bushes.

The driver's door of the Lancia swung open and Inez Torres emerged. Her coat and white trousers showed mud-stained in the moonlight, but her expression as Gaunt came over was one of genuine relief.

"I felt sick back there, just waiting," she said with a quiet sincerity. "It wasn't long—maybe only a minute, *Senhor* Gaunt. But I was afraid of what might have happened."

"I was counting on Sergeant Costa," said Gaunt with a mock solemnity. "He claims there's a law against shooting tourists out of season." He grinned at her, then his manner changed as he nodded towards the Lancia and the silent figure hunched in the front passenger seat. "Like some help?"

"It's all right now." She shook her head at the offer. "Luis knows we're home. I can manage."

Going round, she opened the other door. Her passenger left the car slowly, almost timidly, while she made soft encouraging noises and took his hand. Giving Gaunt a nervous glance, Luis Torres looked away again quickly and let his sister lead him towards the house. Gaunt followed them quietly, waiting while the girl opened the front door and switched on a light.

He followed them in, closed the door, then, while Inez switched on other lights, stopped with something close to shock as he had his first full view of the strange, frail creature he'd helped rescue.

Luis Torres shared his sister's raven-black hair and fine-boned features. He was over medium height and clean-shaven and though his grey wool sweater and slacks were now muddy and torn they looked new and had cost money.

But his face was thin, parchment pale and child-like in its expression. Dark eyes stared at Gaunt with a puzzled, struggling emptiness while he rubbed his boney hands nervously, one against the other. It was like looking at the shrunken, helpless husk of a man who had been drained both physically and mentally.

Shrunken and helpless—Gaunt felt shock give way to pity, then Inez Torres came back.

"I'll get Luis to bed," she said with a forced cheerfulness then gestured towards one of the lighted rooms. "Help yourself to a drink in there. I won't be long. Luis—" she turned, holding out a hand.

Her brother took it, gave Gaunt another puzzled, empty look, and went away with her.

Gaunt entered the room. It had a polished wood floor with sheepskin scatter rugs and had been furnished in a modern,

almost Scandinavian style. A long bookcase and a professional stereo tape and record player unit shared most of one
wall, a natural stone fireplace with a copper hood occupied
the main area on the opposite side. But the really eye-catch-
ing feature was a full-length portrait in oils, life-size, of Inez
Torres in the traditional black dress of a *fadista* singer.

Whoever had created the portrait had tried for a conventional dramatic presentation, complete with a background of
velvet drapes. But he'd caught something else in the process,
a face with a special, compelling quality of warmth and zest
for life. A quality that so far Gaunt had only glimpsed
briefly and occasionally in the original.

There was a small cocktail bar in a corner. Going there, he
poured himself a full three fingers of whisky and this time he
didn't add water. He took a long swallow and sighed appreciatively as the liquor soothed and tingled its way down,
drowning a tiredness which had been creeping in on him now
that excitement had ended.

Carrying the glass, Gaunt went over to the stereo unit
and thumbed through some of the records lying beside it.
Most were *fado* discs, a few with Inez Torres' name on the
label. Others were modern jazz and a couple of Frank Sinatra
oldies, well worn.

Leaving them, he stopped at the bookcase, puzzled. One
shelf held manuals on car maintenance, another was half-filled
with electronics textbooks. Even allowing for the novels and
travel books which made up the rest, it was a collection which
didn't match the positive feminine personality responsible for
the rest of the room.

Going back to the portrait again, studying the vibrant mood
and beauty caught by the brush and canvas, he heard footsteps and turned.

"He's sleeping already," said Inez Torres, coming into the
room. "He was exhausted—and right now I feel that way
too."

She had removed her coat and changed shoes for soft, open-backed slippers. Going over to the bar, she poured herself a drink, very deliberately added a couple of ice cubes, swirled them in the glass, tasted the result, then sat wearily on a cushioned stool beside the fireplace and looked up at him.

"I haven't thanked you yet," she said quietly.

"No need." Gaunt shook his head. "Inez, how long has he been that way?"

"About two years—there was a car crash, a bad one." She shivered a little, bent, switched on an electric fire in the hearth, and watched it begin to glow. "The *medicos* said he would die. He didn't, not the way they meant."

"Brain damage?"

She nodded. "They say Luis has a mental age of about four. Some still hope there's a chance he'll improve—but only a chance." Looking up, she continued to shut all emotion from her voice. "Before it happened, he was very different—a lieutenant in the Navy, big brother."

"I'm sorry." Gaunt meant it, understanding more than she could realise. "It can't be easy."

"I can afford help, a woman who was a nurse. But I give her time off when I'm not working, like tonight." Inez Torres sipped her drink again and shrugged. "I thought it would be all right to leave him alone while I went to see Manuel Costa —but it was a mistake. He'd gone when I got back here."

She took the cigarette Gaunt offered. He lit it for her, took another for himself, then stood with his back to the fire.

"Still, you knew where to find him," he mused. "Was that just luck?"

"I looked in several places." A sudden caution showed on her face then had gone, but stayed in a careful choice of words. "Luis thinks like a child, goes to places he knew as a child—"

"And can get lost or frightened the same way." Gaunt nodded and drew on his cigarette. "I said it before—it can't be easy. Was it some problem about Luis that took you over to Sergeant Costa?"

"No." She shook her head quickly. "I—that was another matter, a private matter."

"I wondered, that's all," soothed Gaunt. "Does he often wander off?"

"Hardly ever." Her eyes showed a gathering anger. "Even when he does, he wouldn't harm anyone—I told you, he's like a child."

"That's what I meant," said Gaunt more grimly. "I still saw three armed men hunting him like an animal. If they'd caught him—" he stopped and shrugged. "I think Sergeant Costa would like to hear about it. And that he'd have all three of them in the local jail within the hour."

Waiting, he took another drink of whisky and watched her, already guessing what was coming.

"No." She bit her lip. "I—I don't want trouble. Not when it might involve Luis. Perhaps later—or if I see Doctor Sollas" —she paused helplessly—"but not now, please."

"If that's how you want it." Gaunt set down his glass and nodded, his face devoid of expression. "Thanks for the drink. I'll get on my way."

"There's no hurry." She rose quickly, flushing. "I didn't mean—"

"I hoped you didn't." Gaunt smiled at her. "You know, I'm here for a couple more days anyway, and I won't be working all the time. When I've the chance, how about helping me be a tourist for a few hours?"

"All right." She managed an answering smile. "But I have to work in the evenings."

Gaunt nodded. "And I'm getting a conducted tour round the digging site tomorrow morning. How about the afternoon?"

"I'll be ready." The smile came more easily, then she had a new thought—or one she'd saved. "Before you go, let me show you something."

Curious, he went out with her into the hall and deeper into the house. She stopped at a half-opened door and beckoned him nearer. Standing beside the girl, her warmth close and tantalising, he looked and understood.

A small night-light burned beside a single bed, throwing a glow over Luis Torres' sleeping figure. He was breathing gently, the thin, pale face relaxed and peaceful, and suddenly it wasn't too hard to imagine how he'd once been.

The room was a man's room, with photographs of naval vessels on the walls and an electric razor lying on the dressing table. But a child's jigsaw puzzle was on the floor beside the bed, abandoned half-completed.

Gently, with a sudden compassion, Gaunt laid a hand on Inez Torres' arm and drew her away. She said nothing till they were at the front door of the house then, as Gaunt opened it, she moistened her lips.

"Can you really imagine him harming anyone?" she asked almost bitterly.

"No." He didn't know if it was a lie or not. There were other questions he wanted to ask her, about Francis Preston, about the digging site, about what had happened after the funeral. But they would have to wait. "Inez, do one thing for me. Have a talk with Sergeant Costa, as a friend."

"Perhaps." She looked out into the night, where the sky now sparkled with stars. "Let me think about it. And—and you?"

"It's not my business—I'll say nothing."

"Thank you," she said, openly relieved. *"Boa noite* . . . good night, *Senhor* Gaunt."

"People call me Jonathan."

"Jonathan. I'll remember." She smiled almost shyly as he went out, then the door closed gently behind him.

It was after midnight when he parked the Fiat outside the Hotel Da Gama. The spotlight on the fountain in the square had been switched off and the houses around were in darkness. Claras apparently had an early to bed, early to rise philosophy, whatever its inhabitants did with their day.

The brief case under one arm, Gaunt found the hotel door unlocked. Inside, a light was still burning over the reception desk and beneath the light, white jacket unbuttoned and head lolling, Jaime was dozing in a chair. Quietly passing the young porter, Gaunt reached the stairs and started up towards his room.

A board creaked underfoot and he heard a yawn.

"*Chame, Senhor* Gaunt?" asked Jaime from below, pausing for another yawn. "Would you like a call in the morning?"

"I suppose so." Stopping, he looked back and nodded. "Make it for eight o'clock."

"*Oito horas*—okay." Jaime chalked the time on a slate then grinned up again. "I was waiting here to see you, *senhor.*"

"So you could report back to Sergeant Costa?" suggested Gaunt acidly. "Keep up with the market, laddie. You've been wasting your time—ask Costa."

"I did." Jaime grimaced at the reminder. "But there was another reason—one that might interest you. At least, I think so."

Gaunt raised an eyebrow then came back down a couple of steps.

"Well?"

Sadly, Jaime spread his hands. Digging into his pocket, Gaunt flicked a five-*escudo* piece towards the desk. It was caught smartly in mid-air and vanished.

"A man from the digging camp came here maybe half an hour ago," said the youngster, grinning. "He was most anxious to know if you were back in the hotel. His name is Alfredo—I have seen him in the bar before."

Gaunt frowned. "What did you tell him?"

"What I thought you might want, that you had just gone to bed." Jaime paused and winked. "He too gave me five *escudoes*—I was to say nothing."

"How long till you buy your own hotel?" asked Gaunt bleakly.

The brown, cherubic face wrinkled in a serious frown. "I

reckon five, maybe six years. But it will be nearer Estoril, where the money is."

Gaunt sighed and leaned on the bannister, considering the sharp-eyed gaze which met his own.

"I'll bet on you making it—unless you land in jail first," he agreed with conviction. "And here's a chance to make a bonus ten *escudoes* towards it. What kind of grudge would make anyone start throwing bricks at the mourners after *Senhor* Preston's funeral? I want an answer, Jaime, otherwise I'm going to come down and belt you around the ears till I get one."

The boy started to grin then saw his expression and had a change of mind.

"People liked *Senhor* Preston," he said cautiously. "If we— if they hadn't liked him, it wouldn't have mattered."

"What wouldn't have mattered?" Gaunt came down another step in menacing style. "No riddles, Jaime. I'm too tired for them."

"Okay—okay, *Senhor* Gaunt." Jaime swallowed hard and nodded. "Then maybe it was because those men he worked with laugh about how he died—that he was drunk when he fell into that trench." His young mouth tightened with a surprising anger and contempt. "Sure, *Senhor* Preston drank a lot. An' sometimes he looked like he should be poured back into a bottle. But not that night."

"What makes you so sure?"

"Because he stopped here for a drink late on—one glass of brandy, no more." He saw the doubt on Gaunt's face and gestured emphatically with both hands. "It is the truth—I even served him myself."

"Does Sergeant Costa know?"

"He did not ask. I only tell him what he asks," was the sullen reply. "Why do more?"

"That's your business." Gaunt rubbed a hand along his chin, feeling the rasp of the day's stubble. "Was Preston alone?"

"*Sim,* when he came an' when he left. All he said was he'd been in Lisbon—but he was angry about something."

The story had a ring of truth. Nodding, Gaunt reached for his pocket.

"No—not this time." Jaime stopped him with a headshake. "For *Senhor* Preston, make it what you call 'on the house'— okay?"

"On the house," agreed Gaunt softly. "Thanks, Jaime."

Leaving the boy, he went up to his room. He found the bed had been turned down and the balcony window closed with the curtains shut. Otherwise, everything seemed as he'd left it.

Or almost everything. Going over to the dressing table, he checked the drawers and smiled. Someone had been rummaging through them, someone not as neat or experienced as Sergeant Costa.

But nothing was missing. Maybe Jaime left that till later.

He undressed slowly, his back aching from the sheer fatigue of a long, long day. Still—he brightened, remembering how he'd carried Luis Torres at a run across that slope. He'd managed it.

Maybe because he hadn't had time to wonder if he could.

Finding the painkiller tablets, he swallowed a couple before he slid naked between the cool, white sheets. Then he lay thinking. About Luis Torres and where he'd been the night Francis Preston had died. About Inez Torres and Preston— then, irrelevantly, about the stock market back in Britain and his brewery shares.

But when sleep came he dreamed of being hunted through a strange, nightmare labyrinth by awesome, giant half-man, half-beast figures.

The kind of nightmare a child might have.

He woke to the swish of curtains being drawn and sunlight pouring into the darkened room. A plump, busty hotel maid finished the task then turned, looked at him with widening eyes, and giggled before she made a swift retreat from the room.

Yawning and puzzled, Gaunt propped himself up on his elbows and saw he'd kicked off the sheets sometime during the night. He grinned at his naked body, thinking it might have been more of a compliment if she'd made another kind of noise, then yawned again and got up.

There was a coffee-and-rolls breakfast on a tray beside the bed and outside the window the sky was bright blue. The coffee pot was blistering hot to the touch so he shaved and dressed first, choosing a dark blue shirt and matching slacks, topping them with an oatmeal sports coat, and laying out a dark red tie. Then, once he'd eaten, he lit a cigarette, stuffed the tie in a pocket, and left.

The same hotel maid was busy with a vacuum cleaner in the downstairs lobby. He winked at her and heard another giggle as he went out.

Claras was already wide awake. Farm trucks were rumbling through the square and a row of makeshift market stalls had sprung up around the fountain, their owners carefully arranging displays of fish and vegetables, used clothing, salvaged auto parts and anything else likely to find a buyer. There was no sign of the knitted lace, carved wood or metalwork of the *artigos regionais* variety . . . the souvenir stall owners made their killing in the season and were probably holidaying in the south of France on the proceeds.

Flicking away his cigarette stub, Gaunt headed over to where he'd left the Fiat then slowed his pace and gave a wry grin. Sergeant Costa was already there, wearing his sunglasses and a shirt even more dazzling than its predecessor but with a far from happy expression on his lean, leathery features as he considered the car's crumpled bodywork.

"Good-morning," said Gaunt warily. "I—uh—went into a ditch."

"*Bom dia.*" Manuel Costa returned the greeting gloomily. "I heard, *Senhor* Gaunt—in detail."

Gaunt nodded, rubbing a hand along the bent metal. It dislodged a heavy flaking of paint in a way that made Costa wince.

"From Inez?" he asked.

"Partly." Costa brought the sunglasses lower on his nose with a forefinger and eyed Gaunt oddly over their rims. "But the rest came from Doctor Sollas. He telephoned us late last night, reporting a new incident at the digging site. It—ah— seems three of his brave labour squad might well have caught an armed intruder if a certain damned fool Englishman—"

"I'm from Scotland."

"*Muito obrigado.*" The policeman gave a nod of mock solemnity. "If this damned fool Scotchman visitor had not come blundering in. I can tell you the good doctor is not amused." His thin lips tightened. "On the other hand Inez Torres also telephoned me but unofficially. I'm glad you were there, *Senhor* Gaunt—if my brother-in-law asks you to pay for the damage, tell him to go to hell."

"Thanks." Gaunt propped himself against the Fiat's roof and looked out at the busy square. "What can you do about it, Sergeant?"

"Nothing—or the next best thing," said Costa wearily. "She refuses to make an official complaint."

"In case it comes out her brother might have killed Preston?" asked Gaunt in a mild voice.

"She told you that?" Manuel Costa's mouth fell open.

"No," admitted Gaunt. "But I think it's there."

Costa sighed, then forced a smile and an answering wave as a truck driver leaned out of his cab and shouted a greeting. He switched to a scowl as the truck rumbled on.

"Then it's a damn fool idea," he said with a sour irritation. "Don't blame me for it. I know Luis—and he liked Preston." He paused, sucking his teeth. "Still, it explains why she came to see me yesterday, with a crazy story about being worried in case their house was ever burgled—we have had some burglaries lately, petty things, probably two men involved. Still, Inez isn't the nervous kind and—yes, she asked a lot about Preston and how he died."

"And?"

Costa grimaced. "She is a friend. Maybe I hinted a little more than I should, which wouldn't help. But—no, not Luis. He wouldn't hurt a fly."

"Even if the fly frightened him?" Gaunt drew a finger along the Fiat's dusty metal and examined the result. "You can't hide from that, Sergeant."

"No." Costa gave a reluctant scowl.

"And we don't know how often Luis manages to sneak out of that house at night—"

Costa swore. "I said Preston was his friend. That was why Preston saw Inez so often, not the other way round. He would spend hours with Luis, showing him puzzles, games —trying to make his mind work." A bitter smile twisted across his thin face. "Preston said all *medicos* were failed garage mechanics, that the mind was just another machine to be repaired."

It rang true to Francis Preston's character. Nodding, Gaunt let an old tractor go by in a noisy stench of exhaust fumes then asked a question that had been puzzling him.

"Aren't there other relatives?"

"Didn't she tell you?" Costa eyed the departing tractor bleakly, the exhaust cloud still belching. "Luis had two passengers when he crashed, their mother and father. They were killed. Until then"—he sighed—"most people envied Luis. He was good-looking, popular, that navy uniform brought the girls swarming around—though he was an electronics specialist, the kind of sailor too important to send out to sea. Now—well, you've seen him."

"But you've still got that hunch about Preston," mused Gaunt. "Maybe it's contagious, Sergeant—and there are other possibilities."

"Of course." Costa brightened.

"What did the post-mortem report say about liquor?"

"That there wasn't enough to be significant." Costa frowned. *"Porque . . .* why?"

"Jaime said the same—Preston stopped at the Da Gama on his way back from Lisbon. He was alone then."

Costa muttered under his breath. "I wasn't told that."

"He says you didn't ask," grinned Gaunt. "But it doesn't help much. What about the people he visited in Lisbon?"

"I have a list." Manuel Costa looked worried. "They were only asked when he left to come back here. But for the police to ask them questions again would mean giving reasons. Unless—" he paused hopefully.

"I could look up a couple." Gaunt saw Costa's delight and added a warning. "But remember, I've got my own interests. They come first."

"All I want is one hard fact," said Costa fervently. "Get me that, from anywhere, one my superiors can't ignore and—"

He stopped, frowning, as a car horn beeped almost beside them. The car drew in, Georges Salvador's blue Jaguar with the plump, sallow-faced owner at the wheel.

"Sollas's landlord," murmured Gaunt as Salvador beckoned him over. "I'll be back."

He heard Costa grunt as he left. The sound was far from polite.

"Senhor Gaunt." Salvador greeted him with a white-toothed smile as he reached the car. "How are you after last night's experience?"

"On the hill?" Gaunt grinned. "Fine—but news seems to travel fast."

"I heard from Doctor Sollas. He had to telephone me this morning—it was about a detail in the lease for the villa." Salvador chuckled and ran a hand along the car's leather-rimmed steering wheel. "Well, now you have more respect for our ditches, eh?"

"A lot more," said Gaunt dryly. "How did things go at the Casino last night?"

"Win a little, lose a little—my usual. Though my friends were less fortunate." Salvador eyed him keenly. "Will you be here long enough to try your own luck?"

"There's that chance," agreed Gaunt vaguely. "If I save hard, I might manage to play a fruit machine or two."

"If you do, be my guest—just let me know." Salvador blipped the accelerator lightly. "Arrangements could be made, discreetly, of course. I know your position."

"Thanks." Gaunt nodded neutrally. "On your way to see Sollas?"

"No, I have another little interest to attend to." Salvador blipped the accelerator again. "Anyway, take care. And remember what I said."

Gaunt stood back as the blue car purred away. It had disappeared round a corner before he got back to Manuel Costa.

"I've had an offer," he said dryly. "A free night at the Casino."

Costa's nostrils twitched in disgust. "Will you go?"

"That depends what he's selling," mused Gaunt. "You don't like him?"

"Me?" Costa grimaced. "As a humble sergeant of detectives—" he stopped and gestured his disgust. "*Jesu*, no! I don't like a man who makes money so easily."

"Meaning?"

"He plays the stock market in Lisbon. Read a few newspapers in bed, make a few phone calls—what kind of man would call that a day's work?"

"Jealousy, Sergeant," murmured Gaunt. "It's not so easy, believe me. I've tried but never got far."

"My heart bleeds," said Costa cynically, giving the Fiat's nearest tyre an experimental kick. "I'll leave those names for you at the Da Gama. Have a good day—and don't fall down any holes, eh?"

Whistling a tune, he ambled away.

CHAPTER FOUR

Moonlight might satisfy song writers, but daytime brought its own compensations as Jonathan Gaunt motored the hill route to the Castelo de Rosa digging site. Where the Fiat had ditched on a nightmare-edged track was now a pleasant, jolting but uneventful drive through a leafy lane. Pine and poplars, tall and majestic, cast their shade and were punctuated here and there by an occasional, isolated patch of bulky, ancient cork trees.

When he cleared the trees, the old Moorish watch-tower stood like a cool, austere sentinel dominating the little valley ahead. A simple, geometrically precise structure, slab-sided, the upper section's tumbled, broken walls telling of some past calamity, it was built of a coral-hued stone which seemed to glow in the rays of the sun.

Gaunt stopped the car for a moment, remembering landmarks from the night before—and seeing them in a new perspective.

The scrub bushland where Luis Torres had been so relentlessly hunted had become a dark green patchwork of shrubbery set in a rich, pastel carpet of long grass and delicate wild flowers, splashed here and there by a yellow blaze of myrtle. On either side of the clearing the timber began again. But not as thickly as he'd imagined and starting a lot further back than he'd realised.

Wryly aware of the way his luck had held, Gaunt switched his attention to the digging site. Broad brown furrows of earth, marking trench excavations, radiated out from the watch-tower's base to join other, narrower furrows which traced an outline like the pencilled shape of the Roman villa he'd seen on Arthur Sollas's map. A few small figures were moving around the trenches and there were cars parked beside the two wooden huts which seemed to form the team's base.

But the fence interested him too. Built of high mesh wire laced to concrete poles, it surrounded a long, oval area which contained the Castelo trenches and a lot more—he guessed the total at some four acres of ground. And, like a stopper in a bottle, it blocked the route of the track winding through the middle of the clearing.

Open, the track was a gateway to the high, wooded hills beyond as it had probably been for centuries, perhaps even back to a time when the watch-tower had been built to guard it.

Closed, it was the kind of irritation any peasant farmer wanting to get to shops or market would find hard to tolerate. Even when the reasons were known to have firm official backing.

But for the moment how the locals felt was among the least of his worries. Releasing the handbrake, Gaunt flicked the Fiat into gear and let it trickle on.

He'd been seen. As the car neared the site gate a workman hurried from the direction of the huts and swung the gate open, waving him through and pointing over to where the other cars were parked. Gaunt stopped beside them and climbed out, his mouth shaping a greeting as he saw Arthur Sollas striding towards him from the nearest hut.

"So you made it this time." Sollas was wearing old baseball shoes, a grubby khaki shirt and shorts which emphasised his paunch. The bulky figure stopped a few paces away and eyed Gaunt stonily. "What the hell was your idea last night?"

Gaunt grimaced apologetically. "I saw lights and got curious."

"Curious?" Sollas grunted the word. "You could have wrecked that car—and you might have got your head blown off."

"The deer hunters?" Gaunt showed innocent surprise. "I was glad enough to see them."

"Maybe, but they weren't after deer—Pereira didn't want to alarm you." Sollas hesitated, rubbing the scar on his nose. "We had a prowler. So—well, they went out to scare him off."

"They'd enough firepower," mused Gaunt.

Sollas nodded. "Pereira says they're pretty certain he had a shotgun. Anyway, he got away—and now you're here, we might as well get started on the guided tour." He gave a cynical grimace. "Unless you want to wait for Marsh and his wife —they're coming over."

"No thanks." He could do without meeting Francis Preston's relatives again unless it became essential—and he hoped it wouldn't. "How did they make out last night?"

"If they'd found anything, you'd have heard." Sollas booted a stray pebble almost viciously. "Bernie Ryan looked in after midnight and found them ripping the lining out of one of Preston's jackets—and they're still trying. That's why they're coming here." He scowled out across the site for a moment then shrugged. "Well, let's begin at the beginning, the watch-tower."

Gaunt followed him and they tramped along a narrow wooden boardwalk which spanned its way across the nearest trenches. Here and there Gaunt caught a glimpse of exposed patches of broken mosaic flooring down below, and once Sollas thumbed towards the butt edge of a fragment of wall which had a triangulation mark chalked across its face.

"These were early stage probings." Sollas stopped as they reached the tower and gestured back. "We were lucky— we got the proof we were right almost first go, only about five feet down, though we had to go a lot deeper later."

"All because of this." Gaunt felt dwarfed beneath the weathered pink-hued stonework. He rubbed a hand over its rough texture. "What made it so special to Preston?"

"The stonework was obviously quarried, but all different-sized blocks pieced together like a jigsaw—he reckoned they'd been salvaged from something a lot bigger." Sollas sucked his teeth in mournful admiration. "As usual, he guessed right—almost right, anyway."

Going over to a gaping archway, Gaunt looked inside the tower. It was shadowed, weed-choked, and smelled of mildewed decay. A crumbling stone stairway led up to the next floor but was blocked halfway where a small tree sprouted from a crack, its long, thin branches reaching almost hungrily towards a few rays of sunlight filtering down from somewhere above.

"Well?" demanded Sollas. "What do you think of it?"

Gaunt shook his head. "It's not my line, Doctor. If I was asked, I'd probably slap a demolition order on it."

"At least you're honest." Sollas chuckled almost amiably. "That's half the trouble. Today's slum can be tomorrow's treasure-house. Like to see more?"

"Yes." Gaunt cleared his throat diplomatically. "How about where the accident happened?"

Sighing, Arthur Sollas nodded and led the way again. They went back the way they'd come and along more boardwalk, skirting trenches which gradually deepened and widened, their loose earth often supported by timber and corrugated iron shuttering. In one, Gaunt glimpsed two workmen slowly and carefully scraping away earth from an emerging stone bench. In another, a man with a hand trowel was down on his knees cleaning a patch of mosaic flooring.

"Down here," said Sollas curtly, stopping and matching action to words by clambering down a runged ladder.

Gaunt followed him. The trench was about twelve feet below ground level, just wide enough to let two men stand side by side, and supported by piling and corrugated sheeting. A stretch of plain stone paving underfoot ended in a mixture of clay and rubble, and a few paces beyond, where there were signs of experimental cuttings into the sides of the trench, it all ended in a caved-in mess of soil, collapsed timber and twisted sheeting.

"We dug him out from under there." Arthur Sollas stuck his hands in the pockets of his shorts and scowled, his booming voice a full tone grimmer. "You see what happened before—we ran out beyond the Roman villa's boundaries. But Preston took convincing before he'd agree we stopped."

"Because it meant defeat for him?"

"That's how he saw it." Sollas stopped and turned as a voice hailed him from up above. One of the workmen beamed down hopefully at them. Sighing, Sollas waved a hand then turned to Gaunt. "A problem—wait here and I'll be back."

Gaunt watched him climb up the ladder and disappear. Then, lighting a cigarette, he went closer to the collapsed tangle of debris and considered it with some care. Rain-soaked, water-logged soil and loosened timbers—it wouldn't have taken much to bring the lot down. If Francis Preston had come this way after dark at the whim of some stubborn devil of impulse, a stumble against one of those timbers might have been enough.

But the word was still only "might."

Shrugging, ready to turn away, he saw something glint just clear of the fall. It was a tiny piece of broken glass, thin and curved. Puzzled, he stooped and saw other, small fragments—the remains of a broken watch-glass.

On impulse, he gathered a few of the pieces in his handkerchief then rose thoughtfully. Carlos Pereira hadn't been wearing a wrist-watch—but the mark of a strap had been there on his left wrist.

A grunt from above brought him round as Arthur Sollas began coming back down the ladder. Gaunt quickly stuffed the handkerchief back in his pocket and tried hard to slip back into his role of interested by-stander.

"False alarm," said Sollas, as he reached the bottom of the trench and came over. "Someone found a chunk of kitchen pottery—not worth a damn, but they know we pay a bonus for anything worthwhile, so they always come running." He chuckled and looked around. "Gaunt, if you know your history, you don't need me to tell you these Romans were sophisticated people. We've found traces of warm-air central heating, a heated bath, even piped water and drainage—things the world lost afterwards and had to invent again. I'd say whoever lived here was important, maybe even a provincial governor."

"Then what went wrong?" Gaunt relaxed, deciding the man hadn't spotted what he'd done.

"Fire and sword—I'll show you." Beckoning, Sollas set off down the trench. They joined another, not as deep but wider, then followed it round an angle.

On the other side the way was partly blocked by a heavy stone pillar, ornately carved but broken in the middle like a stick of seaside rock. The top section lay against one side of the trench, and the digging team had jammed in a couple of struts of timber to hold it in position.

"Careful now"—the big man squeezed past, waited till Gaunt joined him, then pointed—"and in there."

A narrow archway in an unexpected wall formed the entrance to a small, cell-like room and there was light inside. Stooping, Gaunt went in, saw Martin Lawson squatting on the sandy floor, nodded as the fat archaeologist beamed a greeting—then stopped and blinked.

Lawson was hunched down beside a row of five yellowed, fragile human skeletons. He'd been clearing sand and grit from the nearest with a small paintbrush.

"Good, aren't they?" said Lawson happily. Reaching over, he dragged a kerosene lamp closer and sat back on his heels, wiping a hand across his bald head. "We don't find this kind of thing often, Gaunt. But when that pillar fell outside it sealed the door—a real stroke of luck."

Two of the skeletons had shattered skulls. Beaming, Lawson used the paintbrush to point to a blackened metal spearhead still jammed in the breastbone of another.

"Fire and sword, like I said," rumbled Arthur Sollas, squeezing in beside them.

"No doubt about it," declared Lawson enthusiastically. "Almost certainly the villa was attacked in some local uprising. These would be early Roman casualties, killed and brought down here. Then, later, there was a final storming —the entire household slaughtered, bodies stripped and plundered—"

"Don't make a meal of it, Martin," said Sollas wearily. "He can imagine the rest."

Gaunt nodded and shivered a little without knowing why. Sollas noticed and grinned a little.

"If you've seen enough—" he nodded towards the archway.

Thankfully, Gaunt eased back out into the open and stood upright. He heard Arthur Sollas grunting a way through behind him, glanced back—then sensed as much as heard a strange, soft, almost groaning noise. Out of the corner of his eye he caught a movement at the top of the trench.

Then the great carved stone pillar was falling towards him, one of its wooden supports splintering with a crackle, dirt and gravel fogging the air.

For a moment he was paralysed, then he threw himself straight backward, smashing into Sollas, sending the big man reeling, then bringing his hands up over his head in a final futility of protection.

The pillar wasn't falling straight. An edge caught the opposite wall of the trench, it twisted—then landed with a reverberating crash on the stone slabs inches from his feet. For a moment more the air was filled with dust and the noise of trickling earth and gravel.

Then there was silence. Absolute, total silence—till Arthur Sollas pushed and cursed his way out of the little cell. He stared at the fallen pillar then at Gaunt, who was leaning shakily against the wall, and shook his head in something close to stunned disbelief.

"You all right?" he demanded finally.

Gaunt nodded. There was a deep indentation in the cor-

rugated iron shuttering where the pillar had struck. The flag-
stones at his feet were shattered. If he hadn't dived back, if
the pillar had fallen fractionally straighter—then he'd be
dead, a smashed, bloodied smear for Sergeant Costa to theorise
about.

"How the hell did it happen?" Scowling, red-faced, Arthur
Sollas glared around, then focussed his rage. "Carlos, get
down here, damn you!"

The foreman was peering at them from the lip of the trench,
his swarthy face almost sickly, his eyes fixed unbelievingly on
Gaunt.

"Did you hear me?" rasped Sollas.

"*Sim* . . . yes, Doctor. *Immediatamente!*" Carlos Pereira
scrambled away.

As he vanished, Martin Lawson squeezed out into the
open from the archway and blinked like a plump, confused
dormouse as he saw the pillar.

"Is—is it damaged?" he asked weakly. "Ah—are you hurt,
Gaunt?"

"No." Gaunt managed a grin. "And I'll try to catch it for
you next time."

"Damn the damage," snarled Sollas. "And stay out of this,
Martin. Get back to your blasted boneyard."

Lawson shrank back, shaking his head. Hands on hips,
legs apart, Sollas switched viciously as Pereira hurried towards
them along the trench from some nearby ladder.

"Well?" grated Sollas, his nostrils flaring. "Didn't I tell you
this blasted pillar was to be made secure?"

Moistening his lips, Pereira fidgeted a moment then nodded.

"Then how the hell did this happen?"

The man spread his hands vaguely and tried a nervously
apologetic grin. "I don' know, Doctor Sollas. Maybe *Senhor*
Gaunt—"

"*Senhor* Gaunt did damn all. The thing just fell." Two
strides took Sollas to the foreman, two massive fists grabbed

him by the shirt and nearly dragged him off his feet. "Now you'll fix it this time. *Pressa* . . . right now, understand?"

Nodding quickly, Pereira looked relieved as Sollas relaxed his grip. Then he turned to Gaunt, forcing the same sickly grin.

"Accidents happen, *Senhor* Gaunt. I am sorry."

Gaunt shrugged. "I'm still in one piece, Carlos. Luckier than *Senhor* Preston, eh?" He paused then grimaced as he added, "I suppose you helped dig him out?"

"*Nao, senhor* . . . not me." Pereira shook his head quickly and glanced sideways at Arthur Sollas. "I—uh—was in Estoril that night. I did not get back till much later."

"He's got a woman there," said Sollas wearily. "Get on with it, man."

Nodding, Pereira turned away and began shouting orders to some of the other workmen who were now gathered above.

"Tour's over," said Sollas bleakly. "Gaunt, you look like you could use a drink."

"And I feel like I look," agreed Gaunt fervently.

They left Lawson still making tutting noises over the fallen pillar and went along to where they could climb out of the trench. From there, Sollas steered a direct course towards the huts near the gate and led the way into the larger of the two, which was laid out as an office.

"Enjoy your tour?" greeted Bernie Ryan, grinning up at Gaunt from behind a desk made of old packing cases. Without waiting for an answer, he switched his grin towards Sollas. "What was the excitement? Have some more of your early Roman chamber pots turned up, Doc?"

"No." Sollas went straight to a locked cupboard, produced a key, and opened the door. "We damned nearly had a second body on our hands."

Raising an eyebrow, the white-haired photographer gave a startled whistle.

"How?" he demanded.

They told him, while Sollas brought three tumblers and a brandy bottle from the cupboard and splashed a stiff measure of brandy into each tumbler.

"God give us all patience." Ryan rubbed his chin appreciatively as the story ended, then neatly caught the drink that slid across the desk top towards him. "Gaunt, between this and last night, I'd hate like hell to be your insurance company." He raised the glass in a general toast, sipped, then said with a total irrelevance, "The locals have a neat name for a drink before noon, a *matibicho* . . . a germ-killer. See some of their sanitation and you'll know why." Stopping, he frowned. "Hey, where's Martin? He can usually smell a drink being poured at half-mile range."

"Still talking to his skeletons," answered Sollas.

"An appreciative audience at last," declared Ryan solemnly. He gestured around. "Well, here's where the real work is done, Gaunt. See and admire—it's time somebody did."

Gaunt grinned. The timber walls were covered in pinned-up photographs of the excavation area, some of them general views and others close-up studies of pottery ornaments, fragments of statuary or rusted sword blades. But the only trace of the originals he could see was an elaborate mosaic tile which Ryan had as a drink mat.

He asked why.

"Most of it goes straight into a crate and off to the museum people in Lisbon—another of their rules." Arthur Sollas slumped heavily into a camp chair and shrugged. "Not that we're worried. The real prize here has been just finding the place."

"And what happens when you leave?" asked Gaunt.

Sollas frowned. "That's been agreed. There's one small section which will stay fenced off and private—for another year. The Romans weren't necessarily the first people here and I'd like to try going deeper. But that depends on backers and money. The rest is handed back to the Portuguese authorities, and they'll probably open it as a tourist attraction. Lawson's boneyard should bring them running."

"Don't knock the tourists," murmured Ryan lazily. "They could be bread-and-butter to an out-of-work photographer. Maybe I'll stay on and earn the odd *escudo* as a guide or something." He swung his feet up on the desk top and grinned at Gaunt. "It's that or a share of the Treasure Trove reward money you're waving around."

"It's there," mused Gaunt. "Somebody's going to earn it."

"But not me." Ryan grimaced. "And not Marsh and his wife, if there's any justice. When are they due here anyway, Doc?"

"About eleven. Any time now," answered Sollas shortly.

"My cue to leave," said Gaunt with a grin. He finished his drink and laid down the glass. "I'll be in touch."

"Just take care, then," advised Ryan without moving. "Third time might not be so lucky."

Gaunt had already thought of that. He said good-bye, left the hut, and was over at the Fiat when he heard a shout and turned.

A camera clicked. Standing in the hut doorway, Ryan took a second shot then lowered the camera.

"One for the visitors' book," he called. "Order your copies now."

Gaunt grinned, got into the Fiat, and set it moving. Then, as he neared the gate in the fence, he slowed again. Pereira was there, standing bleak-faced and talking earnestly to another of the workmen. Stopping beside them Gaunt wound down his window and beckoned the foreman over.

"Forget about that business with the pillar, Carlos," he said easily. "Accidents happen."

"*Obrigado, Senhor* Gaunt." Pereira nodded gloomily. "You are going now?"

"Back to Claras, to meet someone." Gaunt eyed him innocently. "I said I'd be there before noon. What time do you make it?"

The man hesitated then shook his head. "I don't have a watch, *Senhor* Gaunt."

"I just wondered—mine is misbehaving." Gaunt raised a hand in farewell and set the Fiat moving again. Another workman opened the gate and he drove through without a backward glance.

But one shove from above would have been enough to send that pillar crashing down. Pereira had tried to kill him in the trench. Kill him or at very least frighten him off.

Exactly why didn't matter. It was personal now, and the little fragments of glass nestling in his handkerchief might prove very interesting to a certain humble sergeant of detectives.

A leisurely ten-minute drive brought him back to Claras. He left the Fiat in the square near the fountain and was walking over to the hotel when two determined figures hurried from a shop doorway to intercept him. John and Sarah Marsh looked tired-eyed and pasty-faced in the bright sunlight, but they greeted him with a resolute purpose.

"Gaunt, we're going to stay on an extra couple of days," said Marsh without preamble. "I'm damned if we want to, but with the kind of money you're offering we can't take chances."

Sarah Marsh nodded. She had a paper carrier bag in one hand, bulging with small parcels.

"Including whether somebody here isn't hiding more of Uncle Frank's stuff, just waiting till we've gone," she said grimly.

"Somebody—or anyone in particular?" asked Gaunt.

Husband and wife exchanged a glance then Sarah Marsh sniffed. "Well, there's Doctor Sollas for a start. He—he's the kind that might. Big and noisy but probably desperate for money."

"Aren't we all?" Gaunt sighed sympathetically. "I thought you were visiting this morning, both of you."

"We are." John Marsh flicked a strand of his long, mousy hair back from his forehead and brightened a little. "That photographer character Ryan says he thinks there's maybe some of Uncle Frank's notebooks and papers still out there."

"So we'll find out," said Sarah Marsh. She stabbed an indignant forefinger. "But if any of them are trying a fast one on us—"

She left the threat unfinished. Her husband nodded.

"The other thing we've done is cable the solicitor in London who has Uncle Frank's will. My uncle used a hotel in Bloomsbury as a base—he can check if there's anything maybe in store there."

"Good thinking," agreed Gaunt mildly and nodded at the carrier bag. "Shopping?"

"Souvenirs." Sarah Marsh flicked a smile on and off. "For our friends—might as well let them know we've really been. And the stuff's cheap. We can keep some of it till next Christmas."

They left him. A couple of moments later he saw them again, two straight-backed, purposeful figures in the rear seat of a jeep being driven out of the square by one of Sollas's men.

Glad to know they'd gone, he went into the Da Gama and glanced into the bar as he passed. Jaime was there, polishing tables while another youth loafed over by a window. He strongly resembled the second stone-thrower in the cemetery incident and was laughing at something Jaime had said.

"*Senhor* Gaunt—"

The clerk at the reception desk signalled him and had a letter in his hand. Taking it, Gaunt saw his name scrawled across the front in a bright blue ink and the heavy *Policia de Seguranca Publica* seal across the flap.

He went up to his room and lit a cigarette before he opened it. Sergeant Costa's broad, bold handwriting filled the single page but came down to the fact that he'd be out of Claras most of the day chasing witnesses on a robbery that had been reported. Then came the names Gaunt had wanted, five people, each with a Lisbon address, each known to have been visited by Preston the evening before he died.

Gaunt tucked the list in his wallet pocket. There were envelopes and notepaper in one of the dressing table drawers and he thought for a moment then scribbled a quick note of his own. Taking the handkerchief with the broken watch-glass, he folded it carefully, put it in an envelope with the note, sealed the envelope, then went out again.

His first stop was to leave the envelope at the *policia* station for Costa's return. From there, he located the village post office and had them dig out a cable form.

"PROBLEMS HERE BUT WEATHER FINE." That seemed about right—he signed it, addressed it to Falconer at the Q. and L.T.R. office in Edinburgh, then let the counter clerk struggle to work out the cost.

After he'd paid, he went over to a telephone booth in the corner, checked the Lisbon directory, then dialled the British Embassy number and fed coins into the slot while the number rang out. When the Embassy answered, there was the usual minute or two of delays while he battled to get past the operator and a couple of secretaries and was finally connected with the Duty Officer.

"Gaunt? Ah . . ." There was a pause and a noise which sounded like the Embassy man sipping tea. "Yes, we had a signal about you and this Preston business. Like to come and see us about it?"

Gaunt grimaced at the receiver. That was about the last thing he had in mind. He'd learned early on in this new career that whatever the flag, Embassy protocol could waste hours.

"No time," he said sadly. "I've to wrap this up quickly then get the first plane home. It's the time of year—the Department pipe band practices have started."

A swallowing, spluttering sound came over the line. But Duty Officers were trained to keep their cool.

"I'll tell my wife," came the acid reply. "She's from Scotland too. All right, Gaunt, exactly what the hell do you want?"

"Nothing complicated," he soothed. "I'm involved with a Doctor Arthur Sollas, also a Bernard Ryan, photographer, and a Martin Lawson, archaeologist. Can you see what you've got on them?"

"All ours?"

"As far as I know—I haven't seen their passports."

"Quite." The Duty Officer thawed a little. "Gaunt, have you any idea how many thousand British subjects are permanent residents in this country? How many more are just passing through? The only ones we really know about are the people who land in some kind of trouble." He paused. "Could—ah—"

"That's what I want to find out."

The Embassy man sighed. "Well, hold on."

He'd smoked a cigarette and was thinking about another before the Duty Officer came back on the line.

"Doctor Sollas we know about," he said warily. "He's on the Ambassador's list for cocktail receptions. Not the 'A' list, of course, but he certainly rates a 'B.' He's in private practice in Lisbon with shares in a clinic—more of a sleeping partner than anything, but he knows the right people."

"And the other two?"

"Nothing. Anything else?"

"In a way"—Gaunt hesitated—"though it's more personal—"

"As long as it's not money," warned the Duty Officer stiffly. "I've orders from the top on that—we've had too many visiting firemen wandering through and thinking we're some kind of loan office. The Embassy budget can't take any more."

"Not money. Have you a *Financial Times* handy?"

"We get it air edition from London, daily. But—" the Duty Officer stopped, puzzled.

"Get it," invited Gaunt.

That took a moment or two.

"Now check a couple of prices for me, will you? Consolidated Breweries and Malters Holding Stock."

He heard a mutter of indignation then a rustle of paper.

"Consolidated closed yesterday at 124, Malters rose to 160"—a gathering interest crept into the voice at the other end—"something happening with them? I've a little money in the family piggy bank that's looking for a profitable home so—ah—"

Gaunt grinned. "Suppose you check out Ryan and Lawson again, then I'll let you know."

"Yes, but—"

"I'll call back. Wait till then."

Gaunt hung up. When he'd bought in, Consolidated had already been shading at 130 and Malters had been on the upswing at 146. Now it looked as though a lot more investors were stepping into the situation. Most wouldn't stay on for the full ride, when the real risk came. They'd settle for a fast if modest profit and get out . . . while his own gamble would still just be warming up.

If it all came off, he'd had his eye on a neat little Japanese colour TV set and there could be a useful chunk of money left over. Though "if" was a big little word.

Half an hour later he ate lunch in a cafe off the square. The table didn't have a cloth and the wine came in a chipped carafe, but it washed down one of the thickest steak sandwiches he'd ever seen and the bill was small enough to make him double the size of tip he'd planned.

It was warm and bright and getting warmer when he finally drove the Fiat out to Inez Torres' bungalow. As he swung into the driveway a middle-aged woman in a green overall looked up, broke off from sweeping the front steps of the house, and went inside. By the time he'd climbed out of the car, Inez had appeared on the porch to greet him.

For a moment he said nothing, knowing he had an idiotic grin on his face but not able to do anything about it.

This was the girl he'd seen in the painting—a welcoming sparkle in her dark eyes, a smile on her lips and supple vitality in every movement. She'd chosen faded blue jeans, a gay open-necked shirt-blouse tied in front at her midriff and a matching cotton headscarf which all but hid her jet black hair. The plain gold chain was on her wrist and she had simple, open-toed sandals.

The effect was total and complete, and he had a feeling she both knew it and enjoyed it.

"Reporting for duty, *Senhor* Gaunt," she said demurely. "Have you any plan for this safari?"

"No." Still looking at her, he rubbed a pensive hand along his chin. "But that's liable to change."

She laughed, a husky, pleased sound. "Well, you wanted a guide and I've thought of a few places. But remember, I have to be back in time to go to work." Her dark eyes twinkled again. "The Casino management goes berserk if anyone turns up late."

"But you'll be going to Estoril." He had an idea. "Look, Inez, I've people to see in Lisbon later. That means going through Estoril." He paused hopefully. "We'd have more time if I drove you there without coming back here. I could see these people, come back again to Estoril and—well, bring you home after the last show."

"There's Luis—but Anna will be here." She frowned slightly, considered for a moment, then nodded. "Why not? As long as we use my car, Jonathan. The things for my act are in the trunk."

Gaunt compared the battered Fiat with the sleek lines of the Lancia and didn't feel like arguing.

"Good." Inez reached into a pocket of her jeans and

handed him the keys. "I'll tell Anna—it'll only take a moment. Then I'll say good-bye to Luis. He's round the back."

She disappeared back into the house. Putting the keys in his pocket, Gaunt strolled over to where the Lancia was parked, eyed it appreciatively, then walked slowly round towards the rear of the bungalow.

Luis Torres was standing beside a rabbit hutch inside a patch of grass fenced off knee-high from the rest of the garden. He had his back to Gaunt, but turned quickly as he heard footsteps. For a moment he eyed Gaunt nervously and seemed ready to back away, then he stayed where he was, both arms round the sleek, white rabbit he was holding.

"Hello, Luis . . . *como esta?*" Gaunt kept the same unhurried pace then stopped at the fence. "Remember me?"

After a moment a slow, undecided smile crossed the thin, pale face and Torres nodded.

"Inez and I brought you home last night." Gaunt stepped over the fence, came up to him, and deliberately turned his attention to the rabbit, stroking it behind one ear. Then he looked up. "Home from the Castelo, Luis."

"Castelo." Luis Torres got the word out with an effort then after further effort his mouth twitched again. "*Senhor* Gaunt."

"That's right. You like going to the Castelo, don't you?"

"Like?" The haggard face twitched and those eyes showed a struggle as if something was trapped there, trapped and fighting to get free. Suddenly Torres shook his head quickly and edged away towards the hutch, the rabbit hugged closer, looking past Gaunt towards the house.

His sister was coming. Torres brightened as she came up to him and kissed him on the cheek.

"*Adeus,* Luis." She added something quietly and Torres gave a hesitant nod.

Biting his lip he came forward slowly and held the rabbit out towards Gaunt. Gently, Gaunt let the tiny teeth nibble his fingers, saw Torres watching him anxiously, and felt a sudden angry sympathy with what was left of Lieutenant Luis Torres.

"I'll look after her, Luis," he said quietly.

Maybe it got through, maybe it was only the tone of his voice, maybe he only imagined it.

But the thin face seemed to relax, as if thanking him.

CHAPTER FIVE

The Lancia had a Zagato coachwork body, leather upholstery, a five-speed gear-box, and a high-compression alloy engine which sucked fuel through twin carburettors with a muted roar.

Jonathan Gaunt treated it cautiously for the first few kilometres, watching the rev. counter and getting the feel of brakes and steering. Then, gradually, he gave the car more throttle, heard a new, tight, rasping note throb from the exhaust, and felt at home. On the next length of straight he slammed the car up through the gears and counted the seconds while the speedometer swept round.

He saw it quiver past the 170 k.p.h. mark then eased back on the accelerator as the next corner appeared ahead. Over a hundred in miles per hour in less time than his tuned Mini took to get to sixty . . . and a lot more waiting.

"Well?" Curled up comfortably in the passenger seat, Inez Torres watched him with amusement in her eyes and an unlit cigarette held between her fingers. "Do you like her?"

"Like?" Gaunt concentrated on taking the corner then grinned as he settled back. "After this, I'll feel underprivileged."

"My agent would give you her free, gift-wrapped, if he had the chance." The cigarette lighter on the dashboard popped out and she used it. "Every time he knows I'm driving he thinks about what happened to Luis—and worries about his percentage."

"And you?" He kept his eyes on the road.

"He can go to hell." She smoked the cigarette for a moment, watching the fields and hedgerows slip past. "Jonathan, I talked to Manuel Costa, like you asked."

Gaunt nodded, but said nothing.

"He said—well, anyway, I think I can forget about something now." She stretched lazily, like a cat, then smiled at him. "Thanks for that. Now be a good tourist and enjoy yourself. That's what I'm going to do."

First there was Sintra, a fairy-tale town of palaces and vast gardens of flowers high in the hills where they left the Lancia and solemnly hired a horse-drawn open garry complete with a driver who wore an old top-hat and insisted on singing.

Then the car took them north again, climbing through rocky passes and wooded gorges to Mafra, another hilltop fantasy with a castle of 5,000 doors, a treasure-house library and carillon bells.

And so it went on, flickering impressions—a cafe in a deer park where they had coffee and tiny sweet cakes while fawns nuzzled the windows. A village without a name but with a souvenir shop where Gaunt bought a feather-light white shoulder square of soft, crocheted wool when she lingered over it for a moment. And more—until at last, chewing candy they'd bought from a roadside vendor, the Lancia came over a rise and began murmuring down towards the blue haze of the coastline.

A few white-washed cottages became the outskirts of a fishing village with a tiny harbour and brightly painted seine net boats which had high, sharply curved bow and sternposts. Two kilometres on, as the road swung inland again, Inez touched Gaunt's arm and gestured towards a farm track leading off to the right.

The track, two ruts with a grassy centre strip, ended at the edge of a small, sandy bay. Off-shore, the heavy Atlantic rollers spent their white force on a reef of black rock leaving the bay a quiet, peaceful place where the water rippled in. Sea-birds were feeding along its edge, and they were completely alone with not as much as another car or house in sight.

"Let's stop," said Inez almost sadly. Leaning over, her hair brushing his cheek, she switched off the engine then sat back with her eyes half-closed for a moment. "When will you go back to Britain?"

"I don't know. Maybe in a couple of days, maybe more." Gaunt wound down his window and the steady roar of the waves breaking on the reef came flooding in.

"When you do, you can say you've seen Cape Roca." She pointed to a broad headland of rock to the north. *"Cabo de Roca*—that's the most westerly point in Europe."

He looked at the headland, towering above the rollers pounding white around its base. It had a lighthouse and, further back, he saw a cluster of small buildings surrounded by tall, thin masts and large dish aerials.

"It looks busy," he mused. "Radar?"

"And satellite communications—North Atlantic Treaty Organisation, maritime headquarters, Eastern Atlantic." She shrugged, her face clouding a little. "Luis was stationed there. That's when we found this beach—we used to picnic here sometimes."

He said nothing for a moment, understanding. Then, rubbing a hand along the rim of the steering wheel, he asked quietly, "What was it all about, Inez?"

She frowned. "What was what all about?"

"The panic about Luis." He waited then shrugged. "All right, I'll guess it. Last night wasn't the first time your brother slipped off after dark to the Castelo. And you were scared he might have been there the night Francis Preston died. Scared sick ever since Sergeant Costa let it slip Preston's death maybe wasn't an accident. Right?"

Inez came bolt upright, staring at him, fists knuckle-tight

on her lap. Gaunt only smiled a little then lit two cigarettes and held one out towards her.

Slowly, almost reluctantly, she nodded then took the cigarette.

"Was he out that night?" asked Gaunt.

"*Sim* . . . yes, somewhere." It came like a sigh. "Anna was in the house as usual and thought he was sleeping. But I found mud on his shoes in the morning."

"And it wasn't the first time?"

"No." She looked down at her hands. "Jonathan, I know something did happen to him that night. It showed the next day—he was restless and upset, more nervous than I'd ever seen him."

"You tried asking him about it?"

"Luis?" She gave a tight, helpless smile. "Sometimes I think he does understand. Sometimes I even imagine that the real Luis is still trapped somewhere inside what he's become. Trapped and—well, trying to get out. But it just can't happen."

"Yet you say things have changed," reminded Gaunt. "Why?"

"Because I finally had the couage to ask Manuel Costa when the police thought Preston died. They say some time before midnight. Midnight?" She shook her head firmly and confidently. "Luis was still in the house at eleven-thirty, when Anna went to bed. Even if he'd run all the way, Luis couldn't have got to the Castelo in half an hour."

"So you can forget about that notion." Gaunt nodded but wondered.

"I have." She laughed, a soft, wry throb of a sound. "I should have known better." Then she noticed the dashboard clock and her eyes widened in alarm. "Jonathan, the time! I must be at that rehearsal—"

"You'll be there." Flicking his cigarette out of the window, Gaunt started the Lancia then, his hand resting on the gear lever, asked a last question. "Where do you think Luis maybe did get to that night?"

"I don't know." She shook her head. "I don't suppose I'll ever know. But it doesn't matter now—and I'm going to have that window fixed so it can't happen again." Her eyes strayed to the clock again. *"Por favor* . . . please, Jonathan. If I am late—"

"The management will throw a fit," he completed for her. "All right, Estoril."

He slapped the car into gear.

It was near to five-thirty P.M. when they reached Estoril. A stiffening breeze from the sea had begun snapping the row of national flags outside the Casino frontage and the long expanse of gardens sweeping down towards the shore road was deserted. But the Casino was already preparing for the night's business. As Gaunt stopped the Lancia near the main entrance a uniformed porter hurried out to greet them and he saw cleaners working with mops and dusters on the other side of the plate glass windows.

Sliding out, Inez had the porter take a couple of small suit cases from the trunk then, as the man started back with them, she came round to Gaunt's side of the car.

"My last show is just after midnight—I can leave about one A.M.," she told him through the open window. "I'll tell them to keep a table for you. All right?"

"I'll be there." Gaunt smiled up at her. "Though I may have a try at the gaming rooms first—I've a lucky feeling about today."

"That's when things usually come unstuck," she said dryly, then chuckled. *"Adeus,* Jonathan—just don't use my car as a side-bet."

She hurried after the porter. Gaunt watched till they'd disappeared into the Casino then lit a cigarette and set the Lancia moving.

It was early dusk when he made Lisbon. Stopping at a news

stand, he bought a street map of the city and spent a few minutes checking it against the list of addresses Sergeant Costa had provided, addresses which traced Francis Preston's last evening.

During the next half-hour he disposed of two, a travel agency in Avenida Aliados, in the centre of town, and a car rental firm only a couple of streets away.

At the travel agency, Preston had booked a 'plane seat on a London-bound flight for the following week. At the rental garage he'd paid his account up to date and had advised the desk clerk that he'd only need the car he was using for a few more days.

It was the first hint that Preston had been considering leaving. But the next address on the list took that an unexpected stage further. Doctor Arturo Burnay lived in a fashionable block of terrace houses on the fringe of old Lisbon, looking across parkland to a skyline of modern hotel blocks. A brass plate said Burnay was a consultant neurologist and when Gaunt rang the doorbell the man-servant who answered treated him with the kind of smooth courtesy which added 10 per cent to any medical bill.

Shown into a small, comfortably furnished study, Gaunt waited several minutes before the room door opened again. The stout, middle-aged man who entered had a round, pleasant face and thinning black hair and was in an old sports jacket and slacks.

"Doctor Burnay?" asked Gaunt, rising.

"*Sim . . .*" The man nodded cheerfully. "Forgive my dress, *Senhor* Gaunt. But if this is a professional visit, one usually makes an appointment—"

"I came because of a man named Francis Preston, Doctor," said Gaunt quietly. "The police say he was here the evening before he died."

"True." A frown creased the round face. "And your interest, *senhor*?"

Gaunt shrugged and twisted fact a little for simplicity's

sake. "I'm working through the British Embassy, Doctor. Preston's death raises some awkward legal details we're trying to sort out."

"*Obrigado* . . . then I will help if I can." Burnay gestured him back into the chair and sat down opposite. "But you must understand that Preston did not come to me as a patient. In fact, that evening was his first visit—as well as his last."

"I'm just trying to tie up some loose ends." Gaunt grinned a shade wearily. "As far as I can make out, he was getting ready to leave Portugal. Did you know that?"

"He told me." The neurologist offered Gaunt a cigar from a small silver box. As Gaunt shook his head, the man smiled, chose one for himself, and lit it carefully. Then, drawing on the smoke, he added, "In fact, that was what brought him here."

Gaunt frowned. "Could you explain that?"

"*Sim* . . . or I will try. *Senhor* Preston first telephoned for an appointment. But when he came, it was to ask me about a young man who had been under my professional care for some time."

Suddenly, Gaunt understood. "Luis Torres?"

"You know him?" Burnay lowered his cigar and looked surprised.

"Well enough to know Preston spent a lot of time with him." Gaunt sensed he was on delicate, medical ethics-type ground but probed on. "Did Preston want to try to help him even more—through you?"

Burnay nodded. "He offered to pay for any medical or surgical treatment which might improve the young man's condition. But I told him the simple truth, that everything possible already had been done." His plump shoulders shrugged sadly. "Brain surgery can certainly achieve many things today which were impossible a few years ago—but not for Luis Torres. There was too much damage in that car accident."

"His sister seems to think there's still hope for improvement," murmured Gaunt.

"Is it wrong to hope?" queried Burnay quietly. "The human body can repair itself in strange ways. Even with the brain, it can confound the medical profession by unexpected recovery." He shrugged a little. "We accept it can happen, though we don't understand why. In Luis Torres' case, such a recovery would be a miracle—but even miracles can happen, and hope can sometimes help. Does hope hurt his sister?"

"I don't think it ever hurt anyone." Gaunt showed his understanding then pursed his lips for a moment and moved on. "What about Preston, Doctor? Did he hint why he was leaving Portugal?"

"No, nor did I ask." Placing the cigar carefully on a silver ashtray, Burnay rose and gave a polite but firm smile. "He was a man who came and went, *Senhor* Gaunt. There is nothing more I can tell you."

Night had arrived outside, the sky a rich, dark velvet with stars brighter than he could ever remember having seen before. But there were still two names on the list—back behind the Lancia's wheel, Gaunt used the dashboard light and checked the street map again.

José Andella and Jorge Dias . . . Sergeant Costa had bracketed them in ink, then, under the addresses, had added, "Try Jeronimos Monastery first. They are on Museum staff."

Gaunt knew the Monastery. He'd gone there with Patti on a sight-seeing tour on their honeymoon trip. He remembered a great sprawl of Manueline architecture located beside the River Tagus, its back to the city, an overwhelming grandeur of stone and stained glass.

There had been a great fountain in a broad central garden, they'd walked along tree-lined avenues—and he'd taken photographs of Patti standing beside the gigantic Monument to the Discoveries down at the river's edge.

It brought back other memories too. The kind he supposed he should be trying to forget—except that they still mattered.

Wryly, he forced his mind back to the street map again, made sure of his route, then slipped the Lancia into gear and set off.

Lisbon's traffic was as heavy as ever, but with a difference in character. Now it was pleasure-bent. The streets seemed ribbons of neon-lit clubs and restaurants only broken by vast, flood-lit squares where more traffic swirled and hooted and swung in lane-changing aggression. The Lancia drew its share of horn-blasts and near-misses as he battled through the confusion, but at last things became quieter and the Monastery appeared ahead.

Gaunt parked outside, stood for a moment looking up at the long sweep of its stonework, then walked towards a door where he saw lights and an attendant. He gave his name and asked for José Andella.

"*Senhor* Andella?" The attendant showed an immediate respect, disappeared into a little cubicle, and used an internal telephone. After a moment he hung up, came back, and gestured Gaunt to follow him.

They walked along a series of vast stone corridors, past silent, cloistered courtyards and once he caught a distant glimpse of the Discoveries monument. A choir was singing in another part of the Monastery, but they went away from the sound, entered a different part of the building, and climbed a narrow stairway. At the top was a small, plain doorway. His guide knocked, waited till a muffled voice answered, then opened the door and gestured Gaunt through.

"Good-evening, *Senhor* Gaunt." A thin, elderly man with a bald head and a neat, silvery beard rose from behind a desk in the brightly lit room. It was a long, narrow room with a high ceiling and stone walls which seemed almost lined with books.

"*Senhor* Andella?" queried Gaunt.

"*Sim* . . . that is correct." Andella, who wore a dark, slight old-fashioned suit topped by a stiff white wing-collar and a large, loose bow-tie of dark red silk, nodded his thanks to the attendant. As the attendant went out and the door closed, Andella smiled a greeting. "How can I help you?"

"You're a museum official here, *senhor?*" asked Gaunt.

"Among other things, yes." The smile remained. "My official title is executive curator of archaeology." Andella paused and considered Gaunt with a slight puzzlement. "Have you an interest in the subject?"

"Not directly," said Gaunt. "More in a visitor you had a few nights ago, an Englishman."

"Francis Preston?" Andella refused to show surprise. "I see. Is this interest—ah—personal, *Senhor* Gaunt?"

"I work for a British government department," said Gaunt carefully. "That gives me no particular official status—but you can check with our Embassy. Or this might do." He produced his Remembrancer's Department warrant card.

"*Por favor . . . ?*" Andella took the card, studied it for a moment, then gave a dry chuckle and handed it back. "I have an idea now why you are here, *Senhor* Gaunt. Francis Preston told me a strange story about a disagreement he had with your Department over some church plate you classed as Treasure Trove. Now he is dead, you are anxious to find where that church plate might be, eh?"

"That's how it started," agreed Gaunt neutrally. "Now I've got other problems."

"I see." Andella looked at him oddly then turned, dumped some books from a chair to the floor, and brought the chair nearer his desk. "I don't know where your Treasure Trove is hidden, *Senhor* Gaunt. But sit down—tell me of these 'other problems.'"

Gaunt took the chair and waited till the other man was again behind his desk. Andella had keen, bright eyes, sharp enough to make him wonder how far he could go.

"The police say Preston came to see you the evening before he died," Gaunt began slowly.

"In this room," nodded Andella. "A colleague and I discussed certain matters with him."

"Was the colleague's name Jorge Dias?"

"*Sim* . . . you are well informed." Andella tugged his beard a little and frowned. "Let me save you some time, *Senhor* Gaunt. Jorge Dias left Lisbon today for Italy, to give a series of lectures to students in Rome. He—ah—is our expert in a certain field of archaeology."

"Meaning early Roman remains in Portugal?" asked Gaunt bluntly.

Andella winced then spread his hands apologetically. "Very well informed, I should have said . . . forgive an old man's childishness. So you know about Claras?"

"Arthur Sollas showed me round this morning." Gaunt smiled at the museum executive's discomfiture. "He also told me Preston hoped to find something a whole lot bigger than that villa. But he didn't seem to know Preston was planning to leave Portugal—did you?"

Andella nodded slowly. "Preston came to tell us—and to see if there was no way in which the Claras excavations might have erred." He toyed absently with a pen which had been lying on the desk then shook his head, a trace of amusement in his voice. "Though the man is dead, *Senhor* Gaunt, I must confess Dias and I rather enjoyed the situation. Especially as we had to tell him there was no error. After all, we never did suggest anything more than the villa was there."

It was Gaunt's turn to be puzzled. He leaned forward, frowning. "You mean you knew it was there? I thought—"

"You thought Francis Preston had produced another piece of brilliant deductive discovery?" Andella sniffed and chuckled. "You don't know much about archaeology, *Senhor* Gaunt."

"No," admitted Gaunt grimly. "But I'm willing to learn."

"*Obrigado,*" declared the older man acidly. "Then the first thing to understand is this man Preston—whom I still liked. Preston the amateur who went round the world rubbing professional noses in the dirt with his discoveries?" He made a noise surprisingly close to a raspberry. "That part was a fake, a clever public relations creation."

"I could call that professional jealousy," mused Gaunt.

Andella flushed almost angrily. *"Senhor* Gaunt, I can name you distinguished colleagues in half a dozen countries who will say the same. Archaeology is cursed by hair-brained idiots who use everything from bulldozers to tame clairvoyants in their search for fame. Preston's only difference was that he was much more clever. When he started a project he was already half-sure of success—because of other men's work!"

"You mean someone else found that villa before him?"

"Yes, almost fifty years ago—some students from Lisbon on a summer school camp. They positively established that they were dealing with the site of a second century B.C. villa, and it has been on our records ever since. But, of course, all they did was nibble at the location."

Coming from behind the desk, Andella walked over to the window at the far end of the room, looked out at the city's night skyline for a moment, then turned. His voice still had a bitter edge.

"We have a rich past, *Senhor* Gaunt. But today you could call us poor but proud—perhaps too proud. We are full partners in NATO. We cling to a scattering of colonies, mostly by sheer military presence. But do you know the cost? We spend more of our earnings on defence than any other country in Western Europe. There is little money left over for luxuries."

"And none for digging up Roman villas?"

"Let us say the Claras villa stayed far down the list of our priorities." The museum man grimaced. "So when a private syndicate suggested they would meet the cost we were interested. When they agreed that all finds would belong to our national museums—well, would you have said no to a man with money like Georges Salvador?"

"Salvador?" The unexpected name made Gaunt sit up. "I thought he was just their landlord—"

Andella seemed to smile into his silvery beard. "I can assure you, *Senhor* Gaunt, that whatever you may have heard the first interest in the Claras site came from Georges Salvador. Then he, in turn, interested *Senhor* Preston—who, of course, as an archaeologist of some popular fame carried out all the formal negotiations with the authorities."

"No inspired hunches?" Gaunt scrubbed his long jaw wryly. "All right, if Salvador is a sleeping partner in the dig, what's his particular angle?"

"Angle?" Andella frowned then understood. "Ah—unofficially, a certan tourist hotel development is planned for Claras. It is a pleasant spot, but shall we say that a historic Roman villa, newly uncovered, might be a very useful attraction?"

"Very useful, if you were an investor." Gaunt could imagine the kind of selling job Georges Salvador had carried out in interesting Francis Preston—and for once, it looked as if Preston had been hoodwinked in the process. "But it wouldn't exactly please Preston when he found out."

"If he found out," qualified Andella uneasily. "When he came here that last evening he was hardly happy. But all he talked about was his personal disappointment concerning the site—and financial rumours are no concern of this Department, *Senhor* Gaunt." He built a sad, contemplative steeple with his fingertips. "We could only tell him what facts we knew about the Claras villa, facts we could have told him at any time if he had taken the trouble to ask. We even showed him a plan drawing of what we had expected him to find."

"Could I see it?"

"*Sim.*" Andella opened a filing cabinet, carefully selected a folder, and spread out a folded sheet on a small table as Gaunt came over. "This was based on the original student dig—and our experience of similar villas in other areas."

One glance showed Gaunt that the drawing was close enough in basic detail to the plan he'd been shown by Arthur Sollas. There were only minor variations and a few extended dotted lines.

"What about these?" he asked.

"Water supply and drainage," shrugged Andella. "The Romans were highly civilised people."

"I'd heard," agreed Gaunt. He studied the drawing again then nodded his thanks. "Did Preston seem to know he'd been fooled?"

"A man like Francis Preston would not admit such a thing," murmured Andella, folding the sheet and putting it away. He closed the filing cabinet drawer then faced Gaunt again. "Now, *por favor* . . . can I ask why all this interests you so much, *Senhor* Gaunt?"

"Why do you think, *Senhor* Andella?" countered Gaunt neutrally.

José Andella looked at him for a long moment then very slowly shook his head.

"I would prefer to wait," he said softly. "But if you need any further help, you have only to ask."

Gaunt ate in a little cafe near the water-front where the tables were crowded and the view was out towards the Salazar Bridge—a high, moving ribbon of headlights in the night as heavy traffic crossed the Tagus in both directions.

A young, surprisingly pretty girl, one of several at the bar, watched him for a spell. She finally came over to Gaunt's table as he finished a plate of *Cozido* . . . a mixture of boiled beef, ham and smoked sausage with various unidentifiable vegetables stirred in. She wore the inevitable low-cut blouse and short skirt, her blonde wig clashed with natural black eyebrows, and her smile was as old an introduction as time itself.

Gaunt's answer was a fractional headshake. Shrugging, unperturbed, she wandered back to her perch at the bar and resumed her scrutiny of the tables.

Finishing his meal, he paid the bill then squeezed his way through to a telephone booth near the doors. Inside, it smelled of garlic and cheap cigars as he dialled the British Embassy number.

The Duty Officer he'd spoken to that morning wasn't available, but the voice who answered reacted to his name.

"Gaunt? I've a message for you," came the cheerful greeting. "I've to say we're still trying and you should contact us in the morning. Oh—and I've to say thanks for something or other—he said you'd understand."

Gaunt hung up, hoping that didn't mean what he thought it might. But impetuous Duty Officers sometimes had to learn the hard way. Finding more change, he lifted the receiver again.

This time, his call was to the police station at Claras. Sergeant Costa's normally lazy voice briskened when he heard who was calling.

"Where are you?" demanded Costa.

"Lisbon—but I'm heading for Estoril." Gaunt lit a cigarette one-handed as a defence against the booth's atmosphere. "You got my note?"

"*Sim* . . . this afternoon, when I got back to Claras." Costa's voice dropped a conspiratorial tone or two. "You guessed right about the watch-glass. Pereira's wrist-watch is being repaired at a jeweller's shop here—he said it had been damaged at work."

"Anything more on him?" asked Gaunt grimly.

"Not yet—nothing on record at Headquarters, at any rate." Costa paused, then chuckled. "I told them he might be involved in those burglaries we have had lately. Has—ah—Lisbon been interesting?"

"I'll tell you when I get back," answered Gaunt. "But don't wait up for me."

"I won't." Costa sighed over the line. "Can one ask why you are going to Estoril, my friend?"

"One can ask," admitted Gaunt solemnly. "But one needn't expect an answer."

He hung up, grinning, and went out to the car.

Even allowing for inevitable professional cool towards a persistently lucky amateur, the new view he'd been offered of

Francis Preston shattered some previous notions and if anything left the whole tangled puzzle more complex than before. Preston had come to Portugal believing he had a chance of achieving new, almost guaranteed success at minimum cost. Except it hadn't happened—and either he'd kept his feelings tightly bottled to protect a painfully built reputation or those people who had experienced his wrath were maintaining a very deliberate silence.

He considered the second prospect for a moment, a frown crossing his freckled face. Once or twice Arthur Sollas had shown a trace of embarrassment. How much had he known in advance—how much did he knew of it all even now? In the beginning it had been Georges Salvador, who had spun some kind of a story to Preston—but how did the chain go from there?

And after Preston had visited the Jeronimos Monastery that night, after he'd been told the full truth about the long-held knowledge of the villa's existence?

The easy guess was that he'd driven back to Claras in a black anger. But Francis Preston was a more complicated individual than most. Perhaps he'd still refused to accept what he'd been told because he'd already convinced himself otherwise.

Stubborn pride could have taken him to the Castelo de Rosa that night, to look again, to think, to try to force some new inspiration which might yet bring success—

A loud horn-blast and a flashing of headlamps from the rear jerked Gaunt's attention back to his driving. Easing nearer the kerb, he grinned as a small open M.G. sports car snarled past, the lone driver waving a hand in thanks. Another few moments and the M.G. was far ahead, a pair of red tail lights which disappeared round a corner.

He'd lost the thread. If there was a thread to lose—giving up, Gaunt switched off the radio, fed the Lancia more accelerator, and drew pleasure from the way the engine note quickened.

Two kilometres on, he saw the M.G. again, stopped at a filling station. A few minutes more and the lights of Estoril were ahead. He turned off the main road at the Casino, purred the Lancia up towards the car park area at the rear, and reversed into a gap in one of the rows of vehicles.

Switching off engine and lights, Gaunt climbed out. The car park was a pool of dark shadows but he could hear music and laughter coming from the Casino's windows. Locking the car, he started walking towards the main entrance.

Halfway there, he slowed a little with a growing feeling he wasn't alone, an odd uneasiness which seemed concentrated between his shoulderblades.

"*Senhor* Gaunt?"

The voice was soft and came from one of the darker patches of shadow beside a large Mercedes. He peered, saw a figure waiting in the shadow, and stopped.

"*Senhor*—" the figure took a slow step forward, still half-hidden.

At the same time, a faint rustle of movement reached Gaunt's ears, from behind. He spun instinctively—and a blow from a short, heavy rubber truncheon, aimed at his head, brushed his shoulder instead. The man who'd crept up on him snarled, cursed, and raised his arm for a second blow.

Retreating, Gaunt stopped with his back against the radiator of another car and a new threat materialising, a third man who had appeared on his other side and was coming in at a rush with a knife.

Hands pressing for support against the cold metal behind him, Gaunt swung his right leg in a fast, vicious upward arc. He felt the jar as his heel took the knife man low in the stomach, heard breath explode from the figure's pain-twisted mouth, and saw him stagger back, folding and almost falling.

Tight-lipped, Gaunt retreated again. But the man with the cosh was still on his left and the original figure who had hailed him was closing in from the right. They came unhur-

riedly, accepting they'd lost the initial surprise but professionals who had done it all before—professionals who knew as
many attack variations as a football forward line and needed
fewer signals.

He could shout for help. But even if he was heard above the
music and noise of the Casino any kind of help from there
would come too late. He had seconds left, seconds while these
two tormented him by waiting for their comrade with the
knife to draw breath and join the finale.

Yet Gaunt felt very calm. Calm enough to register that all
three men wore black sweaters and slacks with soft plimsols
and to notice that the man who had hailed him, his face a
wolfish blur in the dim light, also had one of those stubby
little truncheons.

Suddenly, it was like being back on one of those army
night combat courses where a paratroop sergeant had first
taught him to hate—hate sergeants, at any rate. You let the
trained, conditioned part of your mind take over while the
rest remained detached because it was really happening to
someone else.

"Do unto others before they do it to you . . ." the old
chorus from a bawdy barrack-room song swept into his
thoughts. And simultaneously Gaunt catapulted out at the
weakest link, which was still the man with the knife.

Taken off guard, the man sliced a wild, upward arc with
the blade. Left elbow slamming knife arm wide, Gaunt
slid under its threat. His right hand grabbed that black sweater
near the throat, his whole body impetus went behind a slamming head-butt which took his opponent full-face.

It brought a bubbling scream, half-smothered behind
smashed lips and crushed nasal cartilege.

Side-stepping clear, Gaunt still wasn't quick enough to avoid
the others. A truncheon took him near the collar-bone with
close to paralysing force, he swayed as much as dodged the
other truncheon, and missed as he tried a retaliatory judo
hand-stab at the nearest throat.

For a moment, footwork got Gaunt clear. But he collided with the side of a car, stumbled, recovered, warded off another blow—then the two remaining men forced him back against the vehicle. Pinned there, he braced himself as one of the truncheons swept up again.

But it stopped, still poised over his head, the whole scene bathed in a sudden, blinding glare of lights. Tyres screamed and an engine bellowed while the same lights rushed towards them.

It was the little M.G. It stopped by the simple process of slamming into the car where Gaunt was held, the driver coming out as if propelled by an ejector seat, an old-fashioned starting handle swinging in one hand.

Abandoning him, Gaunt's attackers faced this new arrival with a momentary uncertainty. Then the nearest snarled, sprang forward—and howled in agony as the starting handle blurred round to smash against his forearm with bone-breaking force.

Fear in his eyes, the truncheon falling from his limp, useless hand, the thug quickly backed away. Snuffling with pain, the injured knife man was already staggering off into the night.

But Gaunt froze where he was, and suddenly the M.G. driver did the same. The third man was also beginning to edge back, but he was going slowly, and the automatic pistol which had appeared in his right fist stayed pointed in a threat that didn't need words.

The figures continued to fade back. A few more yards, then even the gun owner abandoned any pretence and began running. Another moment and the night had swallowed him up.

The only sound in the car park was the M.G. driver's sigh of disappointment as he lowered the starting handle.

"Thanks," said Gaunt shakily, moistening his lips. "That was getting nasty. *Muito obrigado . . .*"

"Leave it at thanks, friend." His rescuer, chunky and fair-haired, spoke with an unmistakeably American accent and grinned. "Hell, it takes me all my time to ask for the men's room in Portuguese. You're British?"

"Yes." Gaunt tried to rub life back into his shoulder, still numbed from the truncheon blow. "Well, they say the U.S. cavalry always arrive on cue."

"Make it Navy," corrected the other man, tossing the starting handle into the back of the M.G. "The name's Tom Harris." He paused and inspected Gaunt carefully. "Are you all right?"

"There's nothing a drink wouldn't cure. And I owe you one while I'm at it." Gaunt held out his hand. "I'm Jonathan Gaunt. Navy or Army, your timing was good."

"It's a gift," said Harris modestly. He wore a sports jacket with a plaid shirt and string tie and had a bear-crushing grip. Turning, he considered the front of his car. "A couple of fresh dents, but they'll hammer out again. Well, do we whistle up the *policia* or—ah—was it private?"

"Just a plain, old-fashioned mugging," said Gaunt with more conviction than he felt. "But they'll be far away by now —and I don't think they'll be back. Suppose we tidy up here then find that drink?"

"A reasonable attitude." Harris nodded solemn agreement.

He climbed into the M.G., fired the engine, and sent it in a screaming reverse which ended with the little car tucked away in a space at the far end of the row.

The front of the other car was going to need a new grille. Gaunt peeled off some *escudo* notes, tucked them under one of the wiper blades, then saw the abandoned truncheon lying on the ground. He picked it up, felt the weight of lead inside the black rubber, and tucked it carefully in a trouser pocket as Harris walked back.

He'd called what had happened a plain, old-fashioned mugging. But these men had known his name, which meant they must have been watching for the Lancia coming to the Casino. And any sensible professional would have stuck that gun in his ribs as an introduction, not kept it as a last-gasp deterrent.

Unless somebody, somewhere both knew a lot about his movements—and considered him enough of an annoyance to be put out of action though not important enough to be killed.

Dead civil servants could be an embarrassment. It was a useful consolation.

CHAPTER SIX

Gaunt's first whisky went down with only a suspicion of contact with his throat. He ordered another and a refill of bourbon for Tom Harris, then hooked his legs more comfortably round the chrome-framed stool in the Casino's lobby bar.

"Better now?" queried Harris mildly.

"A lot better." Gaunt found his cigarettes, lit one, and offered the pack to Harris as an afterthought.

"Never use them, thanks." Harris signalled the bartender. "Any peanuts left?"

"*Sim,* Lieutenant." The bartender nodded cheerfully and slid a bowl along the counter. "Extra salted, the way you like."

"They seem to know you," said Gaunt, watching Harris munch a handful. "Does that make you a regular customer, Lieutenant?"

"In a moderate way." Harris grinned good-humouredly. "Once-a-week Mad-Money Harris, that's me. A few of us from Disneyland make a weekly date to pool a few dollars against the tables. The old law of averages says we've got to win sometimes."

"Disneyland?" Gaunt was as puzzled as he looked. "Like to translate that one?"

"Office of the C-in-C NATO, Eastern Atlantic." Harris raised his glass in a mock toast then took a swallow. "Ask any cab driver—we're located just this side of Lisbon, beside the main road. Flagpoles and concrete shoe-box architecture gone mad, but that's where it all happens."

Gaunt raised an eyebrow. "I thought Cape Roca—" he began.

"Cape Roca is Super Disneyland," said Harris succinctly. "That's where the electronic hardware is located. Read all about it in any tourist handbook." He grinned at Gaunt. "Sir, are you by any chance an agent of some unfriendly power?"

"Yes, but I'm off duty," confided Gaunt solemnly.

"Good. I'd hate like hell to have to tell Security." Harris chuckled to himself. "They're busy anyway. Somebody lost the Admiral's laundry last weekend and that's got top priority." He helped himself to another handful of peanuts, chewed, and then admitted, "Still, it isn't so bad. Mostly full speed ahead and damn the martinis, and I've had my share of the other kind. Uh—you were driving that Lancia I passed on the road, weren't you?"

Gaunt nodded.

"Nice car, very nice. So if I hadn't stopped at that filling station—" Harris stopped and became suddenly serious. "You're sure it was a mugging?"

"What else?" queried Gaunt calmly.

"Then these Portuguese have an odd way of doing things. We've some characters back home who would give them lessons." Frowning a little, Harris rubbed his chin. Then he glanced at his watch and gave a whistle of surprise. "Hey, I'm going to be late!"

"Mad money time?"

"Uh-huh." Harris finished his drink at a gulp. "Blackjack tonight, and I've got the kitty in my hip pocket. The boys will cut my throat if I don't show up." He realised what he'd said and grinned as he slipped down from the stool. "Figure of speech. Anyway, nice meeting you, and watch your back next time, friend."

He was on his way out of the bar before Gaunt could reply.

With another hour to kill before Inez's midnight floor-show appearance, Gaunt took his time about finishing his drink. Then he decided against another and went exploring.

The main lobby of Estoril's Casino looked more like a brightly lit shopping arcade than a through route to serious gambling. A broad sweep of polished marble floor was punctuated by ornamental fountains, leather couches and strategically placed greenery, the whole area edged by expensive little boutiques offering everything from Paris perfume to airline tickets.

He turned. Immaculate in black tie and dinner jacket, chines. Several close-packed rows of them were located in a partitioned area outside the main gambling salon, a tactful separation of pin-money addicts from the real action, and the custom seemed a mixture of goggle-eyed package tourists and local layabouts. Most of the one-armed bandits were being worked as fast as they could be fed and he watched cynically for a few minutes, seeing the tourists plug on determinedly while the locals stuck to the wiser policy of settling for a small win, priming the machine one turn on, then cashing in.

The main salon was very different. He had to show his passport to enter a vast, almost reverently hushed cathedral of a room lit by candelabra, the rows of tables quietly busy and offering everything from roulette and boule to punto banco and blackjack. Most of the clientele were in evening dress, women glittering with jewellery and their hair stiffly lacquered, their escorts grimly devoid of expression.

Tom Harris was over a blackjack table, surrounded by a group of similarly muscular, purposeful gamblers. Looking up, he saw Gaunt and waved a greeting then returned to the fray.

Five hundred *escudoes* bought Gaunt a handful of chips and he eased along to the nearest roulette table, content to stick with the old, safe-stake play of pair and rouge, six-block and singleton.

A blonde in peach silk with an unbelievable bust was the only player to avoid the croupier's rake on the first couple of spins of the wheel. It was a clean sweep third time, and he felt lucky to win a few chips back on the six-block the next time round.

"I warned you," murmured a sardonic voice close to his ear. "Sometimes a man can spread his luck too thinly."

He turned. Immaculate in black tie and dinner jacket, Georges Salvador stood behind him, a thin smile of greeting on his lips. But it stopped there and the man's eyes examined Gaunt with a cold, almost clinical curiosity.

"The way I'm playing is meant to be a scientific approach," said Gaunt wryly. He glanced at the table and grimaced. "Something's gone wrong with the recipe, that's all. What's your method?"

"One that needs money." Deliberately, Salvador used a one thousand *escudo* plaque to scratch along his small moustache. "Given money, luck is self-generating."

"Old Portuguese proverb?" queried Gaunt.

"Experience, *Senhor* Gaunt." Salvador repeated the thin smile while the wheel began spinning again. "How has the rest of your day gone?"

"Patchy is the best word—patchy, but interesting." Gaunt paused and deliberately lit a cigarette before he went on. "For instance, I looked in at the Jeronimos Monastery. They've got quite a museum there."

A strange flicker crossed Salvador's face, but he nodded. "You like museums, *Senhor* Gaunt?"

"I liked this one," parried Gaunt neutrally. "I learned a few things—and not just about the exhibits. You're a"—he grinned a little—"well, let's say a modest man, *Senhor* Salvador. When do you plan to start building that tourist hotel at Claras?"

Salvador's expression stayed frozen for a moment then he shrugged and gave a noise which might have been a laugh. "Soon. It depends on some financial details."

"With Arthur Sollas among the shareholders?"

"Doctor Sollas?" Salvador's attitude seemed to thaw again in a way that left Gaunt puzzled. "The—ah—arrangement you seem to know about was between myself and Preston. Sollas is happy enough with his Roman villa and later"—he gave another shrug, his voice sinking to a confidential murmur— "well, if he should find out a little of the truth, will it really matter? But I would think it—ah—unfortunate, even cruel to take away the sense of achievement he enjoys at the moment."

"Meaning you're telling me to keep my mouth shut?" asked Gaunt tonelessly.

"Por favor . . ." a wince of distaste crossed the plump sallow face. "I would phrase it more delicately. There are more than business considerations involved. Francis Preston, for instance—a dead man's personal reputation might be at stake."

"How about your own?" asked Gaunt bluntly.

Salvador shrugged and looked past him as a sudden murmur rose from the roulette table. The blonde in peach silk was very deliberately pushing every chip she possessed towards the rouge slot on the table. The wheel spun, the ball bounced round—and it settled on black. As the croupier's rake swept in, the blonde rose tight-lipped and walked away.

"Some people have to gamble for the luxuries in life," said Salvador softly. "Others—" he paused, suddenly hard-eyed. "A wise man might prefer the offer of a business arrangement, free from risk and suitably rewarding. Particularly if the matter involved did not really concern him."

"He might," mused Gaunt, his freckled face staying mild. "But how about if he told you to go to hell?"

Salvador gave a cynical grimace of disbelief. "Then I would give him a second chance and tell him to think again. I might even warn him not to meddle in matters beyond his own little world of form-filling government departments." He stopped and switched to a sudden smile. "A second chance, *Senhor* Gaunt. And my arrangements are always generous. Think about it."

Without waiting for an answer, he went away. As the dinner-jacketed figure vanished among the gambling tables, Gaunt shrugged and considered the few chips left in his hand. He got them down on the roulette table in a last spread just ahead of the croupier spinning the wheel, was conscious of the ball starting its clattering ride, then ignored it, wondering if Arthur Sollas could really have committed himself to the Claras dig on the mere strength of Preston's invitation.

And if he had, how he'd react to the news that he'd been manipulated—

The croupier coughed politely and the rake made a gentle tapping sound on the table. Surprised, Gaunt looked down at the twin stacks of chips which had been pushed his way. It seemed he'd won.

But only on one spin. Soberly, he collected his winnings, tossed a couple of chips back towards the table-man, and eased away to cash the rest. He had his own personal gamble under way now, without being completely sure of the stakes—except that they seemed to be growing by the moment.

It was a few minutes short of midnight when Gaunt went into the Casino's night-club. It was busy and getting busier by the moment, but when he gave his name a waiter led him to a small table near the back then vanished and returned with a glass of whisky and a carafe of water.

"*Quanto* . . . how much?" asked Gaunt, reaching for his pocket.

The man shook his head. "On the house, *senhor*. I will tell Maria-Inez you are here, okay?"

Gaunt thanked him, tasted the whisky, then settled back and looked around. It was a plush setting with a mainly tourist audience, and the show on stage was tailored to match, a line-up of topless go-go girls backed by a band earning its keep with amplified enthusiasm.

A couple of skinny males in black joined the line-up for a final frenetic routine before the dancers high-kicked off to a scatter of indifferent applause. The band sat back, there was a pause while the lighting dimmed and the whole room gradually changed in mood, then suddenly a single white spot-light pinned on the centre of the stage. A loud, demanding chord came from an unseen guitar and as the conversation in the smoke-filled room stilled a small, confident figure in a long, simply cut dress of black silk appeared in the spotlight's glare.

Inez Torres quietly adjusted the traditional black lace *fadista* shawl around her shoulders, smiling a little, seeming to absorb something of the throbbing rhythm coming from the guitar, but still letting her audience settle. At last, she gave a nod, the guitar's throb sank to background level, and she began.

Fado meant fate, *fadista* songs all spoke of human needs and frailties—and that motionless figure in black sang of love and sadness in a voice of elemental, demanding clarity which held and trapped and stirred.

The words didn't have to be understood; hardly mattered. The room seemed to hold only that timeless voice and the simplicity of the guitar. Before the first song ended a woman at the next table to Gaunt had tears running down her cheeks. When the song did finish there was a silence for a moment which was as much of a tribute as the storm of applause that followed.

The guitar began again, Inez shifted her stance just a lit-tle . . .

In all, she sang four *fado* songs, each stripping its way down through her audience's emotions. Then, suddenly, it was over. The lights came back on, the magic ended, a dazed roomful of people finished their applause, and as the figure in black left a knock-about juggling act took over.

It was largely ignored. The Casino audience had experi-enced something from which it took time to recover and ad-just.

When the juggling act ended the go-go girls stormed back on again. Gaunt had ordered another drink when he saw Inez come towards him from a side door he hadn't noticed before. She was wearing a lime-green dress with a scooped neckline,

her black hair was caught up high on her head, and the trans-
formation let her move between the tables without being recognised.

Reaching him, she sat down, took the cigarette he offered,
and cupped one hand round his lighter so that their fingers
touched lightly. Then, after a long draw on the cigarette, she
sat back with a sigh.

"Tired?" he asked.

"Recovering." She grimaced a little. "With *fado,* switching
off afterwards is the problem."

The drink he'd ordered arrived, but she didn't want anything and sat smoking the cigarette, absently watching the
floor show. Suddenly, she brightened.

"I telephoned home before the first performance. Anna
says everything's fine—Luis was sleeping."

"Good." Gaunt nodded vaguely, his thoughts for the moment back on the chances of any more trouble happening at
the car park.

"Jonathan?" She hesitated, puzzled at his mood. "What's
wrong?"

"Nothing that matters." He shook his head reassuringly
but saw no harm in telling her part of it. "Inez, I saw a Doctor
Burnay in Lisbon."

She frowned. "I know him."

"Preston went to him to ask if there was any way he could
help Luis. Preston would have footed the bill."

"I didn't know—but he was like that." Inez smiled a little,
but sadly. "He spent a lot of time with Luis. Sometimes, he'd
bring books or games, like I told you—he was a good man."

Who would still go along with a vaguely crooked proposi-
tion when it suited his own ends. Gaunt looked over at the
twisting go-go girls for a moment and grinned at the thought.

"They're from England," said Inez maliciously and chuckled, drawing her own conclusions. "You'd be disappointed.
They're all tweeds and pearls backstage."

He gave her a mock scowl of protest. "Why shatter the illusion? I was enjoying it."

"Then if we stay here I'll tell you the rest," she countered with amusement. "Like how two of them are married with children and—" she laughed and stopped at his expression. "On the other hand, you could take me home. This is where I work, remember?"

"Fine." Gaunt had had enough of the smoke and the amplified noise. He pushed back his chair then stopped. "Anything to collect backstage?"

"A coat, that's all."

He nodded, glad of the excuse. "Then I'll bring the car around front while you get it."

She looked mildly surprised but agreed.

Outside, there was still the same darkly clouded night with occasional, filtered moonlight. But the car park was empty of life and Gaunt relaxed his grip on the rubber truncheon in his pocket then climbed aboard the Lancia.

Inez was waiting at the Casino main door, a light coat draped over her shoulders. Once she was in the passenger seat, he set the car moving and turned north on the coast road, keeping a careful eye on the rear-view mirror.

They weren't followed. Satisfied as much as relieved, Gaunt settled back and glanced briefly at the girl by his side. Her face was a finely sculpted silhouette in the dim light from the facia instruments and that light, tantalising perfume she used teased at his senses.

Forty-eight hours before he hadn't known she existed. Yet now, she was one person Gaunt felt he knew enough about to trust—and something more, something rooted deeper that scarred instincts told him to avoid admitting. Because when he did, Patti was somehow there in the background. And Patti had another man now, another man whose name and bed she shared as if Gaunt had never existed.

But whether that part was self-pity or something worse, he didn't want to try to work out. It had happened, it was over.

Inez had the radio switched on low to a music station and was lying back on the seat, humming under her breath as the car purred along.

"Do you know what I'd like to do?" she asked suddenly.

"No. But I'll listen." He grinned sideways at her.

"Kick off my shoes and walk on sand." She gave a small, almost apologetic laugh. "That's stupid, isn't it?"

He shook his head and kept his eyes on the road, deliberately.

"I can think of a place," he told her. "I even think I could find the way."

"Por favor . . . let's try." She made a small, contented noise in her throat. Her long, slim legs stretched cat-like in front of her as she shifted in her seat, then her hair brushed his cheek. "Jonathan, who was she—this girl who stays in your mind?" Solemn eyes considered him for a moment. "Don't look so surprised. Any woman knows the signs."

"My wife—ex-wife now." Gaunt answered more curtly than he meant. Talking about it hurt too. "She—well, things didn't work out."

"That's what I thought." Inez smiled to herself then added quietly, "I'm someone else, Jonathan. All I ask is you remember that."

She came closer against him while the car purred on, headlights forming a bright corridor through the night.

At the little bay near Cape Roca he stopped the Lancia near the fringe of the beach. As the engine died, they were left with the steady crash of waves on the shore and the piping calls of sea-birds feeding just above the surf-line. In the distance, the clustered lights on the Cape and what they stood for had a twinkling unreality as if another world away.

They left the car and walked a little way, hand in hand, not talking, the sea and the busy, piping cries a constant, soothing background. At last they stopped and Gaunt very gently brought her nearer till the warmth of her body was against his own.

When he kissed her, she seemed to shiver a little then it passed and her lips were searching too, her whole body meeting and answering his hunger.

It seemed a long time afterwards when they returned to the car. They shared a cigarette there, Inez's head on his shoulder. Finally, Gaunt eased round, flicked the glowing stub that remained out into the night, then faced her again and kissed her.

"Inez—"

"No." She shook her head and put a serious finger against his lips. "Don't say anything, Jonathan. Not now—please." She waited till he nodded, then smiled. "Now take me home before Anna gets worried and starts thinking about telephoning Manuel Costa."

"And Sergeant Costa wouldn't be amused?" Gaunt sighed, started the engine, and let it idle for a second. Then, reluctantly, he slipped the Lancia into gear and set it jolting over the rough track, away from the shore and back to the road.

They reached Claras at two A.M., passed through its sleeping square while a clock tower chimed, and soon were driving up the narrow lane which led to Inez's bungalow.

But as the Lancia reached the end of the lane and the house showed ahead, Gaunt found the kind of surprise waiting he could have done without. The bungalow was a blaze of light, three police cars were lying outside it, and armed, uniformed men seemed everywhere around.

He heard a gasp from Inez, then she gripped his arm. Gaunt slowed the car to a crawl and brought it to a halt beside the other vehicles. Two policemen with leather jackets and shoulder-slung machine-pistols met them as they climbed out, but another figure darted from the bungalow and shoved forward. Sergeant Manuel Costa's habitually lazy attitude had vanished, and his thin, sallow face was hard and grim.

"Inez." His greeting was a curt nod which ignored Gaunt. "I have been trying to contact you."

"Why?" Apprehension in her voice, she looked past him towards the house. "Has—has something happened to Luis?"

"We want him." Costa thumbed back towards the house. "Your housekeeper said he was in his room. But he isn't there now."

She moistened her lips. "Manuel—"

"For tonight I am Sergeant Costa," corrected the detective with a moment's gentleness. *"Desculpe-me* . . . truly, I'm sorry. But this is no social call."

"What's happened then?" asked Gaunt, taking a casual step forward. He stopped short and blinked as one of the policemen prodded a machine-pistol muzzle firmly into his stomach. "And tell him to be careful with that damned thing—it might go off!"

Costa knocked the gun away with a scowl and followed it up with a snarled order which sent the uniformed men fading back.

"Well?" asked Gaunt patiently.

For a moment Costa didn't answer, his hands rammed deep into the pockets of the light raincoat he was wearing, his face a stony, unhappy mask swept by the glow from the police cars' whirring turret lamps. Then he shrugged.

"An hour ago, one of our patrol cars found an abandoned vehicle. Or they thought it was abandoned, till they looked inside—there were two people dead inside."

"Who, Manuel?" It came from Inez like a whisper of fear.

"Senhor Preston's nephew and his wife." Costa met Gaunt's fractionally lifted eyebrow and nodded. "Murdered—stabbed and viciously beaten to death. Almost certainly both died away from the car. But they were dragged back to it afterwards, then an attempt was made to set it on fire."

"And you think that Luis . . ." Inez stared at him as if

hypnotised then flared defensively. "You are supposed to be his friend! Or would you rather forget that?"

Costa winced and shook his head. "The car was on a side road only a few kilometres from here." He brought a hand from one pocket, the fingers holding something already tagged inside a small plastic bag. "We found this beside it, Inez."

It was a battered, ordinary, gun-metal cigarette lighter. But one glance brought a sound like a moan from the girl at Gaunt's side.

"You recognise it?" asked Costa quietly.

She nodded, unable to speak.

"So did I." Bitterly, Costa brought out his other hand to show Gaunt a twin of the lighter. "Luis and I bought these together, years ago, in the same *tabaco* store. We spent an extra three *escudoes* we could ill afford to have our initials engraved on them." He held the lighters closer, the worn lettering still plain. "See for yourself—'M.C.' for Manuel Costa, 'L.T.' for Luis Torres." He shrugged. "Luis does not smoke now. But I have seen him still carrying this lighter. You agree, Inez?"

"He does," she confirmed in a low, weary voice. "He—he keeps it like a toy."

"Perhaps now you understand, *Senhor* Gaunt?" asked Costa tonelessly.

"You've got his lighter," said Gaunt stubbornly. "But you're still talking about a man who'd be more likely to run and hide if he saw a stranger. What the hell would he want to kill anyone for?"

"Can I answer that before we find him?" Costa shook his head helplessly. "I would like that to be soon. For the moment, I am still in charge here. But Headquarters are sending men, and when that happens—" he left it unfinished.

"All I know is that Anna said he was in the house when I telephoned, Manuel," said Inez. She looked around at the night and bit her lip. "Perhaps he heard your cars, perhaps he was frightened—"

Costa nodded. "The woman says his clothes are still here. But the bedroom window was open—if he slipped away, that part is my fault." He shoved the lighters back in his pockets and sucked his teeth, frowning. "I have men searching—and they've been told not to harm him if it can be avoided. I think"—he hesitated then seemed to make up his mind—"yes, I have to go back to where it happened. It is not pleasant, Inez. But if you and *Senhor* Gaunt wish to come—"

"Por favor . . . if it might help." She glanced at Gaunt and looked relieved when he nodded. But that left another problem. "Anna—"

"Is still in the house," confirmed Costa. "I will leave some men here, men who know Luis—he might come back." He glanced quickly at his wrist-watch and grimaced. "If we go now, we will be there before the Headquarters people arrive. And Doctor Sollas will be waiting."

"Sollas?" Gaunt showed his surprise.

"Someone had to identify them," said Costa grimly. "Believe me, it was not too easy."

They went by police car. It was a short ride, which ended on a quiet side road on another of the hill slopes which looked down towards Claras. An old Ford station wagon was there with its nearside wheels on the grass verge and the driver's door hanging open. Other vehicles were parked nearby, headlights blazing and with several men standing beside them.

Leaving the police car, Sergeant Costa led the way. He nodded to a uniformed sergeant with a machine-pistol who came to meet them then stopped a few paces away from the Ford and glanced at Inez, then at the uniformed man.

"The lady will stay here, I think," he said quietly. *"Senhor* Gaunt—"

They left Inez with the other sergeant and went on. As they reached the Ford's open door, Gaunt tightened his lips.

A blanket had been draped over the front seats, but a woman's feet protruded from one edge, shoeless.

Silently, Costa lifted one edge of the blanket. John Marsh and his wife lay across each other inside the station wagon, dumped there in macabre fashion.

"We have to wait for the forensic experts from Lisbon," said Costa in sober apology. "But—well, see for yourself."

He brought a torch from his pocket and clicked on the beam. For a moment Gaunt felt his stomach heave, then he fought the feeling down and moved closer.

Preston's nephew had been stabbed at least once in the chest. But the bloodied shirt-front was nothing compared with the way his head had been smashed in, shattered like some discarded eggshell.

He glanced at Costa, nodded, and the torch-beam shifted.

Sarah Marsh lay face down, half on top of her husband. There was more blood, and a deep slash wound across one arm showed how she'd fought for life. Again it hadn't stopped there—that long, blond hair was almost unrecognisably matted with blood from blows which had smashed through her skull to expose the white of brain tissue.

Mercifully, Costa switched off the torch and lowered the blanket.

"Well?" asked Costa softly. "What kind of man would do such a thing?"

Gaunt could only shake his head.

Looking round, Costa beckoned at one of the shadowy figures and snapped an order. The man he'd summoned brought over a canvas-covered bundle and unwrapped a thick wooden stake. Stains of blood and strands of hair still adhered to one end.

"And the cigarette lighter?" asked Gaunt.

"On the ground, beside the *gasolina* filler pipe—the cap was removed." Costa kicked a loose pebble along the ground, clipping his words to hide his own feelings. "If we assume it was Luis and that he had a knife, then perhaps we can also assume that these people had become lost, saw him, and merely stopped to ask the way."

"So he killed them?"

"I have to shape a picture—but does that mean I like it?" Costa's bitterness came through, then he firmed his lips again. "There are signs Marsh was killed beside the car. There are other signs that his wife tried to run. After—after the killer caught her, he used the stake to make sure then dragged them back here and tried to set the car on fire." He shrugged. "Maybe what is left of his mind decided a fire would burn it all away—except that the cigarette lighter wouldn't work. It was bone dry."

They went back to Inez. Two more figures had joined her at the roadside, a grim-faced Arthur Sollas who looked bulkier than ever in a loose anorak jacket and Bernard Ryan, whose prematurely white hair framed his head like a halo in the weak moonlight. Greetings amounted to nods.

Costa took time off to light a cigarette, looked grimly at his lighter for a moment, then tucked it away and faced them.

"You know how these people were found," he said quietly. "We have been operating extra patrols on roads like this because of petty crime in the area. But I will go over again what little else we know. Doctor Sollas, you were at your villa?"

"Correct," rumbled Sollas, nodding. "With Martin Lawson—we were tidying some paperwork. I left him back there."

"He's probably having kittens by now," murmured Ryan. "Locking the doors and barring the windows"—he stopped, glanced at Inez, shrugged apologetically and finished weakly —"well, you know what I mean."

Costa eyed him frostily. "And where were you, *Senhor* Ryan?"

"In Lisbon, like I told you," answered the photographer wearily. "Pereira drove me in this afternoon, to collect some equipment. Then—well, as a foreman he's maybe more muscle than brain, but he knows a few places." He grinned self-consciously. "We drank around for a spell, then headed back to the Castelo. The watchman was still helping us unload at the site when your *policia* arrived."

"And the watchman says he saw nothing and heard nothing unusual tonight." Costa gave a heavy sigh. "Which leaves the station wagon. Doctor Sollas?"

"If I've got to repeat everything," growled Sollas with a momentary ill temper. "Marsh and his wife were prowling around the villa, doing nothing but complain." He shot a glance at Gaunt. "You know what they were like—so when they said they wanted to drive into Claras I said they could take the Ford. Where they went after they left—" he shrugged.

"They did go to Claras," said Costa, his sallow face impassive. "They were seen around the cafes. But afterwards—?"

"They took a wrong turning," suggested Ryan laconically. He shivered a little in the cold night air. "Hell, this place is in the middle of nowhere, and that pair were the kind who could get lost crossing a road."

Costa didn't find it amusing. But before he could answer a shout from one of the police guards drew his attention to headlights coming fast along the road towards them.

"Headquarters." He pursed his lips. "*Senhor* Gaunt, it would be better if you took Inez home now." Turning to her he added softly, "Believe me, if anything happens you will be first to hear."

The same police car took them back to the bungalow. Once there, the uniformed driver came round to help Inez out, gave a formal salute, then climbed aboard the car and drove away. But another car was still parked on the driveway, its lights out, and as Gaunt went with Inez towards the house an armed policeman watched impassively from the black shadow of a clump of shrubbery.

Maintaining an outward calm, she found her key and opened the front door. But once they were inside and the door had closed again she turned to face Gaunt and tried to speak with lips that, for the moment, could only tremble.

He put a comforting arm round her shouders and she came in close, hiding her face against his chest. When she did look up, the trembling had stopped but she still wasn't far removed from tears.

"Luis couldn't have killed them," she said with a tired but determined conviction. "I don't care how it looks to Manuel Costa—he couldn't. And Anna said"—she stopped, her eyes widening—"Anna! I'd forgotten about Anna!"

She left Gaunt in the hallway and hurried towards the kitchen. A moment later he heard her voice then the other woman's lower, hesitant reply. The conversation in the kitchen went on for several minutes before Inez left the housekeeper and returned alone.

"Could she help?" asked Gaunt quietly.

"No." Inez shook her head slowly and wearily. "All she knows is the police had her check through the kitchen, to see if there was any kind of knife missing."

"And was there?"

"No." Her lips tightened. "So they said he must have got it somewhere else."

"What about earlier, before he went to bed?"

"He was just—just as usual. Anna says he watched some television and looked at some picture books Francis Preston gave him." She moistened her lips, keeping a veneer of control over her voice. "Anna even thought he looked happier than she'd seen him for weeks—"

"They'll find him," said Gaunt, lost for anything else to say. "Manuel Costa won't let him come to harm."

"And afterwards?" She looked at him steadily for a moment. "You're like Manuel. You think Luis killed them."

Gaunt shook his head. "I haven't said that, Inez. But I know Costa's doing his job the best way he can."

"And you've tried to help." She sighed and nodded. "But it's late—there's nothing more you can do for now."

"I'll stay if you like," he suggested quietly.

"*Obrigado* . . . but no, Jonathan." Her mouth shaped a small smile of thanks. "I'll be better alone."

He nodded his understanding, took her hands, and kissed her gently on the lips. Then he turned and went out.

The old Fiat was still where he'd left it that afternoon. Climbing aboard, he took a last glance back at the house then started the car and set it moving.

It was after three A.M. when he got back to Claras and the Hotel Da Gama was in darkness, the front door firmly locked. Gaunt rang the night bell, heard it peal somewhere inside, and eventually the door was opened by the desk clerk, who wore an old coat over his pyjamas and was yawning.

He thanked the man, left him muttering and locking the door again, and caught himself yawning in turn as he climbed the stairs to his room. Going in, he switched on the light, tensed for an instant as he realised someone was already there —then relaxed with a grunt of irritation as he saw it was Jaime.

"What the hell do you want this time?" demanded Gaunt brusquely.

"*Tenho* . . . I am looking for help, *Senhor* Gaunt." The young, dark-haired hotel porter sat up in the chair where he'd been dozing, rubbed his eyes and grinned uneasily.

"Not from me," said Gaunt shortly, and thumbed towards the door. "Out—it can keep till morning."

"*Por favor* . . . please, *Senhor* Gaunt." Jaime got to his feet, a worried earnestness in his voice. "This is too important, believe me."

"Believing you is something I'd worry about." Gaunt peeled off his jacket, dropped it on the bed, then sighed. "All right—keep it short."

Jaime licked his lips. "The police are looking for Luis Torres—I know where he is."

Gaunt froze, staring at him.

"A friend and I have him hidden," declared Jaime quickly. "But it can only be for tonight—we need help to get him somewhere safer."

Gaunt rubbed a slow, confused hand across his forehead. "Jaime, do you know why they're searching for him?"

"*Sim.* They say he killed two people." Jaime combined a crude noise and gesture to make his own opinion clear. "They're the crazy ones."

"Start at the beginning," suggested Gaunt, cloaking a grin. "When did you find him—and where?"

"Maybe an hour ago. My friend Rodrigues and I—uh"— Jaime hesitated, eyeing him cautiously—"we went for a walk."

"At two A.M.?" Gaunt raised an incredulous eyebrow.

"We planned to catch rabbits." The youngster's innocent dark eyes met his own. "There is good money in rabbits, *senhor.*"

"And even better money other ways."

"*Senhor?*" Jaime blinked.

Gaunt stuck a cigarette in his mouth, lit it, and sat down on the bed. "Sergeant Costa's been chasing his tail trying to catch a couple of small-time burglars who operate late at night. But I suppose you wouldn't know anything about that?"

"Of course not, *senhor.*" Jaime shook his head and quickly switched the subject. "But, like I said, we were walking outside the village when we heard something moving behind a hedge an' we thought it was maybe a rabbit. Instead, it was Luis Torres—and we had brought him back here before we heard what had happened."

"Here? You mean—"

Jaime nodded. "He's in this hotel, *senhor.*"

Gaunt swallowed. "He didn't give any trouble?"

"Trouble?" Jaime gave him an almost pitying look. "He was frightened, maybe. But he knows us—and he was tired and cold, wearing only pyjamas." He paused hopefully. "You will help us, *Senhor* Gaunt?"

Gaunt shook his head.

"But"—Jaime's mouth fell open—"but you are a friend of his sister . . ."

"I'm still not crazy enough to risk spending the next few years living on fish stew in a Portuguese jail," said Gaunt grimly. "Not without a damned good reason, anyway. If you want to do Luis Torres a favour, you'll turn him over to Sergeant Costa. Nothing else makes sense—for Torres or anyone."

"I thought—"

"You thought wrong. He needs care—special care," said Gaunt wearily. "Could you give him it, do you know anyone else who will?"

Silenced, Jaime looked down at the floor.

"So I'll see him, then I'll contact Sergeant Costa," Gaunt told him, getting up from the bed. "We'll think of some kind of story that keeps you out of it."

They went out of the room, down one flight of stairs, and stopped at a bedroom door. Jaime knocked lightly and waited, knocked again then, frowning, tried the handle. The door opened a fraction and he looked into the darkened room then hesitated, looking at Gaunt uneasily.

Pushing him aside, Gaunt opened the door wide and found the light switch. The overhead bulb which flared to life showed a figure lying sprawled on the floor. He heard a gasp of alarm from Jaime but ignored him, going over to kneel beside a youth about the same age. His eyes were closed and there was a trickle of drying blood on his forehead. But he was breathing, and whoever had done it had stopped long enough to take a pillow from the bed and put it under his head.

"He's all right," Gaunt assured Jaime, who was still standing nervously in the doorway. "Knocked out, that's all. Get some water."

While Jaime obeyed, filling a jug from the room washbasin, Gaunt glanced around and saw an old-fashioned chamber pot lying on its side on the carpet. His lips twisted a grin. A blow from that kind of heavy pottery could have been lethal—if the user had tried hard enough.

"*Senhor*—" Jaime brought over the jug.

Taking it, Gaunt carefully poured a stream of water on the other youth's face. It brought a groan then a splutter and he stopped as Rodrigues propped himself up on his elbows, squinting painfully in the light.

"Was it Luis who hit you?" asked Gaunt.

A nod and grimace was answer enough.

"But why?" asked Jaime, bewildered. "Why wouldn't he stay?"

"Ever tried to hold a wild bird in your hand?" asked Gaunt softly. "All it has is instinct—and that's Luis."

They stared at him, trying to understand.

He called the *policia* station from a telephone in the hotel lobby and left a message for Costa that Luis Torres had been seen in Claras. Then he called Inez and told her the same, plus a little more.

There were enough men out searching, men who knew the country around and to whom a stranger would be little more than an additional liability. The best kind of help he could give, he decided, might come later with morning.

Going back to his room, he got out of his clothes and saw the bottle of painkillers waiting. But this once he felt too tired to even need them.

Dropping on the bed, he slept till well after dawn.

CHAPTER SEVEN

Morning came warm and bright, accompanied by the strident siren of a police car as it crossed the cobbled square below Gaunt's bedroom. He heard other sirens as he yawned awake and dressed, and when he looked out still another car was turning into the side-street that led to the *policia* post, watched by several interested groups of bystanders.

There was no sign of Jaime when he went down to the dining room, and an attempt at conversation with the plump, dull-faced Portuguese girl who brought him breakfast foundered quickly. Giving up, Gaunt gulped some coffee, left the rest, and went out of the hotel, crossing the sunlit cobbles and past the gushing fountain while curious eyes watched him in silence.

Inside the *policia* post the main office was busy with new faces—police with clipped city accents who seemed equally busy shouting down telephones and at each other. But one of the regular Claras constables came over and greeted him warily.

"*Por favor,* where can I find Sergeant Costa?" asked Gaunt.

"At the Torres place, *Senhor* Gaunt." The man thumbed wryly at the turmoil behind him and lowered his voice. "He told me he would try to stay away till this circus quietens."

Gaunt grimaced his sympathy. "Any trace of Luis Torres yet?"

A slow headshake was answer enough, then the man was called away.

Pensively, Gaunt left the post and returned across the square to where he'd parked the Fiat. He was still thinking about

Luis Torres as he climbed aboard and started the car. A chill night in the open might be a minimal hardship for an ordinary man, but how would it leave a sickly, bewildered, inadequately clad fugitive like Inez's brother.

He caught himself contrasting that picture against another, the battered, bleeding bodies of John and Sarah Marsh left thrown together in their car. In life, they'd been easy to dis-like—but that faded against the savage death which had come their way.

Had it been Torres? The tendril of doubt in his mind had grown considerably with a night's sleep. Because, hazy as it might be, there was a frightening alternative, one that went straight back to the whole chain of doubt and suspicion which surrounded the Castelo de Rosa digging site.

If only that in itself made sense—Gaunt shook his head. Any of the alleged ghosts lurking around the old Moorish watch-tower must be enjoying a grim belly-laugh at it all.

From Claras, he drove straight out to the Torres bungalow. A police car was leaving as he arrived, the driver sitting stiffly behind the wheel and a solitary, high-ranking officer scowl-ing in the back seat. Tyres spattering gravely, it swung off in the direction of the hills in a fast-moving plume of dust.

Shrugging, Gaunt turned in towards the driveway and was promptly flagged down by a constable with a rifle slung over one shoulder. But it was one of Costa's men, and he was waved on towards the house.

Parking outside, Gaunt walked across to the porch steps then saw the door was lying open and heard voices coming from inside. The voices stopped as he rang the doorbell, then, after a moment, Inez appeared in the hallway. She was in a plain blue denim shirt tucked into matching trousers, her face was bare of make-up and she looked as if she'd had little sleep. But she managed a small, tight smile of welcome.

"I hoped you'd come," she said simply.

"You should have known I would." He thumbed past her. "Sergeant Costa?"

"Yes—a police captain from Lisbon is in charge now." Her lips tightened. "He just left. Compared with him, Manuel is a beginner."

She led him through to the front room. Eyes red-rimmed, a stubble of beard darkening his cheeks, Sergeant Costa sat sprawled in an armchair under the *fado* portrait. His greeting amounted to a gloomy wave of a hand. There were mud-stains on his shoes, his clothes were crumpled, and an ashtray beside him was choked with old cigarette ends.

"If I was paid by the kilometre for last night I'd be a rich man, *Senhor* Gaunt," he said wearily, as if reading Gaunt's mind. "Headquarters may have sent us all kinds of damned experts and bosses, but people like me still get left with the donkey-work."

"It's that kind of world—too many chiefs and a shortage of Indians," agreed Gaunt dryly. Inez went over to a sideboard and poured him a cup of coffee from a bubbling percolator. As she brought the cup over, he asked Costa, "You still think it was Luis?"

Costa shrugged awkwardly. "Have I any choice?" For a moment he avoided looking at Inez, frowning to himself. "First, we have to find him. The way he showed up at your hotel last night puzzles me—why would he go there?"

"He was seen, then he vanished again," said Gaunt neutrally, sipping the coffee. "That's all I know."

"Seen by Jaime." Costa treated the point like a bad smell, then sighed. "Inez, now that our so efficient captain from Headquarters has gone, maybe we could try—"

"No, not again, Manuel!" She cut him short angrily, her small fists clenched. "Can't you understand? I've told you every place I can think he might go. I want him found too, for his own sake."

"I know that," soothed Costa. He scrubbed a hopeful thumb along his stubbled chin. "That coffee—uh—smells good."

She glared at him then, still tight-faced, went back to the

sideboard and poured another cup. Costa murmured his thanks as she brought it over, took a gulp, then glanced at Gaunt.

"Every man we have searched the hills most of the night. They started again at dawn, with dogs—and if that doesn't work, some army men may be brought in to help." He scowled at the floor. "The way I feel doesn't matter, *Senhor* Gaunt. He has to be found."

"That part I'll go along with," said Gaunt grimly. "But what about the rest of it?"

"Eh?" Costa didn't understand.

"I can remember when a certain humble sergeant of detectives had other ideas," declared Gaunt icily. "What about Pereira?"

"Now?" Costa gestured his impatience. "He can wait—if he ever mattered."

"Pereira?" Inez looked at them, bewildered. "The foreman at the Castelo site?"

Gaunt nodded.

"Things are different now," muttered Costa uneasily. "Even if Francis Preston's death was murder then—" he left it there.

"Luis?" Inez flared at the unspoken inference. "You can't think that—not after what you told me!"

"About the time of death?" Costa grimaced miserably. "That calculation is always part guesswork. Inez, when it comes to decisions we have to act on what we know—not what some medical examiner thinks might be right." He drew a deep breath, then turned on Gaunt. "And one thing I do know, one thing you might remember, *Senhor* Gaunt. If Marsh and his wife had not been excited by your crazy story of lost treasure and rewards they would have gone back to England yesterday. They would be alive—none of this would have happened."

It was true, though Gaunt hadn't thought of it that way

before. He flushed, a retort ready on his lips. But Inez stepped between them.

"Two grown men—or supposed to be." She eyed them angrily. "Stop it—it doesn't help anyone."

Manuel Costa looked sheepish then slowly shook his head. "*Senhor* Gaunt—"

"Forget it," said Gaunt. "We've all got problems." He remembered one of his own. "Inez, I want to make a telephone call to Lisbon. It won't take long."

She led him through to her bedroom. It was small and neat and pink, with the telephone on a bedside table. Once she'd gone, Gaunt dialled the British Embassy number, waited while it rang out then, when the switchboard answered, asked for the Duty Officer and gave his name. This time he was connected without delay.

"Gaunt?" The Embassy man's voice crackled briskly over the line. "I'll save you time. We've had a report from the Portuguese about Preston's relatives being murdered. Usual expressions of regret to the Ambassador and that sort of thing. Still, they seem to know who killed them, which is the main thing. Have they caught him yet?"

"No, they're still looking." Gaunt answered him woodenly.

"Well, we'll take care of any formalities from this end—not your problem, eh?" The Duty Officer dismissed the matter. "But talking of problems, what the hell did you get involved in last night?"

"Meaning?" Gaunt frowned at the mouthpiece.

"Two separate inquiries asking if we knew anything about you—one from the local NATO security people, the other from a more discreet Portuguese government contact." The voice in his ear gave a mock tut of disapproval. "We said you were clean, of course, and that seemed to satisfy them. But—ah—"

"Some small-time thugs tried to mug me last night, that's all." Gaunt smiled grimly. It sounded as if a certain U. S. Navy lieutenant left nothing to chance.

"Oh." The Duty Officer sounded disappointed. "That's all right then. But—"

Gaunt cut him short. "What about that check I wanted on Lawson and Ryan?"

"Your two digging site friends?" There was a slight pause and he heard a rustle of papers. "Yes, we got a little, some of it interesting. Martin Lawson seems all right, but dull—he came here from Spain about a year ago after lecturing at some Madrid university. But your photographer gentleman, Bernard Ryan, sounds worth watching."

"Why?" Gaunt tensed hopefully.

"He was on the sticky end of some North African gun-running a few years back. Never did get caught, but he knew some unpleasant people—I got that from our own security people. The Portuguese say he's clean."

"Thanks," said Gaunt gratefully. "It could matter."

"I owed you a favour," protested the Duty Officer cheerfully. "Today's *Financial Times,* Gaunt—Consolidated Breweries down two points to 122, Malters another five up at 165. Going well for us both, eh?"

"You bought in?" He asked it in a dull voice, guessing the answer.

"A thousand Malters—I emptied the piggy bank." The Embassy man hesitated with a slight embarrassment. "How high would you let them ride? I mean, when's best to sell?"

"Now."

"Eh? But—"

"You bought the wrong damned company," snarled Gaunt, hung up on a squeak of protest and closed his eyes for a moment.

The Consolidated bid for Malters was real enough. But the real tip, the one that mattered, had been given to him by a douce Edinburgh spinster who had been the long-ago mistress of a Scandinavian beer baron. Their ardour might have died down to mere pen-friend letters, but the Edinburgh spinster lived well.

And while the Consolidated cat was busy trying to swallow the Malters mouse a certain European consortium of brewers were going to grab Consolidated by the tail. When that happened, the Malters price would collapse overnight.

But Consolidated's shares should start flying.

He was only thinking about Bernard Ryan when he went back to Inez and Costa. The tall, prematurely white-haired photographer, so friendly and easy-going, had seemed an unlikely candidate.

Except that Ryan had taken his photograph at the site, that the men who had jumped him at the Casino might have had more than the make of car he was driving to help identify him—and that Ryan was Carlos Pereira's rock-solid alibi for the previous night.

"*Senhor* Gaunt, I must ask a favour." Sergeant Costa was on his feet, still looking sheepish but apparently ready to leave. "*Por favor* . . . I need a lift." Costa grinned his embarrassment. "The Headquarters captain has my car. It would not take long, I promise."

Gaunt glanced at Inez.

"I'm going to wait here," she declared. "That way, if there is news—"

"All right." He nodded his understanding. "I'll come back later, once I've seen a couple of people." A thought struck him. "Inez, you said Preston gave Luis some books. Could you look them out while I'm gone?" He ignored Costa's caustic sniff and added some encouragement. "They might matter."

"I will. It will give me something to do," she said quietly.

It had been cool inside the house, but back in the open the sky was cloudless blue and the temperature was rising. The shrubbery had come alive with buzzing insects and the sun was warm on Gaunt's back as he walked with Costa towards the Fiat.

"Don't you want to know where we're going, *Senhor* Gaunt?" asked Costa with a peeved irritation.

"If you feel like telling." Gaunt stopped and stuck his hands in his pockets. "But suppose we settle one thing first, Sergeant. I didn't come uninvited into this mess—you talked me into it at the beginning."

"True." Gloomily, Costa kicked a stray pebble and scowled. "So I have only myself to blame?"

"Something like that."

"Obrigado . . ." Costa managed a thawing grimace. "Well, first I have to collect the Marshes' car and take it into Claras. The forensic people from Headquarters are finished with it, and as usual the locals are left to tidy up. But afterwards— yes, maybe you are right. Maybe Carlos Pereira deserves more attention. I could begin by talking again to the watchman at the Castelo digging site." Suddenly, a touch of his old, lazy humour slipped through. "Could I impose on you to come along?"

"Sergeant, you're beginning to make sense again." Gaunt grinned and brought out the Fiat's keys. "Sense enough to do the driving, anyway."

They got aboard, and Costa struggled to adjust the driving seat.

"No prize for guessing a long-legged Scottish giraffe has been using this," he complained, finishing the job and putting on his sunglasses.

"And now a short-ass Portuguese peasant has his turn," countered Gaunt easily. It was hot inside the Fiat, and he wound down the passenger window as Costa started the car moving. "Sergeant, if you meant what you said about Pereira, maybe I can help a little."

Costa gave a quick glance of interest, but Gaunt waited till they'd passed the guard at the bottom of the driveway and were travelling on the road. Then he gave a quick summary of most of what he knew, including the Embassy information on Ryan.

When he'd finished, Costa gave a puzzled but appreciative whistle then rubbed a hand along the steering wheel's
rim, leaving a momentary streak of perspiration.

"*Obrigado* again, *Senhor* Gaunt, and this time I mean
it." He frowned at the road ahead, then blew the horn
briefly as they passed a farm cart drawn by an undersized
donkey. "Finding Luis still matters most to me, for obvious
reasons. But if I can produce one firm reason why he could
not have killed these people then—then I will happily spit
in a certain *policia* captain's face!"

Suddenly, he began humming confidently to himself. Glancing at him, Gaunt said nothing but recognised the signs. Sergeant Costa felt he had something worthwhile to do again. But
as the car purred on along the dry, dusty road, scrub and
cactus alternating with almond trees in blossom and an occasional, rocky slope terraced for vines, Gaunt wished he
could share the man's confidence.

To believe that all that had happened had to centre round
the Castelo de Rosa site was one thing. To make sense of it
was another until something emerged to act as a catalyst,
and until then how much could they really do?

It took about ten minutes to reach the farm road where the
Ford station wagon had been found. It hadn't been moved
and a constable with a rifle slung from one shoulder was
still on guard, his pedal cycle propped against a fence.

Costa spoke to him briefly, then led the way over to the
station wagon. Inside, the bloodstains on the seats and car-
pets had been covered in plastic sheeting and a mist of grey
fingerprint powder had been sprayed over everything. Opening the driver's door, Costa snorted his disgust and flicked a
hand at the flies already buzzing around inside.

"Did they find anything?" asked Gaunt.

Costa shook his head. "Nothing that mattered—not even a
decent fingerprint from the steering wheel and the *gasolina*
filler cap was the same." Climbing aboard, he checked the

foot pedals, sighed, and brought the seat forward. "If you follow me back to Claras, then once I am finished, we can go straight to the Castelo site."

"I'll meet you at the site but I've something else to do first." Gaunt stifled the incipient protest. "I'm only taking a drive across to Sollas's villa. A few words there might help stir things up."

"*Quanto* . . . by how much?" queried Costa bleakly, leaning forward to key-start the Ford. "Already we have all the trouble we can handle."

"Then I'll stir gently," promised Gaunt.

Grunting, Costa let in the clutch. Gaunt watched him struggle to turn the big station wagon on the narrow road then, as it drew away and began travelling back down the road towards Claras, he smiled and lit a cigarette. The policeman who had been on guard nodded at him, mounted his bicycle, and solemnly pedalled off in the same direction.

Left alone, Gaunt stayed for a moment looking at the tyre marks on the grass and a small patch of sump oil, all that remained of what had happened. Then he shrugged, went back to the Fiat, and set it moving.

A mud-streaked jeep from the digging site was the only vehicle parked outside Arthur Sollas's villa. Gaunt stopped the Fiat beside it, got out, and went over to the house. He rang the bell twice before the door swung open, and then it was Martin Lawson who peered out at him.

"Oh." The bald, chubby archaeologist blinked at him then stepped back. "Come in, Mr Gaunt. I thought—well, I thought it might be the police." He gestured vaguely to two closed and labelled suit cases lying in the hallway. "They said they'd collect the Marshes' belongings."

Gaunt entered and Lawson closed the door, still shaking his head over the suit cases.

"We packed them this morning. An ordeal on its own, Mr Gaunt. With Frank Preston, it was sad. But Marsh and his wife were so much younger—and to be killed so brutally . . ." he let it tail away. "Has Torres been captured yet?"

"No." Gaunt wondered if the visit was going to turn out a waste of time. "Where's Doctor Sollas?"

"At the site, I think. He left to go there, anyway." Lawson tutted to himself. "In fact, I'm on my own." Then he brightened. "I've some coffee brewed if you'd like a cup."

"Thanks." Gaunt followed him through to a large, untidy kitchen. A brown metal percolator was on the stove and Lawson fussed around. At last, he brought over two steaming mugs and handed one to Gaunt.

"There"—he beamed nervously, nursing his own—"now, can I help?"

Gaunt shrugged. "The Embassy at Lisbon said that as I was here I could take care of a few formalities for them— British nationals killed abroad, the usual reports." He saw Lawson nod wisely, and went on. "You were here with Doctor Sollas when Marsh and his wife took the car?"

"That's right." Lawson rubbed his chin nervously. "They were—ah—restless and wanted to do something, almost anything. Not being able to find any trace of Preston's Treasure Trove expedition had—ah—upset them."

"I can imagine," said Gaunt dryly. "But they didn't say where they were going?"

"Just into Claras." Lawson frowned a little. "The police know all this."

"The Embassy like their own paperwork," soothed Gaunt. "So you were here with Doctor Sollas. But Ryan was with Pereira?"

"Yes." An embarrassed smile crossed the other man's round face and he shifted his feet awkwardly. "Bernard didn't really need to go with Pereira, of course, but it was an excuse to get away for the evening. And by then Marsh and his wife were—well, it had become rather a strain. Bernard isn't particularly good at hiding his feelings."

"I've noticed." Gaunt took a gulp of the coffee, but shook

his head at the offer of a sandwich. "It's been a bad week for you people. You knew Preston fairly well, didn't you?"

"We'd met," said Lawson uneasily. "I couldn't say I knew him, Mr Gaunt. I—well, I suppose it was luck he remembered my name and that I was out here."

"Just luck?"

Lawson looked puzzled. "I don't understand."

"Then let's see if I can help," said Gaunt softly, laying down his mug. "Georges Salvador told Preston he was on a sure thing if he excavated at the Castelo." He saw the way Lawson's expression froze, and knew he'd guessed right. "Salvador wouldn't know that on his own. Someone had to tell him—an expert. Someone like you, Lawson."

"Me?" Lawson licked his lips. "I hardly know *Senhor* Salvador—"

"That's not what I asked," murmured Gaunt. As Lawson tried to look away he grabbed him by the shoulder and brought him round again. "You told him, didn't you?"

Reluctantly, Lawson nodded then swallowed hard. "I— yes, I heard he was interested in Claras, and I'd come across a mention of the site. But—"

"As long as you got paid," said Gaunt cynically. "Does Doctor Sollas know?"

Lawson shook his head.

"That part isn't my business," Gaunt told him curtly. "But last night is. What happened here after Marsh and his wife left?"

"Nothing. I—I went to bed."

Gaunt frowned. "What about Sollas?"

"I don't know." Lawson gestured feebly. "I was asleep— but he woke me when the police came to tell us what had happened."

Gaunt considered him silently for a moment then gave a fractional nod. Marsh and his wife had left the villa about ten P.M., their bodies had been found around one A.M.—

three hours of suddenly unaccounted time against Arthur Sollas's name.

He left Lawson in the kitchen and returned through the villa to the front door. But when he stepped out onto the porch he stopped short. Georges Salvador's blue Jaguar was parked beside the Fiat, and Salvador stood at the foot of the porch steps smiling up at him with all the cold-eyed interest of a hungry fox.

Salvador wasn't alone. Leaning against the Fiat, cleaning his nails with the tip of a long-bladed knife, Carlos Pereira presented a picture of stocky, studied but watchful disinterest.

"We seem fated to meet, *Senhor* Gaunt," said Salvador softly. "What brought you here? More curiosity?"

"Something like that." Gaunt shrugged and came down the steps. "Lawson's inside, if you want him."

"*Obrigado,* but he can wait," murmured Salvador. He signalled with a forefinger and Pereira began ambling over, still using the knife. "I offered you some advice last night, *Senhor* Gaunt, and a second chance."

"I remember." Gaunt nodded indifferently. "The answer stays the same."

"Then you're a fool." The smile died.

"Maybe." Glancing at Pereira, who was still using the knife-tip on his nails, Gaunt grimaced a little. "How long since your little friend joined the payroll?"

"We have an arrangement," said Salvador bleakly. "He protects certain of my investments."

"Nice for you," murmured Gaunt. "But I'd rather buy a large-sized dog—you can trust dogs. And they don't play with knives like they'd just been invented."

Pereira froze, his pock-marked face shaping a snarl. But Salvador gave a fractional, restraining headshake.

"He knows exactly how to use a knife," said Salvador softly. "I would advise you to take my word for that."

"If you say so." Gaunt let his right hand stray into his pocket, where the lead-filled truncheon was waiting. He gripped it and brought it out into view, the short tip still just inside his pocket flap. "Just make sure he doesn't get any ideas about a practical demonstration—because I'd take you first."

Salvador hesitated, glancing with guarded contempt at the little truncheon. Then the decision was taken for him as the villa door clicked open behind them. Martin Lawson came out onto the porch and stopped there, an uncertain smile on his face.

"More visitors for you," said Gaunt grimly.

"I—uh—I thought I heard voices." Lawson bobbed his head anxiously. "Come in, *Senhor* Salvador—you too, Carlos."

"I can recommend the coffee," said Gaunt, keeping his eyes on Salvador but letting the truncheon slide back into his pocket. "Go ahead. You'll have things to talk about."

Tight-lipped, Salvador nodded. Smiling a little, Gaunt stepped past him and brought one heel hard down on Pereira's instep.

"Clumsy," said Gaunt apologetically above the foreman's yelp of pain. "I keep doing things like that."

He walked over to the Fiat without looking back.

A few minutes later he was pulling up at the main gate of the Castelo de Rosa site. When he honked the horn the gate opened and he drove through, to stop beside the huts. A police car was parked there, its driver behind the wheel, while Sergeant Costa was standing outside the nearest hut talking with Arthur Sollas and a small nut-brown man in a coarse wool shirt and old corduroy jeans.

"You again?" Arthur Sollas scowled as he joined them. "Gaunt, you may be doing your job, but you're beginning to get on my nerves the way you turn up every time there's trouble."

"Here?" Gaunt raised an innocent eyebrow. "What's happened now?"

"*Pequeno* . . . a small thing." Sergeant Costa gave him a quick look which might have killed, then cleared his throat uncomfortably. "Doctor Sollas dislikes certain questions I have been asking—"

"Dislikes?" Sollas grated the word. "You're wasting time, Costa. Why don't you get back to where you belong, chasing that damned killer Luis Torres?" He switched his glare to Gaunt. "Or was this your idea?"

"Doctor, I don't know what the hell you're talking about," declared Gaunt sadly. He thumbed at the other man, who stood with an expression of gloomy boredom on his thin, unshaven weasel face. "Who's this?"

"Pracard, our night watchman," snapped Sollas. "Costa seems to imagine he's lying."

"The night watchman?" Gaunt considered the little man with a new interest. "The same one you had the night Preston was killed?"

"No." Sollas kept his temper with an effort. "I fired that idiot. Pracard took over—Ryan dug him up from somewhere."

"More buried treasure." Gaunt nodded solemnly.

"And all I have asked is if he is sure he saw nothing last night," said Sergeant Costa wearily. "That and if he remembers the exact time *Senhor* Ryan arrived. The details are necessary—Headquarters demand a full report on the movements of everyone who knew *Senhor* Marsh and his wife." He gestured defensively. "When *Senhor* Ryan was here, he didn't seem to mind."

"Where's Ryan anyway?" queried Gaunt, glancing around.

"Gone back to work," said Sollas sourly. "We're still trying to keep things ticking over. Pracard"—he turned to the watchman—"is there anything at all you can tell the sergeant?"

"*Nao*, Doctor Sollas." The watchman shook his head wearily.

"That's what I'd expect." Sollas pointed an angry hand towards the wooded hills. "There's a homicidal maniac running loose out there, Costa. I'll warn you now, if Torres shows up here again—"

"Again?" interrupted Gaunt, surprised.

Costa shrugged, unconvinced. "Two of the workmen on the site thought they saw someone among the trees this morning."

"So we went looking for him, and we didn't go empty-handed," rumbled Sollas grimly. "If he turns up again, we'll shoot on sight."

"Do that, and I'll arrest every man involved," countered Sergeant Costa, flushing. "You're talking about a man, not an animal."

"Then if he matters so much, you'd better find him first." Bleakly, Sollas dismissed the watchman with a nod then swung to face them again as the man left. "Finished, Sergeant?"

"*Sim,* for now." Not troubling to hide his spluttering fury, Costa added for Gaunt's benefit, "If I am needed, the *policia* post at Claras can contact me."

He strode off to the police car, climbed aboard, and slammed the passenger door shut. Starting up, the car shot away and vanished out through the gates.

"Which leaves you." Hitching his thumbs into the waistband of his slacks, Arthur Sollas considered Gaunt with ill-concealed impatience. "What do you want?"

"I've a puzzle of my own to solve," said Gaunt mildly. He looked around the site for a moment, noting the very few men who seemed to be working, then combed a hand through his rumpled mop of hair. "I thought maybe you could help."

"If it's still that damned Treasure Trove nonsense, don't waste my time," warned Sollas, bristling. "Not after what's happened."

"There's still a lot of money involved in it," mused Gaunt. "Enough to make a reasonable motive for murder—if it hadn't been Luis Torres the police were after." He took out a cigarette and lit it carefully, not looking at the man. "And things aren't always how they seem. Even alibis—"

"Meaning?"

Gaunt shrugged. "Do I have to spell it out, Doctor? Take your own case. Lawson is your alibi at the villa, but does Sergeant Costa know he was asleep most of the time?"

Arthur Sollas swallowed hard, controlled himself with an effort, then came back with a stabbing fury behind every word.

"If I had your kind of weevil mind, I might have a different notion," he snarled, red-faced. "Motive? What about you, Gaunt? I could dream up the idea that maybe you got a lead to your damned Treasure Trove through the Torres girl. Then the idea that backing her claim and getting a share could be a hell of a sight easier if Preston's relatives were eliminated."

"And I could have given her brother that job?" Gaunt treated the suggestion with a wooden respect. "I never thought of it that way." Deliberately, he switched in a new direction. "Doctor, do you know a man in Lisbon named José Andella?"

Sollas blinked, rubbed the same finger back across his nose, scowled, and shook his head dangerously.

"You'll find him at the Jeronimos Museum," said Gaunt. "Look him up. He'll tell you the real story about Preston and this site—if you don't know it already."

Open-mouthed, the bulky figure stared at him in what seemed genuine bewilderment.

"José Andella," reminded Gaunt softly. "Good-bye, Doctor."

Every step he took towards the Fiat he expected a bellow from Sollas. But he reached it, set it moving—and still the man stood staring as he drove out of the camp.

Once the fence and the coral-tinted stone of the old Castelo watch-tower had been lost along the tree-lined track Gaunt slowed the car and pulled in. Switching off the engine, he slumped back against the stained upholstery, grinned wryly at himself in the rear-view mirror, and took a long draw on what was left of his cigarette.

He'd promised Costa that he'd stir things up—and he'd done it. But how much was it going to achieve?

For a couple of minutes he sat there, trying to force the tangled confusion of it all into some kind of order that made sense. But it didn't happen. If anything, the mess seemed worse than ever.

Giving up, Gaunt stubbed out the cigarette and reached for the starter key. Then he stopped, staring at a thick patch of red-flowered scrub near the track—scrub from which two small black and white birds had just exploded skyward in twittering fright.

A fox, another bird, maybe a deer, half a dozen possible reasons clicked through his mind. But there was still another. Reaching for the door handle, he made a deliberate, unhurried job of climbing out.

For a long moment he stood beside the car, just listening. The black and white birds were still circling overhead, crickets were sawing away somewhere near, and dried leaves rustled when he shifted his feet. But nothing moved over at the red-flowered scrub.

"Luis?" He waited then tried again, louder. "Luis, you know me—*Senhor* Gaunt."

There was no wind, but the scrub stirred a little.

"Let's go home, Luis." Gaunt took a slow step forward, then another. Suddenly there was a louder rustle then he had a brief glimpse of a blurred figure moving on the far side of the scrub. Another moment and the figure was running, heading deep into the trees, vanishing from sight.

Gaunt didn't try to follow. A regiment of men could have hidden in that dense, dark woodland and laughed at one man's attempt to find them. He needed help. Either Sergeant Costa's kind of help, which meant uniformed men and dogs. Or the other kind, the kind Luis Torres was more likely to answer.

Going back to the car, Gaunt drove on again. Reaching the main road, he turned right towards Claras and about a kilometre on found a filling station with a pay phone he could use. When he dialled Inez's number she answered within two beats of the ringing tone.

"Are Costa's men still prowling outside?" he asked without preamble.

She gave a small gasp over the line, a mixture of hope and fear. "Have you found Luis?"

"I think I spotted him." Gaunt glanced round in the booth, but the pump attendant was busy with a Volkswagen which had pulled in. "Dream up some kind of story to get away without a fuss. I'm at a filling station just this side of the turnoff for Castelo de Rosa."

"I know it," she said quickly. "Wait for me." And the phone went down.

About twenty minutes passed before the open red Lancia came snarling along the road and swung into the filling station. It stopped beside Gaunt, who was finishing a can of beer he'd bought from a self-service dispenser and Inez reached over to open the passenger door.

"You're sure, Jonathan?" she asked as he threw away the can and climbed in.

"No," he said bluntly. "Just that there's something up there—and he ran."

She bit her lip and nodded. "I couldn't come sooner. I didn't want it to look as if I was rushing off."

"What did you tell them?"

Inez twisted a smile. "That I was going into Claras to see Manuel Costa."

"That should hold them, unless he comes looking for you." Gaunt glanced at his watch. It was already past noon, a lot later than he'd expected. "You know the roads around here, Inez. Is there another way we can get near the Castelo site without being spotted?"

"Yes, but it would take time." She rubbed a hand thoughtfully along the thigh seam of her trousers. "We'd have to make a wide circle round the hills."

"Then forget it."

The sudden harsh note in his voice made her stare.

"Why?" she asked.

"We've got to get to him before anyone else does." Gaunt left it at that, glanced at the car's fuel gauge, saw the needle reading almost half full, and made up his mind. "Where you hid the car the last time you went up there will have to do, and—" he stopped, staring at the driving seat as if seeing it for the first time.

Inez had it fully forward on the slides. When he'd driven the car, he'd needed the same seat fully back to drive in comfort.

A sudden mental picture of Costa crossed his mind. Costa having to move the Ford station wagon's seat forward before he could reach the pedals properly. Yet, if anything, John Marsh had been smaller than Costa and his wife positively petite by comparison.

Then how could Marsh have driven the Ford?

It would fall down if the station wagon seat had been moved during the fingerprint check. But otherwise—mouth tightening, Gaunt took the thought on. Arthur Sollas was a big man and Bernard Ryan was another member of the Castelo team who must match him in height.

Inez blipped the accelerator with a touch of impatience.

"Let's go," he agreed quietly.

She drove well, with a skilled, unflurried assurance which didn't waste a moment yet kept the car travelling smoothly. Gaunt's first worry began when they left the main road on the secondary route towards the hills, but he was able to relax again when they passed the fork of the Castelo track without meeting other traffic.

Moments later Inez slowed the car, frowning ahead. Then, suddenly, she turned the wheel to the right and they bounced across a strip of rough grassland to stop behind a clump of young trees.

"Here," she said confidently.

Gaunt got out and walked back to the road to check for himself. Satisfied the car couldn't be seen, he returned to find Inez rummaging in the dashboard glove-box. When she emerged, she was carrying a small pair of binoculars and a small, cloth-wrapped bundle.

"You'd better have these," she said almost hesitantly. "They belonged to Luis, before the accident. I thought—well, I brought them anyway."

Gaunt put the binoculars round his neck by their strap then unwrapped the cloth and gave a mild whistle of surprise. It was a service issue FN self-loading pistol, a 9-millimetre automatic only slightly in need of oiling. He checked the pistol, found it still held a full thirteen-round magazine, and stuffed it in his waistband without comment.

"Where now?" he asked.

She led the way, setting a fast pace through the upward slope of undergrowth and trees. In a matter of minutes they were at the edge of the track which led to the Castelo site, waited there a moment to make sure it was clear, and then went across quickly.

From there Gaunt took the lead, working gradually left through the thickening woodland until the blanketing leaves overhead had reduced the sunlight to a dull gloom. When he reckoned they were close to where he'd seen that blurred figure disappearing he called another halt. All around them were the small, living noises of any forest . . . tiny buzzing and rustling noises, the faint sigh of a shifting tree-branch, the distant chuckle of some unseen bird.

But nothing more.

"Anywhere from here on," he said wryly, flicking at a large fly which seemed determined to land on his forehead. "If he's still around, then he'll see us."

"In this?" Inez looked at the dark, shadowy world which

surrounded them, something less than hope in her voice. But she nodded and drew a deep breath. "Can I try calling him?"

"Better not." He was glad she didn't ask why.

They set off again, at a slower pace. Twice they came across traces of litter from some long-ago picnic, once a sudden hope ended as an old coat abandoned by some tramp. Then, gradually, the trees began to thin again and in another moment they were looking down towards the little valley of the Castelo site, still bathed in bright sunlight and with its squat stone watch-tower standing guardian over the long brown scars of the excavation trenches.

"Far enough." Gaunt sank down among the long grass, glad of a chance to rest, his back already beginning to protest at the prolonged exercise.

More reluctant but still wearily, Inez followed his example and lay face down, her arms pillowing her head. Along the way, her long dark hair had come loose and cascaded around her shoulders, the denim shirt was dark with perspiration against her back, and she already looked as though she'd had enough.

Lighting two cigarettes, Gaunt gave her one then, after a moment, reached for the binoculars and focussed them on the digging site. He caught a brief glimpse of Ryan moving between the office huts, but the site seemed strangely empty of life with only a couple of workmen near the gate.

It puzzled him, but he lowered the glasses and nudged Inez gently.

"We'll start again in a couple of minutes. Work further to the right this time." He grinned encouragingly. "If he's here, we'll find him."

"*Quando* . . . and then what?" she asked almost dispiritedly. "What will happen to him? That's what I kept asking myself back at the house." Her small, white teeth showed in a mirthless smile. "The only answer I had was to go and find those books you wanted."

"The ones Preston gave him?" Gaunt felt a jab of interest. "What are they like?"

"A mixture. Picture books, and one or two infant school readers. Luis was beginning to manage some of the simple words—but he lost his temper when a difficult one beat him."

"Nothing else? More personal, I mean—a scrapbook, a diary, old postcards?"

"No." She shook her head firmly. "Manuel told me all about your Treasure Trove thing, Jonathan. But there was nothing that could help you."

"It doesn't matter." Rolling over on his back, Gaunt looked up at the lacework of branches. "Right now, I'd settle for just knowing what makes Luis keep coming back here."

"I told you, we often played near the Castelo when we were young." Her lips shaped a momentary smile. "These woods were like magic to us, full of dens and hideaways. I remember when Luis was working for the Navy in the valley a few years ago, he took a day off and we came back up here together—a long time had passed, but it still just seemed like the day before."

It took a moment to sink in. Then Gaunt jerked round to face her.

"Say that again."

"About the dens and—" eyes widening, she sat up quickly. "The dens and hideaways, Jonathan! Do you think—"

"The other part first," urged Gaunt. "He did a job for the Portuguese Navy here?"

She nodded impatiently. "About two years before his accident. They were laying some kind of underground cable and Luis supervised this section because he knew the area."

Gaunt moistened his lips. "A communications cable?"

"Something like that. Though they all wore civilian clothes and tried to pretend they were laying a sewer—it was supposed to be secret."

He swore under his breath. "Can you remember anything more about it, Inez?"

"I think it was a land link between the NATO people at Cape Roca and their Headquarters outside Lisbon—something like that, anyway." It hardly mattered to her, the new possibility uppermost in her mind. "Jonathan, suppose he went to one of those old dens where we used to play!"

"Wait." Gaunt said it harshly and saw her flinch.

But so much had suddenly begun slotting into place. Cape Roca—a communications centre probably handling everything from satellite links to nuclear submarine traffic every day of the week. With a constant two-way flow of information along the landline from the Cape to Maritime Headquarters.

If it could be tapped, even for a short length of time, the NATO naval cupboard could be stripped bare of secrets. It was a thought big enough to make him shiver.

Inez was watching him, her eyes puzzled and anxious.

"You're right," he told her soberly. "We'll start trying those hideaways, any you can remember."

Trapped inside his damaged mind, Luis Torres must still have sensed something was wrong in the Castelo valley—something that should matter to him even if he couldn't understand why. And some surviving instinct must have forced him out over these hills night after night on a blind, helpless quest beyond outside comprehension.

Because, like the doctor in Lisbon had admitted, there were things about the human mind, even a damaged human mind, far beyond normal understanding.

Things that projected Luis Torres into a new, personal danger.

He got up, drew Inez back into the deeper shelter of the trees, and checked the pistol in his waistband with a feeling it might be needed now.

"Where do we start?" he asked.

She hesitated, frowned to the right for a moment, then changed her mind and pointed to the left instead.

"That way. It isn't far."

A couple of minutes walking brought them to the first of

the Torres family's childhood dens, a mere outcrop of rock forming what imagination might have called a cave. But it was shelter, and someone had been there. Crouching his way in under the ledge, Gaunt brought out the paper-wrapped remains of an old sandwich and some chocolate wrappings. The bread was days old, hard and stale.

"But it means we could be right," said Inez eagerly. "Anna sometimes gives him sandwiches—can we keep trying?"

"We've got to," he said ominously, tossing the finds down. "All right, where next?"

"There's one we called the house den. We both like it, and—"

She stopped short, wide-eyed, at the sudden bark of a gun. It came from not far distant, then they heard a second shot—this time followed by a shout. For Gaunt, it seemed like a sickeningly familiar echo of where he'd come in.

They headed back to the edge of the woodland at a run then stopped. Down below, a jeep-load of men were driving away from the Castelo diggings. The vehicle was travelling fast, bumping and bouncing its way over the grassland and travelling north up the little valley.

Bringing up the binoculars, Gaunt looked along the route it was taking and understood. A rifle in one hand, waving the jeep on towards him with the other, Carlos Pereira was standing at the edge of the trees about half a kilometre along from them.

"What is it?" asked Inez hoarsely, gripping his arm. "What's happened?"

"My guess is they've spotted him." Gaunt lowered the glasses grimly, knowing they had to gamble now. "If he's running, the odds are he's making for somewhere he feels he can hide—somewhere he thinks of as safety."

"The house den is over there." She bit her lip hard. "It's the only place I can think he'd go."

Gaunt took another glance down at the speeding jeep. Pereira had fired twice. It might have been a signal or it might mean that already Luis Torres was dead or wounded. But one thing was certain—if he was somewhere among those trees and trying to escape he stood little chance on his own.

To try to find him meant heading straight into danger. But if Pereira got there first, Torres' fate was certain. It was very clear now that Luis Torres dead was a factor several people needed to protect their plans.

"Let's move," he said curtly.

And called himself a fool.

CHAPTER EIGHT

Leading the way through the dark woodland, ignoring clawing scrub and barely slowing to dodge the hazards of half-buried tree roots, Inez Torres set a fast, loping pace born from fear and kept going by sheer determination. Keeping up with her slim, fleet-footed figure needed all of Gaunt's energy while his breath became a rasping rhythm and perspiration soaked his body.

He heard no further shots or shouts. But he had no time to think about it as the raven-haired girl continued on her way. When she did finally slow and stop he had lost all sense of distance and direction. But they were at the edge of a tiny gorge carved by a small, dried-up stream.

"There it is," she said, breathless but triumphant, pointing to where an old pine tree lay uprooted like a bridge across the gap. "That's the house den."

Moistening his lips, Gaunt nodded then looked around and listened. He thought he heard a faint shout somewhere, but it was distant, as if the searchers were heading away from them.

He hoped that, anyway.

"Try calling him," he managed hoarsely. "But keep it low."

She called Luis's name softly, waited, then tried again.

Suddenly, there was a rustling movement beneath the fallen tree. A dark head looked out, and with a noise like a sob Inez went scrambling down and began running along the puddled stream.

Gaunt followed her down and arrived beside the fallen tree

to find her hugging a haggard, unkempt Luis Torres. Seeing him, Torres made a quick, struggling movement.

"*Nao* . . . no, Luis," said his sister in a quick, soothing voice. "You know *Senhor* Gaunt. He came to help."

Subsiding, Torres looked at Gaunt again then nodded and grinned weakly. He was wearing an old sweater and slacks, he had shoes, and the one-time play-den beneath the tree held a grubby sleeping bag and an ancient rucksack. Puzzled, Gaunt lifted the rucksack flap, saw the food packed inside, and suddenly understood.

"Jaime," he said wryly. "It couldn't be anyone else."

"Luis, was Jaime here?" asked Inez.

"*Sim.*" The grubby, unshaven scarecrow brightened at the name. "Jaime came."

"Where is he now, Luis?" asked Gaunt with a swift foreboding.

Torres stared at him helplessly and shook his head. Then, without warning, he tried to stand but sank down again with a moan of pain. For the first time Gaunt noticed his left ankle, which had a crude rag bandage tied round it above the shoe.

"He's been hurt." For a moment Inez showed a trace of panic then recovered and knelt down, unwrapping the rag. Badly bruised, Torres' ankle looked swollen to twice normal size but didn't seem broken. She glanced up at Gaunt, dismayed. "What will we do? He can't walk like this—"

"We'll manage," Gaunt reassured her. "Try to fix him up the best you can—and ask him what's been happening. I'll be back."

Climbing up to the lip of the little gorge, he stayed there for a full couple of minutes peering out at the surrounding scrub and timber while down below Inez talked softly and drew low, mumbling replies. At last, satisfied the area was still clear, Gaunt slithered down again to join them.

"All quiet," he confirmed. "What does he say?"

"He fell this morning, when some men were chasing him."

She had soaked the rag bandage in one of the small pools beside them and was busy binding it round her brother's ankle again. "But he hid, then managed to crawl here and—well, Jaime appeared."

"How would Jaime know where to look?"

She shrugged, finishing the task. "He knows Luis and he grew up here too—so he knows these woods." Then, as a new thought struck her, she looked up with a sudden horror. "If it was Jaime they were shooting at—"

"He's pretty good at taking care of himself," said Gaunt soberly. "He's also got enough sense to lead them well away from here."

"If he had the chance."

"Jaime makes his own luck." Gaunt eased past her and smiled reassuringly at Torres. *"Para tras . . .* time to go back home. Okay?"

Torres nodded eagerly. Stooping, Gaunt helped him upright, gripped him round his thin waist, and felt Torres clutch at his shoulder for support.

"We'll try it this way," he told Inez. "Let's go."

There was an easy way out of the stream bed not far along. Once they were out, Inez led the way again through the trees while Gaunt assisted Torres a few paces behind. They moved slowly, Inez murmuring an occasional warning as she skirted a rabbit hole or half-concealed root, her brother hopping along with only a few muttered protests.

After a spell they stopped for a brief rest. Torres was breathing hard and, when they started again, Gaunt let him go only a couple of paces then halted and lifted him on his back. Two thin arms clinging round his neck, he nodded to Inez and they moved off.

They made better time that way. Soon the downward slope became steeper and the trees showed a first sign of thinning.

"Not far now," encouraged Inez, glancing back anxiously.

Though he felt like a plodding pack-horse, Gaunt managed an answering grin and hefted Torres fractionally higher on his shoulders. Then, as his feet sank into a soft patch of leaf and mould, Gaunt heard Inez give a gasp.

He looked up again—and stopped in mid-stride. Heavy face a carved, scowling mask, Arthur Sollas stood a few yards ahead with a pump-action shotgun held at his hip, the muzzle pointed squarely.

"Stay like that," rasped Sollas. He took two more steps away from the thick clump of scrub which had concealed him then halted and raised his voice. "Pracard!"

The little foxy-faced camp watchman emerged from behind a tree to their right. Similarly armed, he came over grinning with satisfaction and stopped with his gun inches from Gaunt's stomach.

"Put Torres down," ordered Sollas curtly. "Then move away from him."

Tight-lipped, Gaunt eased Torres from his back, sat him on the ground, then was prodded clear. Shoving him on, Pracard brought him facing a tree, stopped him there, then lowered the shotgun and rapidly checked him over. The automatic and truncheon were found and stuffed into one of the watchman's pockets, then it was Luis Torres' turn.

Torres tried to shrink back as the grinning figure approached him. But Pracard cuffed him hard across the face, repeated the task roughly, then glanced at Sollas and shook his head.

"Make sure of the girl." Sollas's shotgun still hadn't wavered.

Pale-faced and angry, Inez was subjected to the same pawing process then the man stood back. Satisfied, Sollas raised his gun in the air and fired three times. As the spread of pellets brought twigs and leaves raining down from overhead three similarly timed shots answered like an echo from the distance.

"Now what?" asked Gaunt wearily.

"Pick that object up again." Sollas glared in angry contempt at Luis Torres, who cringed like an unhappy schoolboy. "We're going down to the Castelo." He sniffed hard and grunted. "Three of you—that's two more than I expected when I said I'd watch this end in case Torres tried to double back. All right, Gaunt, lift him."

"And what happens once we're down there?" Gaunt's half-step forward ended as Pracard's gun jabbed hard against his side.

"What you deserve. Though it wouldn't take much to make me finish it right here," answered Sollas bleakly. "That goes for you in particular, Gaunt. I wouldn't waste time giving you a trial."

Gaunt stared at him, with a sudden, slender hope.

"How much do you really know, Doctor Sollas?" he asked softly.

"Any fool can see it," said Sollas. "Finding you together is the last proof I need. The Marshes are dead, you can get the girl to lodge a claim with your Department—and how you planned to split that Treasure Trove money is no concern of mine, damn you."

Inez shook her head desperately. "You can't believe that. Doctor, we can prove—"

"Do you think I'd even listen?" Sollas cut her short with an outraged snarl. "Don't waste your breath. I'd bet you can get that poor damned wreck of a brother to do anything—and Gaunt can probably do the same with you."

She stood white-faced and speechless but Gaunt tried again.

"You're being fooled," he said bitterly. "You're surrounded by men who couldn't care less about your piddling little Roman villa—hell, they knew it was there all along."

"You're a talker all right." Sollas gave a twist of grim admiration then slowly brought the shotgun round until it was trained on Luis Torres. "Well, talk all you want later. But either pick him up—or watch him die."

Gaunt began moving towards Torres then looked back for one last attempt.

"Sollas, there's a NATO communications cable down there. That's what they—"

Pracard's gun-barrel cracked him across the side of the face. He staggered, tasted blood in his mouth, and saw the gun raised again. Dazed and shaking his head, he stopped and lifted Torres.

A few trudging minutes brought them to the edge of the woodland at a spot little more than a stone's throw away from the bulk of the Castelo watch-tower. Bernard Ryan's jeep-load of men was on its way back too and skidded to a halt beside their procession as they arrived at the digging site gates.

"Nicely done, Doc!" Jumping down from the driving seat, Ryan came over and greeted Sollas enthusiastically. "All three together—any trouble?"

"None." Sollas rubbed his scarred nose, glanced at Gaunt sardonically, and shook his head. "They walked right into us up there."

"Well, it looks like I was right all along, eh?" The tall, white-haired photographer looked round as the other men from the jeep reached him. "Carlos—"

"*Sim, Senhor* Ryan?" Pereira pushed forward, a mocking delight on his pock-marked face as he considered Gaunt.

"Shove them into the office," ordered Ryan.

"Then call the *policia* at Claras and get them out here," added Sollas grimly. "I want rid of them."

Turning, Pereira gave some quick instructions to his companions—and Gaunt, taking the chance to look around, felt a last hope fade. The whole site area was empty and deserted, there were only the men around them and two more, armed with rifles, waiting by the huts. Perhaps half a dozen in all —before he could check again he was being shoved forward, Torres still clinging bewilderedly to his back and Inez being dragged along beside them.

The one relief when they were inside the hut was that he could drop Luis Torres into the nearest chair. Pereira waved his companions out again then stood covering his three prisoners with a rifle. Too tired to do more than cling to the edge of a bench, Gaunt watched Inez whisper reassuringly to her brother then pulled himself upright a little as Arthur Sollas come in, followed by Ryan.

"Happy now?" asked Gaunt wryly. "You're still a fool, Sollas."

"You don't give up, do you?" His shotgun crooked under one arm, Sollas gave a snort of contempt.

"Try getting that call through to the police like you wanted," suggested Gaunt caustically. "Go ahead—try."

"What does he mean, Doc?" asked Ryan with an unusual mildness, coming between them.

"They tried to make me swallow a wild story up there— the kind you'd expect." Sollas propped the shotgun against the wall, opened a cupboard, and brought out a whisky bottle. "The general idea was I should let them go."

"What kind of story?" persisted Ryan.

"Wild, like I said." Sollas found a glass and poured himself a drink without looking round. "All about how some of our people must have killed the Marshes. Then some nonsense about the Roman villa and a piece of idiocy about a military cable." The filled glass in his hands, he turned and frowned a little as he saw Pereira hadn't moved. "Carlos, get that call in."

Pereira stayed where he was and raised a faint eyebrow towards Ryan, who shook his head.

"Sorry, Doc," murmured Ryan sadly. "It's not convenient."

A Luger pistol had appeared in his hand and was trained on Sollas's middle. Sollas froze, staring at it, the glass almost at his lips. Then, open-mouthed in disbelief, he glanced at Pereira and met a lop-sided grin.

"We tried to warn you, Doctor," said Inez quietly.

"It sounds like you did," mused Ryan. "But he always was pig-headed. Move, Doc—over beside them."

For a moment Sollas hesitated then he made a snatch for

the shotgun. The Luger barked, its bullet blasting splinters of wood from the stock of the gun and knocking it clear.

"Next time is for real, Doc," said Ryan softly. "Get beside them."

Tight-lipped with fury, Sollas obeyed reluctantly.

"Good." The Luger swinging from his trigger finger, Ryan perched himself on the edge of the bench and sighed as he said, "Life gets complicated, that's for sure."

"Like now?" asked Gaunt ironically, flexing his stiffened back muscles and stretching upright. Ignoring Pereira's warning scowl, he brought out his cigarettes and lit one. "I've a feeling the good doctor thinks the same."

"All I feel is that the world is going mad," exploded Sollas. He was still clutching the whisky glass, though most of the contents had slopped down his clothes, and he drained what remained at a single, gulping swallow then abandoned the glass to point a quivering, angry finger at Ryan. "Damn you, I don't care what kind of fraudulent idiocies have been going on. We can talk about that later. But we've got Torres, the police want him for double murder—and maybe these other two as well before they're done."

"Forget it," said Ryan curtly. He eased down from the workbench, came over to where Torres was sitting, and grimaced as the puzzled, dishevelled figure gave him a hopeful smile. Ryan sighed again and looked at Inez.

"Don't think we wanted it this way," he said almost apologetically. "Things just happened, that's all."

The hut door swung open and one of the men from the jeep strode in. Ignoring Sollas, he murmured briefly to Pereira then went out again.

"That's how it is, Doc," nodded Ryan, amused at Sollas's expression. "You okayed me sending most of the squad home for the day—anyone still around is on our side in this."

"And what the hell side is that?" bristled Sollas.

Ryan shrugged. "Ask Gaunt. He seems to know."

Swearing, the big man swung on Gaunt.

"Make some sense out of this," he appealed.

"Go ahead, Gaunt," encouraged Ryan softly. "I'm interested too—things were going smoothly enough until you turned up."

Gaunt looked at the white-haired, oddly smiling figure and knew a lot of things didn't matter any more. Any hopes he had left were slim, and for the rest there was little to lose.

"Including Preston's murder?" he asked, and heard a startled grunt from Sollas. "Preston—then John Marsh and his wife. They were complications too, I suppose."

Ryan's mouth shaped a sudden, hard line. Then, unexpectedly, he shrugged.

"You're guessing—and that disappoints me," he complained, scratching his chin lightly with the Luger's foresight.

The sound of a car drawing up reached them from outside. Hearing it, Ryan gave a faint, reassuring nod to Pereira. Then he considered Gaunt again.

"I'll take a bet you've been guessing most of the way," he declared. "Guessing, with no one else in on the game. Right?"

Suddenly, Inez Torres had had enough. Too fast for anyone to stop her, she reached Ryan and slapped him hard across the mouth. The sound echoed in the hut like an angry whipcrack and Ryan's head jolted back. For a heart-stopping moment his grip tightened on the Luger—then instead he laughed and shoved her back towards the chair.

"*Obrigado,* sweetheart," he said dryly. "But don't try that again. Once is enough."

"For you?" Raw contempt in her voice, Inez put a sheltering arm around her brother. "You've made people hunt Luis like—like some kind of animal. Does that make you feel proud and clever?"

"I didn't enjoy it, sweetheart." Ryan felt his mouth gingerly, then turned to Gaunt as if he found that easier. "Guessing or not, I'll give you first prize—Preston and the Marshes."

"Preston because he saw too much that night?"

Ryan nodded.

"And the Marshes?"

"Like I said, life gets complicated," said Ryan defensively, ignoring a click behind him as the hut door opened again.

"Very complicated by the look of things," murmured a new voice from the doorway.

Arthur Sollas stared open-mouthed and made a throaty noise of complete disbelief. Jerking round, Gaunt felt the same way as he saw Martin Lawson standing there, the sunlight from outside glinting on his bald head and fluffy halo of hair. Lawson stayed in the doorway a moment more, his expression one of customary mildness. But as he came in and closed the door again there was an unmistakable authority in the way he nodded to Pereira and Ryan.

"We'll talk outside," he said curtly.

"We'd better," agreed Ryan heavily.

With a struggle, Arthur Sollas managed a choked, dazed whisper.

"You, Martin?"

"That's right." Lawson's smile faded as his glance flickered over to Gaunt. "All unexpected, believe me—but I haven't forgotten what happened at our last meeting, Mr Gaunt."

"I was afraid of that," said Gaunt wryly. He dropped his cigarette and stubbed it out under one heel. "But that was when I thought Salvador gave the orders."

"Salvador?" Lawson found the notion amusing. "He makes a good contact man."

"When he doesn't over-reach," grunted Ryan.

"Many people do that," murmured Lawson.

He beckoned Ryan and they went out of the hut together. A moment passed, then Pracard and another man, a stolid, dull-faced figure with a shotgun, came in. Pracard carried a length of rope and had Gaunt's FN automatic jutting from one pocket and their arrival was the signal for Pereira to leave.

The two newcomers began with Gaunt and Sollas, lashing

their hands behind their backs. Unemotionally, ignoring his feeble protests, they did the same to Luis Torres then, after completing the same task with Inez, they made all four captives sit on the floor.

Satisfied, Pracard began wandering around the hut examining the site photographs pinned to the walls. His companion relaxed against a filing cabinet, yawning a little.

"Damn them all," said Arthur Sollas in a low, grey voice. "Gaunt, it doesn't help. But I'm sorry."

Gaunt shrugged, more concerned with testing the rope round his wrists. It was tight and unyielding.

"At least you know what's going on—or some of it," muttered Sollas bitterly. "You could tell me that much."

"And you'd listen now." Inez put a sting behind the words.

Glumly, Sollas nodded.

It was always something to keep their minds off what was being discussed outside. Gaunt talked, keeping his voice low though the men on guard showed no interest. He left out a few details, including Jaime having been in the forest, because it still seemed better that way. Sollas listened intently, and some of it was also new to Inez.

At the finish, Sollas swallowed hard then squirmed round to look at Luis Torres, who was sitting calmly and blank-eyed, as if in some secret world of his own.

"But it all seemed so—so positive." He moistened his lips. "There was that cigarette lighter—"

"They'd chased him other times," mused Gaunt. "Maybe they found it, or maybe they took it if they caught him earlier. Then—well, he was getting to be a nuisance and he made a perfect suspect."

Cursing under his breath, Sollas nodded. "And all the time they had me fooled."

"They had Preston fooled too, and he knew plenty of tricks," reminded Gaunt dryly. "But give them credit—they put a lot of work into all this, long-term work. They knew they couldn't just dig down to this NATO cable without being spotted. Instead, they found the other way."

"A full-scale, drum-beating archaeological dig—" Sollas sighed his understanding.

"Great big trenches all over the place and a lot of un-official overtime," agreed Gaunt. "Now you know why the Portuguese were so edgy about permissions—even when you and Preston were being used as a high-class front."

"Does any of it matter now?" asked Inez in a low voice. "Jonathan, they're going to kill us, aren't they?"

The door opening again saved him from having to answer. Martin Lawson came in alone and stood over them, frowning a little and sucking his teeth.

"We've found where the girl hid her car," he said suddenly. "I'm going along with Ryan on the rest—that you were in this on your own and that there's no risk of anyone missing you for a few hours. That's all we need." Coming closer, he prodded Gaunt with a foot. "Get up—that goes for all of you. I'm putting you somewhere else for now."

"Then what?" asked Gaunt bluntly.

"Get up," said Lawson without answering.

"Por favor . . ." Inez spoke wearily. "My brother will need help. He—his ankle is hurt."

"Look for yourself," growled Sollas. "Any fool can see that's true."

"A medical opinion too?" Lawson gave him a watery smile. "The girl can help him."

He gave an order to Pracard, who produced a knife and cut Inez and Torres loose. Then, pushed and prodded to their feet, Inez half-supporting her brother, they were bundled out of the hut and hustled past the excavation trenches towards the ruin of the Castelo tower. Ryan and Pereira were there, standing beside the archway.

"Opened up?" asked Lawson.

Pereira nodded.

"Ryan and I will cope here," Lawson told him. "You stay around the huts in case of visitors."

Obediently, Pereira strode off while Ryan led the way through the archway into the dank, shadowed gloom of the old tower. Gaunt and the others were pushed along after him, squeezing past blocks of fallen masonry and into a short, narrow passage which led to a small inner room. Two of the slabs of its flagstone floor had been removed and a bright glow of light came up from below.

"Down there," said Ryan briefly, gesturing to the top rungs of a sloping iron ladder.

"With our hands tied?" queried Sollas in disgust. "We could break our necks."

"You worry me," said Ryan cynically. He nodded to Pracard, who grinned and disappeared down the rungs. Then he beckoned Gaunt. "You first."

Keeping his back to the sloping ladder, Gaunt managed to get down about a dozen rungs before he missed his footing. He bumped and slid the rest of the way, to land with a thud on another stone floor only a few more feet down. Sollas was less lucky, tumbling after he'd hardly started and crashing down. He was still groaning with pain as he was kicked back on his feet.

Lawson climbed down next then, as the others followed, Gaunt found himself being pushed on again through a low, narrow tunnel built of old, rough stonework but with new electric lights wired along one side at intervals. He had to stoop to get through, while cobwebs brushed his face and large spiders scurried to escape into crannies in the stone. Here and there, he saw places where cement patches repaired gaps in the original structure.

"It dates back to Roman times," said Lawson suddenly, crouching along behind him. "This was the villa's water culvert—they tapped a stream from the hill." He kept on in the same almost conversational voice, as if he was lecturing to a favoured student. "From here it went to a cistern in the villa, then they drew it off as required. The—ah—Moors used it later, but only as a form of sewer. Still, they were clever people too."

"And the rest was all your own idea?" Gaunt swore as a low projection grazed his head.

"That's right," agreed Lawson modestly. "I counted on something like it—and it saved a lot of work, believe me." He sighed a little. "We weren't so fortunate beyond the villa. I'd hoped for a drainage culvert—but we hit nothing but inferior clay piping, most of it broken."

"Maybe the Romans ran out of pennies," suggested Gaunt sourly.

"That's possible," Lawson mused on the notion for a moment. "Yes, you could be right. It's a pity we can't talk about it more—I really mean that."

They had reached the end of the tunnel, or more exactly the lip where it fell away into what had once been the Roman villa's vast underground cistern. Stone walls and a smooth stone floor were lit by more electric bulbs, and Lawson pushed him on down a new ramp of earth into the middle.

Able to stand upright again and left alone for a moment as the others stumbled down, he looked around quickly and felt a reluctant admiration for what had been done.

The old cistern was saucer-shaped, about twenty feet across, and perhaps half as high as it was broad. On one side the original Roman-built wall had been hacked away to form a smaller chamber which held a litter of shovels, timber props and other equipment. Beside it, the black mouth of a low, new, and much smaller tunnel than the one he'd come through had two thin cables trailing out to link to a trio of small, grey-finished metal cabinets. A small diesel generator stood beside them, linked to a bank of lead-acid batteries, its exhaust pipe a flexible tube snaking back into the main tunnel.

"Look, but don't touch," said Bernard Ryan sardonically, blocking his way as he took a tentative step nearer the cabinets. He thumbed to where Pracard and the other guard were herding Inez, Sollas and a surprisingly calm Luis Torres against the opposite wall. "That's your side of the fence."

"Let him stay," murmured Lawson, with a chilly benevolence. "Ryan's sensitive about his equipment, Gaunt. But one could say you've earned this much."

"A last favour before a carbon copy of the Marsh business?" asked Gaunt bleakly. "Four of us will take a lot of explaining."

Ryan winced, but stayed silent, glancing at Lawson.

"That disgusted me—but was necessary," declared Lawson slowly. "We—" he stopped and shook his head. "Leave it. Gaunt, I am a professional, and my masters in Moscow dislike unnecessary violence as much as I do, even if for slightly different reasons. But sometimes there is no option. The Marshes, for instance"—his mouth tightened—"an objectionable couple, for a start. They were caught inside the office hut, after breaking into Ryan's desk. Obviously they were hoping some of their uncle's papers might be hidden inside. Instead, they found some"—he glared at Ryan—"some unfortunate drawings and paperwork which should not have been there."

"So they were killed, and you framed Luis Torres."

"We had a lot to lose," shrugged Lawson. "We've been through to the NATO cable for almost two weeks. Monitoring its signal impulses is no great technical problem, and analysing the tapes isn't our concern. We simply pass them on. But this is a long-term project—no here today, gone tomorrow affair."

Abruptly, he went over to the bank of equipment, quickly flicking switches and not looking back.

"Talking's over—back with the rest of them," ordered Ryan quickly, gesturing with the Luger. He twisted a humourless grin. "I've work to do. Cape Roca has a computer feed chatter with Lisbon due in about ten minutes—it's becoming one of our regular tapings."

The equipment bank was coming to life as Ryan herded him over to where Inez, Torres, and Arthur Sollas were already squatting on the stone floor under Pracard's sharp-eyed supervision. Ryan beckoned Pracard's thick-set companion, who slouched over casually nursing the shotgun in his grasp.

"*Quero* . . . I want this one watched," warned Ryan.

"*Sim*." The man grinned and shoved Gaunt down next to Inez.

Leaving them, Ryan went back to join Lawson at the recording equipment. Gaunt tried to wriggle into a more comfortable position, found having his hands tied behind him made it difficult, then felt Inez helping him.

"Thanks." He grimaced wryly and looked around. Arthur Sollas was still tied and met his gaze with a gloomy scowl, but so far no one seemed to have bothered about Inez or her brother.

"Did they say what will happen?" asked Inez quietly.

"I don't think they know themselves," he lied. "How's Luis?"

"Happy." She said oddly but meant it.

Torres was sitting staring at the equipment bank, almost drinking in its murmur of sound. At that moment, a high-pitched tone howl, as Ryan adjusted a control, brought a smile to his haggard, unshaven young face and his lips began moving, silently shaping words to himself.

It was as if some long-buried memories were being stirred awake, their plight a completely obscured irrelevancy.

In a few minutes the recording gear was ready enough to satisfy Lawson. He left Ryan, crossed the cistern floor, and spoke for a moment to Pracard. Then he frowned down at Inez.

"Tie her hands again—the same with her brother," he ordered, and switched his attention to Gaunt. "You'll be here for a spell. I wouldn't try any heroics—that would be fairly senseless."

Without waiting for an answer he turned and went away, going up the earth ramp and into the culvert tunnel towards the Castelo tower.

Ryan was still working at the recording gear as Pracard

began wandering around, poking at the digging equipment and looking for something to use as rope. He found a section of cut cable, frowned down at it, then changed his mind and was starting to search again when Ryan called him over.

"Can't we do anything?" muttered Sollas, watching the two men moving one of the recording units and Ryan making adjustments to some hidden control at the rear.

"Like what?" Gaunt looked up wistfully at the remaining guard. "Will I bite his ankle and then hope he bleeds to death?"

Sollas glared and faced away, muttering to himself. After a moment, Gaunt eased closer to Inez then casually turned to screen her from view, nudging with his hands. She understood, shifted her own position with a deliberate sigh—then, seconds later, her fingers were working on the tightly knotted rope at his wrists.

Suddenly, the man on guard stopped being sleepy-eyed. He shoved forward, kicked Gaunt angrily on the side, and forced Inez over until she was beside Luis.

"Next time—" he scowled and gestured with the butt of the shotgun.

At last, Ryan had finished with the recording unit. He had Pracard help him shove it back, checked the result with another warbling tone note which echoed round the stone walls, and was ready. Glancing at his wrist-watch, he grinned coldly across at Gaunt.

"They're finishing their coffee-break at Cape Roca. Those computer operators stick to routine. They'll be making their own line-checks in a minute or two."

A flick of a switch brought a pale glow of lights along the smaller tunnel. Going over to it, Ryan went down on all fours and disappeared inside.

Whistling thinly through his teeth, Gaunt tried to calculate how long the tunnel might go. From the middle of the Roman villa, probably, to somewhere in the open ground outside the site fence. Maybe a hundred yards, a reasonable construction job on its own. At the other end, once they'd reached the cable, he expected installing the monitoring "bug" equipment had been simple by comparison—a question of skill, just as deciphering the signals it captured and taped was something for other skills.

And he couldn't do a damned thing about any of it.

He sighed as the soft-tone note from the recording gear switched to a new, broken rhythm. Then, suddenly, he noticed Luis Torres.

As the new rhythm warbled on, Torres frowned, looked puzzled, and before Inez could stop him was on his feet, holding to the wall for support and hobbling nearer. Pracard saw him, nudged the other guard, and grinned, watching but doing nothing.

Slowly, Torres came nearer to the recording banks. His face was twisted in concentration, Inez was staring at him in bewilderment—and Gaunt winced, sensing what was coming a moment before it happened.

Strolling over, Pracard stuck out a foot and tripped him. The other guard came over, gave a coarse laugh at the way Torres lay sprawled, and deliberately hit him in the stomach with the shotgun butt. As Torres gave a retch of agony the heavy butt swung back again, this time aiming for his head.

The blow didn't land. Inez Torres was there first, throwing herself bodily at the thick-set figure, nails scratching raw furrows down his face as she clawed for his eyes. Cursing, her opponent tried to fend her off while Pracard joined in, seizing her by the hair and trying to wrench her away. Both men were cursing, Arthur Sollas was struggling upright, Gaunt was trying to do the same—and for the moment Luis Torres was forgotten.

Suddenly, Inez gave a cry of pain as the thick-set man twisted her arm viciously. Up at last, Gaunt started forward— then stopped, mesmerised.

Luis Torres was also up again, somehow staying on his feet, a twisted, determined fury on his thin face—and a metal crowbar in his hands. He took two swaying, hobbling steps forward, balanced on his good ankle, and smashed the bar down with both hands on the thick-set man's skull.

The thud of the blow blended with the louder noise as the guard tumbled limp, the shotgun clattering. Inez stumbled back while Pracard spun, grabbing the automatic from his waistband.

He triggered twice at the thin, swaying figure before him and Luis Torres fell, his mouth opened wide in a soundless surprise. Snarling, Pracard brought the automatic round again, aiming for Inez—but the bullet went wide as Gaunt body-charged him back against the wall and next moment Sollas was there too, hurling his massive weight in a bull-like desperation which threw Pracard down on the stone floor.

The automatic was still in Pracard's fist, and he was wriggling clear. Gaunt kicked, took Pracard hard on the wrist, and the weapon went skidding across the floor to stop near Inez. She stared at it then, as Gaunt shouted, picked it up.

Pracard scrambled to his feet, saw her, and made a dive towards the fallen shotgun. She pulled the trigger three times, and he screamed once, jerked, and died with his fingers still scrabbling.

The echo of the shots faded and, for a moment, there was only the monotonous warbling of the recording banks. Arthur Sollas was sitting back against the stonework, breathing heavily and with blood staining his left shoulder. Inez hadn't moved, the automatic held limp at her side, her face the colour of parchment . . . and her brother still lay as he'd fallen.

But there was still Ryan in the cable tunnel. Gaunt moistened his lips.

"Pracard had a knife," he said urgently. "Get it, Inez."

She looked round slowly, her eyes blank.

"The knife, Inez," he insisted. "Get it."

It sank in. Listlessly, she found the knife, brought it over, and cut the rope from his wrists. Wincing at the first return of circulation, Gaunt took the knife over to Arthur Sollas, cut him free, and looked round again.

Inez was down on her knees beside her brother, sobbing quietly. Gaunt went to her, removed the gun gently from her hand then turned and saw the lights in the cable tunnel had gone out. He reached its entrance at a run, flopped down beside it—and a shot slammed out at him, the bullet ricochetting wildly off the stonework above his head.

Bringing the automatic up, he fired once in a blind reply and heard a startled, muffled curse.

"Ryan"—he raised his voice in a shout, but kept clear of the tunnel mouth, a perfect target frame—"we've taken over at this end. You can come out, but throw that gun out first."

There was silence for several seconds, then Ryan bellowed back.

"Like hell—and try coming in, Gaunt. I'll sit this one out till you're taken care of from up top."

Another shot from the darkness slammed the stonework in emphasis and Gaunt gave up, looking round as Arthur Sollas crawled beside him, tight-lipped and bringing the shotgun.

"Torres is dead," said Sollas grimly. "Pracard the same—the other one's name was Martinez, and he won't trouble anyone." He propped himself beside Gaunt, sighed, and thumbed back. "The girl's in the next best thing to shock, so don't expect much help there."

"What about you?"

"A nice, clean shoulder wound—Pracard's third shot." Sollas grunted almost amiably and hefted the shotgun. "That's the least of my worries right now. How about using this?"

"Just watch him for me," said Gaunt.

Easing back, he went over to Inez. She had stopped sobbing but was still kneeling beside her brother, and when she looked up her face held its own silent agony.

"He's dead," she said simply.

Gently, Gaunt coaxed her to her feet and over beside the recording equipment. He stopped long enough to find a switch that shut off the monotonous chattering tone then went back, took off his jacket and carefully covered Luis Torres' face.

Stepping back, he chewed his lip thoughtfully. Despite the echoing din of these shots, there was every chance nothing had been heard above ground. But Ryan, stuck like a mole in his tunnel, was still right. Any moment might bring someone down from the Castelo—and when that happened there could only be one bloody result.

Yet he had to be sure of Ryan first . . . looking round again, he suddenly saw that part of the answer in the little diesel generator and the cans of fuel which lay beside it.

The generator was on a wheeled trolley, it took only seconds to use the knife to cut its output terminals, and a minute more to slash through the snaking exhaust pipe a few feet from its source. Pracard's body was in the way. He dragged it clear, then wheeled the generator over to be greeted by a frown from Sollas.

"What the hell?" Suddenly, Sollas's expression changed and an appreciative grin twisted across his scarred face. "It should work, but it takes time."

"Maybe he doesn't know that. Keep an eye on the Castelo side for me." Carefully, Gaunt fed the exhaust tube's length down into the tunnel. It slithered along, with enough noise to bring a shot from Ryan, then again there was silence.

"Ryan, listen for a moment," shouted Gaunt. The engine had a simple pull-cord starter and burst into noisy life at the second pull. He gave it full throttle for a few seconds then shut it off again. "Do you know what that was?"

"Don't play games," came a snarled reply from somewhere in the tunnel.

"Remember your science?" called Gaunt. "Exhaust fumes equal carbon monoxide—colourless, odourless, tasteless, but it kills. Symptoms start with shortage of breath and giddiness, then your heart starts racing before you pass out." He crossed his fingers. "Five minutes at most and you're dead."

He heard a curse and two shots whined off the stonework.

"Throw the gun out when you're ready." Gaunt started the little engine again and sent it racing.

A full minute passed then he heard a muffled shout above the throbbing beat. Grinning at Sollas, he closed down the engine and Ryan's automatic came skidding out of the tunnel.

Sullen and grimy, Bernard Ryan followed it out. He emerged coughing and spluttering, looked nervously at the dead men on the floor, doubled in another bout of coughing, then allowed himself to be frisked without uttering a protest.

"Inez, help me." Gaunt gave a faint smile of reassurance as she came over slowly, then handed her Ryan's gun. "Keep him covered."

Silently, she trained the Luger on Ryan's middle and it stayed like that, unwavering, while Gaunt used a length of electrical wiring to secure the man's hands.

"You still haven't a hope," said Ryan cautiously as he finished.

"That's part of your worry now," Gaunt told him softly. "How many men has Lawson up there?"

Ryan shrugged, growing more confident. "Another four, not counting Pereira. Long odds, friend—unless we maybe do some kind of a deal."

"See that gun Inez is holding?" said Gaunt stonily. "Her brother is dead, Ryan. The only deal left us is that maybe you get out of here alive."

Thin face growing paler, Ryan saw the hate in Inez's eyes and cringed back a little.

"I didn't kill anyone," he said urgently, sweat suddenly beading his forehead. "That was all Pereira—he did for Preston."

"What about the Marshes?" rasped Sollas from the background.

"The Marshes too," agreed Ryan hoarsely. "I drove the car the last stage, that's all. Pereira did the rest, Marsh first then the woman." He licked his lips. "It was Pereira's idea to make it look like Torres did it too. He had that cigarette lighter—Torres dropped it one night when we chased him off."

"And you just drove the car." Gaunt considered him with an open contempt. "Congratulations."

Arthur Sollas came over and pushed Ryan back with unconcealed relish. Turning away, Gaunt checked the FN automatic which had been Luis Torres' and saw it had six rounds of its thirteen-round magazine remaining. There were four rounds left in the Luger when he took it from Inez, but he shook his head and returned it.

"I'll come too," she said, reading his mind. "I—*por favor*, Jonathan. I don't want to stay here."

He frowned. "Sollas?"

"Another hunk of flex round this character's legs and he wouldn't go far," rumbled Sollas, glaring at Ryan. "Though a bullet would be quicker."

Ryan stared at them, naked fear in his face. "Gaunt—"

"Flex," said Gaunt. Then he touched Inez gently on the cheek and nodded. "We'll all go."

They left Ryan bound hand and foot and started back along the old culvert tunnel which led to the Castelo, Gaunt in the lead with Inez and Sollas close behind.

On the way, Gaunt noticed details he'd missed before. Another time, and he'd have asked Arthur Sollas about some of them, like the apparently perfect blocks of carved masonry lumped in at intervals with the rest of the culvert material because of some probable tiny flaw. He saw other blocks with crudely scratched lettering which might have been the Roman equivalent of graffiti and, strangest, a few broken sections of an oddly veined white marble, worn by surface time but still showing a separate, more delicate carving which had to be from an even earlier age.

Another time . . . what mattered more was his first glimpse of the iron rung ladder which led up to the Castelo.

They were almost there when, unexpectedly, the stone-slabbed hatch above began to grate open. He signalled Sollas and Inez back against the tunnel walls and waited while the slabs were dragged clear and a figure began hastily clambering down.

The man's back was to them. Cat-footing forward, Gaunt could hear him breathing heavily on the last few rungs. Then, as the stranger reached the bottom, Gaunt tapped him lightly on the shoulder.

Yelping in surprise, the man tried to turn—and Gaunt slammed him over the head with the butt of the FN pistol, catching him as he fell.

Leaving the unconscious figure to Sollas, he swarmed up the iron ladder with the FN ready. But the Castelo room above was empty and the only sound a faint murmur of wind.

Climbing out, he looked back and saw Sollas busy binding and gagging the man with his own tie and belt. He let him finish then signalled them up.

Inez came first and gave him a shaky smile as he helped her out. Sollas was slower, his shoulder troubling him and the slung shotgun bumping, but there was still a triumphant grin on his face as he sat with his legs still dangling over the edge of the hatch.

"That's it," declared Sollas cheerfully. "Hell, we could fight our own little war from this place."

Gaunt nodded and gave Sollas a minute more to recover before he gestured them on again. Quietly, they made their way back along the rubble-strewn passage to the Castelo door, the bright glow of sunlight pouring in from outside a welcome on its own.

But at its edge Gaunt stopped and stared in sheer disbelief. Down below, a police car was stopped beside the site huts. A couple of uniformed police lounged beside it and Sergeant Costa was strolling casually towards the excavation trenches with Lawson by his side.

Pressing past him in the archway, Arthur Sollas gasped then drew in a deep breath, ready to yell. Gaunt stopped him in time, looked again, and saw that three of Lawson's men clustered in a tight knot close by the car.

Even if Ryan had been right when he'd talked, that still left Pereira—and Pereira was the most dangerous.

"Stay here," he said quietly. "I'm going down."

Inez looked at him blankly but Sollas gave a frown which showed he understood and looked wryly at the shotgun.

"There's no real range with this thing," he warned.

Gaunt nodded, checked the FN again, then stepped out into the open.

Nobody noticed him at first and he walked quietly down the slope, taking a line to intercept Sergeant Costa and Lawson. Then, about halfway down, he heard a warning shout from the men at the huts, saw Costa turn, stare, and reach for his holster—and Carlos Pereira step into view from behind one of the spoil-heaps, a rifle coming up to his shoulder.

Gaunt threw himself sideways, triggering the FN as the rifle barked. Pereira's bullet whined close over his head—then the echo of their shots was drowned by the staccato, cyclic rasp of a machine-pistol.

It came from the police car, a long, hosing burst of fire which sent Pereira jerking and twisting like a maddened doll. As it ended, he sank slowly to his knees then collapsed in the dirt.

Then it was quiet, and Gaunt rose slowly. The uniformed men by the police car were no longer lounging, and Lawson's trio had their hands in the air. A third officer was climbing out the car, the machine-pistol in his hands—and the car was going to need a new windscreen.

He walked down to where Pereira lay, saw he was dead, and went straight on to where Manuel Costa was waiting with Lawson. Costa had a revolver in his right hand, covering Martin Lawson, but Lawson still managed a sad, wry smile.

"The others?" asked Costa without preamble as Gaunt reached them.

"Inez and Sollas are all right," said Gaunt, his eyes on Lawson.

"And Luis?"

"Dead." More cars were driving into the camp, filled with police. He watched them for a moment, puzzled, as they stopped and their crews poured out. "How the hell did you know?"

"Jaime," said Costa with a wry pride. "He came with a crazy story about being chased and hiding, then seeing you and Inez and Luis—" he stopped and shrugged his slim shoulders. "So I—ah—took certain precautions before I came."

"But you wouldn't have found them," said Lawson, a bitter, weary figure who seemed suddenly aged and drained. Lips tightening, he looked around him. "What happened, Gaunt?"

"Some luck—and Luis Torres," said Gaunt grimly. "Mainly Luis Torres."

Lawson shook his head in near disbelief. "I told you I was a professional, Gaunt," he said hoarsely. "A few more years and my masters had agreed I should retire. It may amuse you. There would even have been a pension. But now—"

"We call it *fado*," said Manuel Costa unemotionally. "Fate is something no one can forecast." Then he brightened as he saw Inez coming down from the Castelo with Arthur Sollas close behind her. "My men will take care of the rest here, *Senhor* Gaunt—I want to be with you when you meet a certain Headquarters captain."

"And Jaime," reminded Gaunt.

Costa nodded wryly. "My little black sheep relative, whom I may have to throw in jail some day." He saw Gaunt's raised eyebrow and nodded. "My nephew—you hired his father's car."

Gaunt managed a grin, then went to meet the slim, proud girl coming towards them.

Two days later they buried Lieutenant Luis Torres with full naval honours in the little cemetery outside Claras.

Inez was there in black mourning, Gaunt on her one side and Manuel Costa on the other. But an Embassy car from Lisbon was waiting by the cemetery gate as the service ended and two hours later Gaunt was on *Trans Aeros Portugueses* flight out of Lisbon for London.

It was the middle of the following morning, a grey day of gentle rain in Edinburgh, when he walked into Henry Falconer's room in the Queen's and Lord Treasurer's Remembrancer's office in George Street.

Falconer was behind his desk, looking out at the misting wet with a resigned gloom. He turned and greeted Gaunt with no particular enthusiasm.

"Lisbon sent us a full telex," said Falconer in his gloomiest Senior Administrative Assistant voice. "You had a busy time."

"It shaped that way," agreed Gaunt carefully.

"Quite." Falconer built a small steeple with his fingertips. "But the Treasure Trove inquiry—?"

"Nothing." Gaunt shook his head.

"So it died with him. A pity." Falconer frowned and unlocked a drawer of his desk. "I—ah—didn't show you this before. Francis Preston gave it to the Remembrancer as—well, he called it a token."

He laid a small, exquisitely shaped silver chalice cup on his desk top and touched it carefully with one finger. "The experts say early Celtic Christian. If the rest was like this—well, we'll just have to hope they turn up some day."

Some day or maybe never. Gaunt looked at it for a moment then reached into the brief case at his side.

"Yours," he said briefly, placing a bottle of vintage port beside the glinting chalice.

"You remembered—excellent!" Falconer brightened. "The true wine of the country, eh?"

Gaunt nodded. He'd bought the bottle that morning in a shop along Princes Street.

He could afford that much. The financial pages were leading with the story of a surprise European bid for Consolidated

Breweries, which had made an overnight rise of twenty points. The price for Malters shares had crashed.

There was another bottle in his brief case, for a little old lady out in Morningside.

But he'd be drinking alone.

Which meant thinking of Inez. Though he knew he now stood for too many memories of a kind she wanted to forget.

Fado . . . Manuel Costa had been right when he'd talked about fate.

"Yes, I'll look forward to this," said Falconer, examining the bottle again. "In fact, we could sample it now, eh?"

Gaunt grinned, considered the glinting chalice for a moment, then went for some paper cups.

5/74